GLOBAL CHANGE AND REMOTE SENSING

WILEY-PRAXIS SERIES IN REMOTE SENSING
Series Editor: David Sloggett, M.Sc., Ph.D.

Editor, *EARSeL Newsletter*
Co-Director, Dundee Centre for Coastal Zone Research, UK
Deputy Chairman, Cray Systems, UK

This series aims to bring together some of the world's leading researchers working in the forefront of the analysis and application of remotely sensed data and the infrastructure required to utilize the data on an operational basis. A key theme of the series is monitoring the environment and the development of sustainable practices for its exploitation.

The series makes an important contribution to existing literature encompassing areas such as: theoretical research; data analysis; the infrastructure required to exploit the data; and the application of data derived from satellites, aircraft and *in situ* observations. The series specifically emphasizes research into the interaction of elements of the global ecosystem publishing high-quality material at the forefront of existing knowledge. It also provides unique insights into examples where remotely sensed data is combined with Geographic Information Systems and high-fidelity models of the physical, chemical and biological processes at the heart of our environment to provide operational applications of the remotely sensed data.

Aimed at a wide readership, the books will appeal to professional researchers working in the field of remote sensing, potential users of the information and data derived from the application of remote sensing techniques, and postgraduate and undergraduate students working in the field.

EARTHWATCH: The Climate from Space

John E. Harries, Professor of Earth Observation, Imperial College, London, UK

GLOBAL CHANGE AND REMOTE SENSING

Kirill Ya. Kondratyev, Scientific Research Centre for Ecological Safety, Russian Academy of Sciences, St Petersburg, Russia; A. A. Buznikov, Electrotechnical University of St Petersburg, Russia; O.M. Pokrovsky, Main Geophysical Observatory, St Petersburg, Russia

HIGH LATITUDE CLIMATE AND REMOTE SENSING

Kirill Ya. Kondratyev, Scientific Research Centre for Ecological Safety, Russian Academy of Sciences, St Petersburg, Russia; O.M. Johannessen, Nansen Environment and Remote Sensing Centre, Bergen, Norway; V.V. Melentyev, Nansen International Environmental Remote Sensing Centre, St Petersburg, Russia

REMOTE SENSING AND GEOGRAPHIC INFORMATION SYSTEMS: Geological Mapping, Mineral Exploration and Mining

Christopher A. Legg, United Kingdom Overseas Development Administration, Forest and Land Use Mapping Project, Forest Department, Colombo, Sri Lanka

SATELLITE OCEANOGRAPHY: An Introduction for Oceanographers and Remote-sensing Scientists

Ian S. Robinson, Department of Oceanography, University of Southampton, UK

GEOGRAPHIC INFORMATION FROM SPACE: Processes and Applications of Geocoded Satellite Images

Jonathan Williams, Consultant, Space Division Logica plc, Leatherhead, UK

GLOBAL CHANGE AND REMOTE SENSING

K. Ya. Kondratyev
Scientific Research Centre for Ecological Safety
St Petersburg's Russian Academy of Sciences, Russia

A. A. Buznikov
Electrotechnical University of St Petersburg, Russia

O. M. Pokrovsky
Main Geophysical Observatory, St Petersburg, Russia

JOHN WILEY & SONS

Chichester • New York • Brisbane • Toronto • Singapore

Published in association with
PRAXIS PUBLISHING
Chichester

Published in 1996 by
John Wiley & Sons Ltd
in association with Praxis Publishing Ltd

Wiley Editorial Offices

John Wiley & Sons Ltd, Baffins Lane,
Chichester, West Sussex PO19 1UD, England

John Wiley & Sons, Inc., 605 Third Avenue,
New York, NY 10158-0012, USA

Jacaranda Wiley Ltd, G.P.O. Box 859, Brisbane
Queensland 4001, Australia

John Wiley & Sons (Canada) Ltd, 22 Worcester Road,
Rexdale, Ontario M9W 1L1, Canada

John Wiley & Sons (SEA) Pte Ltd, 37 Jalan Pemimpin 05-04,
Block B, Union Industrial Building, Singapore 2057

A catalogue record for this book is available from the British Library

ISBN 0-471-96078-0

Printed and bound in Great Britain by Hartnolls Ltd, Bodmin

Table of contents

Foreword

The 1992 Rio de Janeiro Earth Summit, officially the United Nations Conference on Environment and Development, was a landmark in international cooperation to develop a truly global strategy for sustainable development. The political commitments at Rio and the follow-up strategies now being implemented in individual nations would not, however, have been possible without the solid scientific foundation provided by the many national and international monitoring and research programmes of the preceding decades such as the World Weather Watch, the Global Atmospheric Research Programme and the World Climate Programme; and these in turn were built on the fundamental capabilities for *in situ* and remote sensing of the atmosphere, land and oceans that emerged from the various research institutes around the world earlier this century.

There are few individuals who have contributed more to, or who are better equipped to describe, the fascinating story of the development of remote sensing as a tool for earth observation than Professor Kirill Kondratyev. For a generation he has been the acknowledged father figure of atmospheric radiation studies and I doubt if there is anyone in the field who has not learned greatly from his prolific and lucid writing over more than fifty years. In this book, he and his co-authors provide a comprehensive overview of the development of aircraft and satellite remote sensing as an observational tool and of its application to global environmental monitoring and research. They provide both the detailed science and the big picture and lay the foundation for a better understanding of what must be done to build an effective global environmental observing system for the next century.

John W. Zillman
President, World Meteorological Organization
February 1996

Introduction

An accomplishment of the International Space Year (1992) programme stimulates an analysis of the present state of the environmental remote sensing, perspectives of their further development, and substantiation of key directions of further research. The International Space Year has become a culminating point in the most urgent fields of remote sensing. It goes without saying that in the late twentieth century there is no problem more urgent than the ecological one. A wide range of problems—from environmental pollution in individual regions to global ecology, on the whole—reflects an acuteness of the situation.

The economic and social development of society has come to an obvious controversy with limited resource-reproducing and life-maintaining abilities of the biosphere. At present one can observe a depletion of natural resources of both land and ocean, irretrievable loss of various species of plants and animals, technogenic breaking of the biogeochemical cycles of substances, contamination of all environmental components, loss of biodiversity and degradation of ecosystems. All kinds of land use—industrial, agricultural, forestry, recreation, etc.—are accompanied by not only obtaining the needed results, but also diverse ecological, ecologo-economic and social consequences (Kondratyev, 1990c, 1988c; Programme..., 1988). An appearance of these consequences has determined a critical situation in many regions and over the globe, on the whole.

The change in the land use strategy, its continuous improvement to overcome negative ecological, ecologo-economic and ecologo-social consequences in various regions, in various countries and over the globe are the basic scientific problem of the ecological optimization of nature use.

Discovering the laws of interaction of the geospheric and biospheric components requires extremely complicated interdisciplinary studies. Complex studies of geosphere and biosphere have been carried out for a long time. In recent decades, studies have been accomplished within numerous large-scale programmes: the International Geophysical Year (IGY), the International Quiet Sun Year (IQSY), the World Weather Watch (WWW), and the Global Atmospheric Research Programme (GARP). Since then, the large-scale Middle Atmosphere Programme

(MAP), International Lithosphere Programme, World Climate Programme (with the World Climate Research Programme (WCRP) as a component), specialized International Satellite Cloud Climatology Project (ISCCP) and the International Satellite Land Surface Climatology Project (ISLSCP) as well as a large-scale Russian programme "Sections" aimed at studies of the role of oceans in short-term climate changes have been undertaken. There are two new international programmes with the same objective: The World Ocean Circulation Experiment (WOCE) and The Tropical Ocean and Global Atmosphere (TOGA) programme. The Global Climate Observing System (GCOS), Global Ocean Observing System (GOOS), and Global Terrestrial Observing System (GTOS) serve the purpose of comprehensive environmental monitoring.

The following international projects on studies of biogeophysical cycles of various components have be accomplished under the aegis of SCOPE and UNEP: the American Programme of the Global Tropospheric Chemistry, the International Hydrobiological Programme, and the Man and Biosphere Programme (within the framework of UNESCO, etc.).

Each of the enumerated programmes is characterized by a complex approach to solving respective problems. An analysis of the global ecological problem, on the whole, shows, however, an urgent need for coordinated efforts to achieve the goals of various programmes and for substantiating a "super-programme" covering the key aspects of geosphere–biosphere studies.

These circumstances have stimulated the development of the long-term International Geosphere–Biosphere Programme (IGBP) aimed at studies of global changes, especially with a view to the anthropogenic impact on the biogeochemical cycles of carbon, nitrogen, sulphur, phosphorus, water, and the dynamics of such factors of life support as solar radiation, the quality of air and natural waters, soil fertility, as well as interrelationships between biospheric and geospheric events (Bolle and Rasool, 1985; Kondratyev, 1988c, 1989b, 1990c; Kotliakov et al., 1988; Rasool, 1984, 1987).

Bearing in mind that the growing anthropogenic impact on the environment tells upon practically all the components of geosphere and biosphere and in some cases is of the global scale, the problem of global change cannot be solved without using a systems approach to study the processes considered (Kondratyev, 1990c).

The representatives of the USSR Academy of Sciences and the US National Academy of Sciences, having agreed in December 1988 on the formation of the International Committee on Global Ecology, formulated the following key problems in this field:

1. Global energy and biogeochemical cycles; industrial and biospheric processes; prospects of the development of energy production and its possible impact on the ecological systems; global-scale monitoring of the state of soils and vegetation, with special emphasis, first, on the data for Russia and the USA; estimation of ejected industrial pollutants in the USA and in Russia, both in the past and now.
2. Substantiation of the observation systems to assess the global-scale changes:

development of new observation systems both conventional and space-borne; programmes for exchanging the data obtained from satellites; analysis of the adequacy of both existing and planned observation systems to assess global changes.

3. Global changes in biodiversity: description and observations of biodiversity in the USA and in Russia and, if possible, over the globe; development of efficient observation systems to obtain approximate estimates of biological extinction through reducing the processes of species extinction and diversity loss; establishing connections between biogeochemical cycles and biodiversity.

4. Theoretical and methodological bases for understanding the ecological changes: revealing the approaches based on techniques of non-linear physics and current mathematics to study the instability of ecological systems; analysis of the methodological basis to forecast global ecological changes.

5. Discussion of, and support for, the respective international efforts: the IGPB and other international programmes; bilateral and regional intergovernmental programmes; study of, and support for, the international agreements in the field of environmental studies.

Solutions of the enumerated problems require global observation systems making use of both conventional and space-borne means. In solving the problems of global change a combination of conventional and space-borne means plays an increasing role (Beregovoi et al., 1972a; Buznikov, 1986; Buznikov et al., 1986; Kondratyev, 1987a, 1990b, c; Kondratyev and Buznikov, 1981). Naturally, the problem of study of the Earth as a whole natural system can be solved only on the basis of widely used space-borne observational means based on the application of remote sounding.

In practice, for the Earth-resources and environmental studies various capabilities of the remote sounding technique have been used, including photographic, TV, spectral, lidar, thermal, passive microwave, radar, and other kinds of survey of the atmosphere, the surface of the Earth and the World Ocean from the ground, ships aerosphace and other platforms to study their state or for thematic mapping.

Certain progress has been achieved in solving the fundamental scientific problems and in practical use of the space survey data for the Earth-resources and environmental studies. There are experimental and operational space-borne remote sounding instruments functioning in a wide electromagnetic spectral range: from UV to microwave. They have been designed to solve problems of meteorology, climate and weather forecasting, oceanography, studies of Earth's resources and environmental monitoring.

The automated satellites carrying the photographic, TV and multi-spectral instruments are the basic means of continuous monitoring of the state of the Earth's environment and its changes. There are, for instance, continuously operating space-borne systems NOAA, GOES, Nimbus, Landsat, SPOT, "Meteor", "Meteor-Priroda", "Resurs", "Okean", "Kosmos", etc.

The manned orbital stations (MOS) such as "Salyut", "Mir", Skylab and Shuttle have become orbital scientific laboratories to carry out complex experiments to test various scientific instruments, to accomplish visual and visual-instrumental studies.

Both the MOS and automated satellites have opened up wide possibilities to study the surface and the atmosphere of the Earth and the World Ocean making use of the opto-electronic and radio-electronic systems of the remote sounding of the environment.

To accomplish a long-term programme of studies from space, it is necessary:

1. To take into account the available economic resources to create the multi-purpose satellite systems, to substantiate the order of priorities, and to determine the importance of interaction of various kinds of space-borne remote-sensing instrumentation, in particular, automatic and manned space systems, low- and high-orbit satellites.
2. To coordinate the development of the main components of the system of observations of the Earth from space: satellite and conventional observation means; means of transmitting the information to the ground-based stations, where this information is received, processed and archived in the interests of the users.
3. To solve such an important problem as the development of a system of key sites (KS) of the calibration test areas, which should become a component of the remote sensing (RS) system. It should be borne in mind that the costs of such a KS system can be commensurable with those of space systems.
4. To create, on a international basis, the systems of survey from space of the global environmental dynamics, making use of technical means and experience of various countries. In this connection, it is extremely important that the RS systems developed in different countries be compatible and mutually supplementing.
5. That programmes of global change studies should be based on experience, ensuring further development of space systems, techniques and means of remote sensing.
6. That composition and number of space vehicles (SV) planned to be launched should be thoroughly substantiated both from the scientific–technical and technical–economic points of view.

From the viewpoint of ecological studies, the problem of substantiation of the concept of ecological and Earth-resources studies from space remains the first priority. Here it is expedient to proceed from the following classification of the problems.

I. GLOBAL CHANGE PROBLEMS

Here the priorities are quite clear. They are connected, first of all, with the need for studies of violations of the closed nature of global biogeochemical cycles, which result, in particular, in the anthropogenically induced changes in the composition of the atmosphere (e.g. concentrations of "greenhouse" gases) affecting, in their turn, the global climate (Gorshkov, 1994; Kondratyev et al., 1992a,b, 1994). During the last decade a problem has arisen, the emission of chlorofluorocarbons (CFCs) destructing the ozone layer, practically not existing in nature; this changes substantially the pattern of biogeochemical cycles (speaking about ozone, one should also remember the photochemical smog reactions determining the increase of the ozone concentration in the lower troposphere; interrelationships between the problems of global climate change, as well as the dynamics of the stratospheric and tropospheric ozone).

The key role of biospheric dynamics in the problems of global change determines a specific significance of the monitoring of the processes in the biosphere, including the dynamics of primary productivity both on land and in the World Ocean (if, for example, the conclusions about the CO_2-induced "fertilization" of vegetation are valid, one may expect a "greening of the planet"; variations in the oceanic bioproductivity can cause variations in the emissions of dimethylsulphide to the atmosphere, leading to climate changes opposite in sign compared to the "greenhouse" warming: Kondratyev and Grassl, 1993, 1995; Kondratyev and Cracknell, 1995). The second important aspect of global change is a re-distribution of the Earth's heat balance components, connected both with the internal variability and with external forcings (variations in the extra-atmospheric input of solar radiation).

Naturally, the cost-effective development of the RS systems to solve the most urgent problems of global change determines, first of all, the need for an optimized design of a global observation system, including four, most important (and interdependent) directions of development:

1. Optimization of satellite observations and of the ground-based observational networks (models, algorithms, rules of decision making taking into account costs on the realization of space systems, etc.).
2. Problems of geo-ecoinformatics (a function of the value of satellite information for ecological purposes, the information content of observational data, technical means of data processing making use of the pattern-recognition approach, information measure characteristics, texture analysis, *a priori* information, expert systems, etc.); problems of data archiving and distribution are quite complex.
3. The simulation modelling of geophysical and biological processes with analysis of the time series of satellite observation data, development of the concept of the ecologically active zones of the ocean and land surface, parameterization of the biosphere in climate models and the subsequent development of the coupled biospheric models.
4. The theory of the global change predictability based on analysis of the time series of the data of observations and geoinformation models.

The absence, so far, of a substantiation of optimized global observation systems is explained by unsolved problems, such as: (i) priorities of global ecology; (ii) quantitatively substantiated requirements for the observational data (the spatial–temporal resolution, acceptable errors, etc.); (iii) compatibility (comparability) of the data of conventional and satellite observations; (iv) the choice of the KS. In this connection it should be emphasized that, unfortunately, the methodology of the energy-active zones (EAZO) propounded by G. I. Marchuk (Marchuk, 1964, 1974, 1979; Marchuk et al., 1968, 1988) as applied to the problem of mass and energy exchange between the ocean and the atmosphere, but, of course, much more important for the substantiation of the choice of KS has not been given due attention. So far, problems connected with the planning an optimal system of observations have been solved on a qualitatively intuitive and unsystematic level, which, on the one hand, brings unacceptably profuse information and, on the other hand, does not guarantee the lack of gaps.

II. REGIONAL ECOLOGICAL PROBLEMS

Numerous regional ecological problems, both national and international, can easily be outlined. More difficult problems consist in substantiating a system (first of all, ecosystem) approach to the solution of regional problems and, on this basis, planning adequate observational systems based on the results of the numerical modelling simulation. This can be illustrated, in the case of Russia, by the urgent regional problems, such as Chernobyl, the Azov Sea and the Black Sea, Ladoga–Neva–Gulf of Finland (in connection with the building of the dam across the Gulf), volcanic eruptions, strong industrial pollution of the atmosphere of some regions, boreal Siberian forests, degradation of the quality of arable soils, etc. It is a paradox that in all these (and many other) cases there are no adequate systems of observations (in particular, the information contribution from various observation means has not been analysed), and the simulation modelling is either fragmentary or lacking at all.

III. LOCAL ECOLOGICAL PROBLEMS

Of course, the spatial–temporal scales of local problems determine the decisive role of conventional means of observations. However, in many cases the information contribution of satellite data turns out to be extremely important. This refers, in particular, to natural (eruptions, floods, typhoons, dust storms, tsunami, forest fires, etc.) and anthropogenic disasters and catastrophes (accidents at oil- and gas-pipelines, sudden releases of pollutants, etc.), when prompt decisions on the basis of information about the processes taking place often in remote regions are often needed.

IV. EARTH-RESOURCES STUDIES

The Earth-resources studies are closely connected with ecological problems. This refers, first of all, to the problems of water, soil forest and atmosphere resources (note that though the atmosphere has not been considered, so far, as one of the natural resources, such a viewpoint has become obsolete). The problem of various non-renewable resources (coal, oil, gas, etc.) is quite complex, from the viewpoint of both its practical importance and wide application of satellite information in search for raw-material resources.

Extremely important is an unsolved problem—analysis of overlapping requirements for information put forward by ecological and Earth-resources studies. The answer to this question determines the possibility to substantiate a single global system for ecological and Earth-resources observations. An important part of the problem is the role of manned spacecraft (MS). The need for some comparatively highly specialized space-borne observational means raises no doubts. On the other hand, it is clear, however, that a single system of observations should serve the basis.

Complex developments in the context of comparative planetology are the most efficient means to develop studies of the Earth from space (Kondratyev, 1988b, 1992). So far, the case has been confined to declarative statements, whereas a single programme is needed to study the Solar system.

V. INTERNATIONAL COOPERATION

The global and regional ecological problems can only be solved on the basis of international cooperation in the light of recommendations made by the Second UN Conference on Environment and Development (Kondratyev, 1993a). One of the urgent problems is a need for substantiation and realization of international regional systems of observation. For example, the problems of ecological safety of the countries of the Baltic region, the Mediterranean Sea basin, the river Zambezi basin, etc.

A large number and diversity of the channels of international cooperation (UN and such specialized organizations as UNESCO and UNEP, WMO, FAO, WHO, European Space Agency, European Environmental Agency, bilateral agreements, etc.) require, first of all, agreed-upon efforts of various agencies of the countries to formulate the priorities and realize the cooperation instead of the existing unsystematic approaches.

There is a need for the development of an international agreement on designing an optimized system of global ecological monitoring and adopting it at the UN level. Only the use of such observational data as the input information for numerical simulation models of the global ecodynamics (the dynamics of the biosphere, climate, ozone layer, water and forest resources, etc.) will make it possible to realize an early detection of dangerous trends of development of ecological situations, as well as to substantiate possible scenarios of development and mitigation measures needed to prevent catastrophic consequences of anthropogenic impacts on the environment and the biosphere. Thus, we speak about the global ecological safety provision.

The development of space ecology should be based on a long-range international programme of the Earth observations from space with an efficient coordination of development and standardization (unification, comparability, etc.) of the information obtained. The solution of this problem is promoted by such new space missions as the Russian satellite Almaz-1, European satellites ERS-1 and ERS-2, Japan Earth-resources satellite JERS and others; further development in Russia of such systems as Meteor, Meteor-Priroda, Resurs, the Earth-resources module of the orbital station "Mir"; Russian–French developments to measure the Earth radiation budget (ERB) (the programme ScaRab) and for lidar sounding of the atmosphere (the programme "Alissa"); Russian–American studies of the ozone layer (making use of the American TOMS instrumentation on the Russian satellites). The launching in 1991 of the satellite "Meteor-3/TOMS" is the first stage of this development. Very promising are improved measuring complexes carried by the satellites NOAA, SPOT, Landsat; the launching of the Indian Earth's-resources satellite IRS-1; further development of meteorological and Earth's-resources satellite observations in China; developments within the French–American programme TOPEX-POSEIDON; the launching in 1991 of the American satellite UARS to study the upper layers of the atmosphere, etc. (Kondratyev, 1993a).

Of course, the data of global ecological monitoring and the conclusions with respect to an assessment of the trends of development of the ecological situation should be made accessible to all countries. The solution of this problem, like an agreement on the creation of an optimized system of the global monitoring, can be realized only through an arrangement of a UN body responsible for the problem of global ecological safety.

This monograph is an attempt to summarize the results of applying the techniques and remote sensing instrumentation in the problems of global ecology and the possibilities of their solution.

An assessment has been made of the role of satellite observations in global environmental monitoring. Key directions of developments of the global system of ecological monitoring have been analysed, including the Earth's Observing System (EOS). The programme GEWEX and the global system of climate observations have been analysed, as well.

The second part of the book is dedicated to analysis of the complex of space- and air-borne instruments for remote sensing developed and utilized in the f. USSR and Russia. The main types of space-borne systems for the Earth's-resources and environmental studies have been described. Analysis has been made of the techniques and instruments for spectrophotometric observations from space. A description is made of the environmental and Earth's-resources satellites, the MOS "Mir", and its specialized scientific modules. Possibilities are considered to apply radar remote sensing to ecological studies and monitoring of the environmental state.

Taking into account the high cost of the satellite instrumentation, limited weight, power supply and volume of the on-board information; the problem of an optimal design of an observational system, including an optimal design of the systems for remote sensing from space, has become very urgent. In this connection, the third part of the book is dedicated to the problem of optimization of the observation systems. A number of scientific aspects of this problem have been considered.

Since an interpretation of the data of satellite observations is connected with the solution of mathematically non-correct problems (parameters characterizing the state of the environment should be retrieved from the characteristics of emitted, reflected or absorbed radiation), the incorrectness of most of the inverse problems of remote sensing is responsible for the fact that the choice of measurement conditions critically affects the accuracy of the results obtained. An inadequate choice of spectral channels or measurement geometry can much depreciate the results of observation. On the other hand, an underestimation of the significance of the information content assessment can lead to excessive information. The book considers an information model of the ground-based observational systems. An analysis is made of the information content of global systems of the aerological observations and remote sounding of the atmosphere. Methods of the theory of conjugated equations for an optimal planning of the systems of conventional and satellite observations have been applied. Analysis is made of the requirements of satellite information users to the systems of the remote sensing as well as the information content of the existing on-board instrumentation.

The book is meant for specialists in the field of geophysics, geography, oceanology, atmospheric physics, space studies who are interested in applications of remote sensing techniques to solve the problems of global change, for the teachers, undergraduate and graduate students, as well as for the scientific community and the broad circles of readers interested in these problems.

1

Global environmental monitoring: the role of satellite observations

From the viewpoint of the problems of global change, the combined use of conventional and satellite-borne observational means to assess the state of the natural environment and its possible changes in the future plays an increasing role. The problem of studying the Earth as a whole natural system set by the International Geosphere–Biosphere Programme (Kondratyev, 1985b, 1990c; Kotliakov et al., 1988) can be solved only on the basis of the wide use of space-borne observational means (Kondratyev, 1987a, 1989a).

1.1 THE INTERNATIONAL GEOSPHERE–BIOSPHERE PROGRAMME (IGBP). GLOBAL ECOLOGICAL MONITORING

The evolution of the geosphere and biosphere can be characterized by ever increasing interaction between their components, which is due, above all, to the growing anthropogenic impact on the environment. This impact is first of all revealed in the form of the transformation of nature carried out by man, and in the more and more enhanced anthropogenic loading on the environment, which can practically be traced in all components of the geosphere and biosphere (in some cases, on a global scale). Hence the need in a systematic approach to the study of the processes under consideration (Gorshkov and Kondratyev, 1988, 1990; Kondratyev and Pokrovsky, 1989a,b; Marchuk and Kondratyev, 1992; IGBP, 1994 a, b). To reveal certain laws of the impact of geo- and biospheric components, interdisciplinary studies of unprecedented complexity are required; so the whole range of relevant problems is brought to the foreground of contemporary natural science.

1.1.1 Priorities of the IGBP
The scientific community has been aware of the necessity for complex studies of the geosphere and biosphere for a long time. During recent decades, this awareness has revealed itself in a most spectacular way through the implementation of the scientific programmes mentioned in the Introduction.

The following directions of research within the SCOPE illustrate the variety of the IGBP problems:

(1)   The cycles of carbon and nutrients in lakes and estuaries;
(2)   The sulphur cycle in the continental and water ecosystems;
(3)   The processes of acidification in tropical countries;
(4)   The phosphorus cycle in the continental and water ecosystems;
(5)   The budgets of organic substances;
(6)   The effect of pesticides;
(7)   Organisms generated by genetic engineering in the environment;
(8)   The lowering of coastal zones and rising of the sea level;
(9)   Ecotones in the varying environment;
(10) The exhange of minor gaseous components between the biosphere and atmosphere;
(11) The ecosystem experiments;
(12) The pollution of subsurface waters.

The following projects are presently under consideration:

(1)   Flow of particles into the ocean;
(2)   Studies on the problem of genetic engineering and the environment;
(3)   Long-term ecological investigations;
(4)   Biogeochemical metabolism of small water catchment areas;
(5)   Use of scientific information for solving the problems relevant to sustainable development of the biosphere;
(6)   Biogeochemical "trajectories" of radionuclides;
(7)   Effect of climate change on human health.

The Russian programme of biospheric and ecological studies is broader still.

Each of the programmes mentioned above (and many that have not been mentioned) are characteristic of a complex approach to the solution of relevant problems. However, analysis of the set of problems relevant to global ecology shows that a closer coordination of efforts is required and that those efforts should be oriented towards achieving the particular goals of various programmes, and the substantiation of a kind of "superprogramme" encompassing the key aspects of geospheric studies.

It is these circumstances that have stimulated the development of the long-term International Geosphere–Biosphere Programme (IGBP) (the full-scale development of observational systems was started in the 1990s). Its main goal is the study of global changes in the geosphere, especially from the viewpoint of the anthropogenic impact on the biogeochemical cycles of carbon, nitrogen, sulphur, phosphorus, water, and the dynamics of such life-supporting factors as radiation, the quality of air and natural waters, soil fertility, as well as interactions between biospheric and geospheric phenomena.

The current situation requires, first of all, a proper analysis of key problems of the geosphere–biosphere studies. And, in this connection, the following considerations are of primary importance.

The first one is that, on a time scale of the order of a decade or more, it becomes quite evident that geospheric components compose a single coupled system. The interaction between individual components of the system is characteristic of the presence of synergism (feedbacks which sometimes lead to a mutual intensification of various processes). It is this circumstance that makes so important the systematic approach, the interdisciplinary studies of physical, chemical and biological processes based on the realization of an integrated programme.

The second important fact is that the ever increasing level of anthropogenic impact on the geosphere–biosphere indicates even more clearly (than consideration of naturally induced processes alone) the necessity of studying processes and changes on a global scale. From the viewpoint of planning an observing system, this indicates a leading role of satellite observation means (although conventional observing systems must play their positive role now, as well as in the future). Of specific interest for the totality of problems involved are palaeo- and comparative-planetary analogies, which means that geospheric research should be closely associated with the study of the origin and evolution of the solar system. One of the aspects here which is especially significant is that the geosphere–biosphere system is not closed in the sense that it is subject to the influence of various extraterrestrial factors (solar activity, galactic cosmic rays, etc.). Thus, there is no doubt that in the geosphere–biosphere studies, the key role belongs to such objects of these studies as the atmosphere, ocean, lithosphere and solar/cosmic factors (Kondratyev, 1990 a–d).

An important aspect of the problem is that some anthropogenic impacts on the global geosphere are already appreciable (for instance, through the growth of carbon dioxide and nitrogen oxide concentrations—an evidence of impact on the global cycles of carbon and nitrogen), and may become very considerable in a few decades' time, whereas our capability of taking relevant counter-measures requires an equal (or larger) characteristic time scale; hence, the urgency for studying the set of problems under examination.

It is only natural that when an interdisciplinary problem of exceptional complexity is developed, of primary importance becomes the establishment of its priority aspects. One of these, in particular, is the problem of climate and its change. Climate is formed as a result of the interaction of the components of the climatic system (the "atmosphere–hydrosphere–lithosphere–cryosphere–biosphere"), for which the existence of numerous feedbacks is typical. At present, there is hardly any other problem in the natural sciences of this degree of complexity on a global scale, and requiring consideration of the most important and complicated anthropogenic impacts.

Directly relevant to the climate problem is the role of the interaction between the geosphere and biosphere. This role is very well pronounced, for example, in the consideration of the problem of the influence of the anthropogenically induced CO_2 concentration growth on climate. During recent years, this problem has given rise to contradictory statements concerning climate change assessments (Borisenkov and Kondratyev, 1988; Kondratyev, 1988d; Kondratyev and Pokrovsky, 1989a,b; Kondratyev, Adamenko, Henderson-Sellers, 1990). This is mainly due to two circumstances: (1) the lack of sufficiently reliable models of the global carbon cycle (the contribution of the marine and continental biota has not been clearly established so far); (2) the inadequacy of the climate theory from the point of view of interactive accounting of processes in the geosphere–biosphere. Although the climate problem may serve as an illustration of the importance of the consideration of the effect of extra-terrestrial factors, established from observational data, the physical mechanisms determining this influence are not fully known today.

The problem of climate is also so important because of its exceptional practical significance. It is a well-known fact that man's economic activity (and above all, agricultural activity) is strictly dependent on climate conditions. Recently, a new aspect of the problem has become evident—that of the possible effect of a nuclear war on climate and the biosphere (Kondratyev, 1988d). The assessments performed reveal the danger of a global ecological catastrophe which may be caused, in particular, by a strong climate cooling (the "nuclear winter") resulting from a decreased income of solar radiation to the Earth's surface due to its marked attenuation by smoke—the aftereffects of fires in forests and cities—the consequences of nuclear explosions. Still more important may be climate instability under conditions of a strong disturbance of the climate system.

Considering the importance of the problem of climate, a respective interdisciplinary section within the IGBP must be formulated, taking into account the WCRP and other specialized programmes (WOCE, TOGA, ISCCP, etc.). Examination of specific features of programmes of this kind shows that studies of closely interrelated problems of atmospheric physics and chemistry require special attention within the IGBP, including investigation of biogeochemical cycles of such components as carbon, nitrogen, phosphorus, sulphur, and of solar–atmospheric relationships.

Various aspects of atmospheric physics and chemistry are highly important from the viewpoint of estimating the prospects of the existence of the biosphere (its productivity) under conditions of an ever growing anthropogenic stress (Gorshkov and Kondratyev, 1990; Kondratyev, 1990 a, d). Special attention should be given to the problem of the impact on the ozone layer in the stratosphere, which protects the biosphere from harmful effects of hard ultraviolet radiation.

Although assessments of the anthropogenic impact on ozone vary within a broad range of judgement (see Kondratyev, 1990b), there is no doubt that there still is deep general concern about the influence on the total ozone content and the vertical ozone concentration profile of the emissions of chlorofluorocarbons (CFCs), carbon dioxide, nitrogen oxides and methane. It is clear now that the effects of these components are closely interrelated, and therefore estimates for individual (isolated) components cannot be considered correct.

There is convincing evidence (obtained from observational data) of increased concentrations of CFC, methylchloroform, carbon dioxide, nitrogen monoxide and methane. However, the lack of reliable data on the sources and sinks of the above-mentioned gases does not make it possible to obtain realistic forecasts of their trends in the future (this is especially true for methane).

The solution of the ozone problem (considering that ozone is an important atmospheric component) requires the implementation of a broad programme of laboratory, field and theoretical studies of the interrelated physical, chemical and photochemical processes in the troposphere and stratosphere, and monitoring changes in the atmospheric chemical composition (for a large number of components) on a global scale.

With regard to tropospheric chemistry, most urgent must be studies of: (1) the water cycle; (2) processes determining the dynamics of oxidants, especially of O_3, SO_2 and NO_2; (3) the mechanisms of dry and wet deposition of pollutants at the land surface and in water basins; (4) processes determining the concentrations of aerosols and such gases as CO_2, N_2O, CH_4, NH_3 and H_2O in lower atmospheric layers; (5) the effect of optically active atmospheric components on the radiative regime and climate. Just as in all other cases, the interaction between chemical processes in the troposphere and stratosphere plays a most important role.

For a better understanding of biogeochemical cycles, it is necessary to study such factors of their control as: (1) natural and anthropogenic emissions of minor gaseous components to the troposphere; (2) their transport over large distances; (3) chemical transformations (including gas-to-particle conversions); (4) removal from the stratosphere of minor gaseous and aerosol components (in this connection, of special interest is the role of cloud cover). Of primary interest are studies of such biospheric components as forests in the tropics and at temperate latitudes, steppes and savannahs, tundra, agricultural land, and also of coastal upwellings and processes in the open ocean.

Climatic changes are determined by the important role of minor optically active atmospheric components (including ozone) in the formation of the greenhouse effect of the atmosphere, whose variations are the primary energy source of anthropogenic impact on climate. This may be illustrated by the increased content of ozone in the troposphere detected during recent years. Assessments have revealed that the contribution of this increase to the enhancement of the greenhouse effect is equivalent to the effect of increased concentration of carbon dioxide.

In the field of simulation modelling, most urgent is the task of developing interactive models, taking account of dynamical and photochemical processes, for the simulation of global budgets of O_3, CO_2 and other components of crucial importance. Sufficient attention must be paid, as before, to approximate 1- and 2-D models in the studies of regional transport, geochemical balances, and in the search for new important chemical reactions. Long-term tasks must include examination of the role of complex heterogeneous processes in the formation of the global cycles of various components; here special attention should be given to poorly studied processes in remote (background) regions of the atmosphere.

In many respects, the chemical composition of the atmosphere has been formed and is presently subject to changes as a result of the interaction with the biosphere. The biosphere is a major source of hydrocarbons, and of such a volatile halocarbon as methylchloroform. Interactions between respective processes are not always direct and unequivocal. For instance, chemical reactions involving nitrogen oxides in the troposphere may lead to both an increase and a decrease in the ozone content, and this, in turn, influences the vegetation cover. Variations in the N_2O, CH_3Cl and CH_4 concentrations in the troposphere affect the ozone content in the stratosphere, which influences the biosphere.

A problem of major importance is the study of physical, chemical and biological processes responsible for the release and assimilation by the biosphere of various components (within different ecosystems), and also, on the other hand, of the reaction of the biosphere to the variability of physical characteristics and the chemical composition of the atmosphere. A first priority task, in this connection, appears to be the monitoring of such gases whose concentration is already subject to changes as a result of man's economic activity. Such gases are CO_2, CH_4, N_2O, NO_x and SO_x, as well as carbon monoxide.

There are sound grounds to believe that chemical and photochemical processes in the stratosphere and mesosphere which have been changing under the influence of cosmic factors (solar proton events, galactic cosmic rays) are responsible for mechanisms determining the effect of cosmic factors on climate.

A key factor in the formation of the atmospheric chemical composition is its interaction with the ocean, which is a sink area for CO_2 and nitrogen oxides, but a source (in regions of coastal lowlands and productive zones) of CH_4, H_2S and $(CH_3)_2S$, as well as of halogens, nitrous oxide and water vapour for the atmosphere. An urgent problem is that of examining the gas exchange between the ocean and the atmosphere as a consequence of respective chemical, physical and biological processes. The cardinal role of the ocean in the formation of the sulphur cycle requires special attention. The interaction between processes in the ocean and on the land through rivers, estuaries and coastal zones also deserves close consideration. In this case, assessments of the input to the ocean of fresh waters, carbon, phosphorus and suspended matter are needed above all.

Atmospheric aerosols play an important role because it is an optically active atmospheric component affecting the formation of climate (Kondratyev, 1987b, 1990 a,d, 1992). Volcanic stratospheric aerosols causing strong and long-term disturbances in the radiative regime, and climatic changes accompanying them, produce an essential factor of the impact of natural aerosols on radiation and global climate (dust storms are an important regional factor). The presence of anthropogenic tropospheric aerosols is responsible for such consequences as the trend of growing atmospheric turbidity and the formation of an aerosol haze at high latitudes of the Northern hemisphere. The mechanism of gas-to-particle conversion is highly important in all cases (it plays a leading part in the case of volcanic stratospheric aerosols), which determines the interaction between the biogeochemical cycles of sulphur and nitrogen and the processes forming atmospheric aerosols. The effect of aerosols on the processes of formation and destruction of cloud cover has hardly been studied at all, and this is a serious problem. The crucial importance of smoke aerosols produced by fires originated by nuclear explosions has already been mentioned above.

One more first-priority component of the IGBP is doubtless the problem of biological productivity on the land and in the ocean. Conditions required for biological productivity on the land surface are determined by the resources of water, nutrients and light; for the ocean, the latter two factors are significant. Hence it follows that to assess the land surface conditions, one needs information about the spatial–temporal distribution and intensity of precipitation. Flows of nutrients carried by rivers and brought to oceanic coastal zones are of decisive value as factors of oceanic bioproductivity. They are mixed and finally come to deep ocean layers. Equally important is the transport of the matter from the land surface to the ocean through the atmosphere.

Estimations of the second factor are complicated because contemporary climate models are unreliable from the point of view of describing the global distribution of rainfall, and also because it is necessary to take into account the increasing anthropogenic emissions of optically active minor gaseous components. This leads to changes in the temperature regime, affects water cycle, causes the formation of acid precipitation and changes in the concentration of toxic gases, soil fertility, the content of nutrients in rivers and the shelf zone. Essential for the impact on the bioproductivity can also be the variation of the intensity of ultraviolet solar radiation at the Earth's surface level caused by atmospheric contamination. An important task is, first, to reveal the naturally induced variability in bioproductivity and, second, to analyse the anthropogenic impact on the biosphere. To solve this very complicated problem, a whole number of projects along the lines of basic directions of research must be accomplished.

One of these is the global cycle of water, whose formation is determined by the interaction of the thermal regime and circulation of the atmosphere, processes of evaporation (including evapotranspiration), transport and phase transformations of water in the atmosphere; here, atmospheric circulation is interactively coupled with the radiative regime, which is subject to the effect of anthropogenically induced variations in atmospheric composition (chemically and biologically active components included). Among the difficulties arising in the course of the solution of the water cycle problem there are: insufficient reliability of estimates of evapotranspiration on the land, evaporation and precipitation in the oceans, inadequacy of the description of the processes of cloud formation and rainfall. In particular, the role of vegetation cover in the transport of water from the soil to the atmosphere should be further studied. Quite fragmentary remain data on the global climatology of cloud cover, the distribution of precipitation over oceans and evaporation from the ocean surface.

The leading role of the ocean in the formation of the global water cycle and climate determines the key importance of the problem of the interaction between the atmosphere and the ocean, and in this connection, of the Programme "Razrezy" ("Sections") (see Kondratyev and Pokrovsky, 1989). The interaction between the atmosphere and land surface has been studied evidently insufficiently; that is why an International Conference on the Parametrization of Land Surface Processes was held in 1982, and later the International Satellite Land Surface Climatology Projects (ISLSCP) was initiated.

The snow and ice covers are of fundamental climate-forming significance, as well as their variability. The high albedo of snow and ice determines a strong (and interactive) dependence of climate on variations in the extent and properties of snow and ice covers. Sea ice plays an important role as a thermal insulation layer (which accounts for the great contribution of heat exchange through polynyas and leads at high latitudes), and as a thermal-intertial component which transforms the annual temperature variation by shifting the extrema due to the latent heat release during freezing in autumn and the heat expenditure for melting in spring. As a sensitive component of the climate system, ice cover is a good indicator of climatic changes.

A fact of principal importance is that the continental biomass has been assessed to an accuracy of about a factor of 2; changes on a scale of decades are known only very approximately. The situation is aggravated by the enormous scale of the impact of man's economic activity on natural ecosystems during the last 100 years (deforestation, broad application of monocultures in agriculture, etc.). Far more precise estimations are required for the total biomass for individual ecosystems and the land surface on the whole. Such estimations will make possible a more reliable analysis of the effect of changes in land use, climate, and the income of nutrients, on global primary bioproductivity. Here are first-priority directions of research: (1) the effect of the income of biogenic components (in particular, of nitrogen, phosphorus, sulphur), variation of oxidant concentrations, acid rains and heavy metal deposition on carbon reservoirs; (2) the counter-reaction of biota on changes in the environment; (3) factors regulating the carbon ratio between living and dead components of ecosystems, and their dependence on anthropogenic impacts.

The International Geosphere–Biosphere Programme (IGBP), which has been in the implementation phase since 10 September 1990, comprises seven key directions of research:

1. Regular features of chemical processes in the global atmosphere and the role of biological processes in minor gaseous component cycles.

Research within this subject includes two core projects (CP).

1.1. The International Global Atmospheric Chemistry Project (IGAC) is a core project stipulating:

1.1.1. Study of processes responsible for the variation of the chemical composition of the atmosphere.

1.1.2. Examination of the interactions between the atmospheric chemical composition, biospheric and climatic processes.

1.1.3. Forecast of the effect of natural and anthropogenic factors on the atmospheric chemical composition.

1.2. The Stratosphere–Troposphere Interactions and the Biosphere (STIB) is a core project that planned:

1.2.1. To analyse the consequences of the variations of the ozone concentration in the stratosphere for the penetration of biologically dangerous UV radiation to the Earth's surface.

1.2.2. To obtain quantitative estimates of the processes of interaction between the stratosphere and troposphere.

1.2.3. To assess the natural variability of the stratosphere and the impact on it from anthropogenic factors.

1.2.4. To obtain quantitative estimates of the effect of aerosol on climate.

1.2.5. To assess the influence of processes in the stratosphere on climate. A project of this kind has been approved as part of the WCRP.

2. The effect of biogeochemical processes in the ocean on climate and the counter-effect of the climate changes on the ocean. Two projects are envisaged:

2.1. The Joint Global Ocean Flux Study (JGOFS).

2.1.1. Study on a global scale of processes responsible for the dynamics of the income of carbon fluxes and other accompanying nutrients to the ocean, as well as assessment of gas exchange between the atmosphere, the sea bottom, and continental boundaries.

2.1.2. Development of methods of forecasting on a global scale of the reaction of biogeochemical processes in the ocean to anthropogenic disturbances. especially those relevant to climate change.

The first field investigations within the project were accomplished in 1989 in the Atlantic Ocean.

2.2. The Global Ocean Euphotic Zone Study (GOEZS), taking account of the interaction between physical, chemical and biological processes.

3. The effect of changes in land use on the resources of coastal zones of seas and oceans, as well as the effect of changes in the ocean level and climate on coastal ecosystems. This direction of research will be realized through the GOEZS project.

3.1. The Land–Ocean Interactions in the Coastal Zone (LOICZ) is aimed at:

3.1.1. Development of methods of forecasting the effects of changes in climate, land use and ocean level on the functioning and stability of coastal ecosystems under global scales with an account of the first-priority value of the interactions between the varying conditions on the land surface and in the ocean, and possible feedbacks of the effects of physical processes in the environment.

4. Interaction between the vegetation cover and physical processes responsible for the formation of the global water cycle.

4.1. The Biological Aspects of the Hydrological Cycle (BAHC). Research within this project is planned to be complementary to the Global Energy and Water Cycle Experiment (GEWEX), which is a component part of the World Climate Research Programme (WCRP).

4.1.1. Study of the impact of the biosphere on the water cycle on the basis of field observations aimed at the development of models of energy- and moisture exchange in the system "soil–vegetation cover–atmosphere", with spatial–temporal scale from the elements of vegetation cover to the cell of general atmospheric circulation models.

4.1.2. Development of databases which may be used to characterize interactions between the biosphere and physical processes in the environment, as well as to verify the reliability of simulation models of such interactions.

5. The effect of global change on continental ecosystems.

5.1. The Global Change and Terrestrial Ecosystems (GCTE)—a core project.

5.1.1. Development of methods for forecasting the effects of climate change, CO_2 concentration and land use on ecosystems, as well as assessment of consequences of such effects on the formation of feedbacks between the biosphere and the environment. The project will focus on the following three basic directions of research: (1) the physiology of ecosystems; (2) the dynamics of ecosystems; (3) the impact on agriculture and forestry.

5.2. The Global Change and Ecological Complexity (GCEC)—a core project.

5.2.1. Development of methods for forecasting the relationships between global change and biodiversity (ecological complexity).

6. Palaeoecological and palaeoclimatic changes and their consequences.

6.1. Past Global Changes (PAGES)—a core project.

6.1.1. The reconstruction of the detailed history of changes in climate and the environment on a global scale over a period 2000 BC till the present moment, with a temporal resolution of not less than 10 years (better of one year or season).

6.1.2. A reconstruction of the history of climatic and environmental changes over a complete glaciation cycle, aimed at achieving more profound understanding of natural processes responsible for climate change.

7. A systematic approach to simulation numerical modelling of the Earth's system to enable the forecast of its evolution in the future.

7.1. Global Analysis, Interpretation and Modelling (GAIM)—a core project.

7.1.1. Quantitative estimations of the interaction between global, physical, chemical, and biological interactive processes in the Earth's system during the last 100 thousand years, with special emphasis on the analysis of potential future changes.

Further development of the IGBP (IGBP, 1994a) has led to the formulation of six key research questions. Each is now addressed by an established Core Project, with an operational duration of about a decade:

- How is the chemistry of the global atmosphere regulated, and what is the role of biological processes in producing and consuming trace gases? (International Global Atmospheric Chemistry project, IGAC). Priority issues: Chemical transformations, and biospheric sources and sinks (marine and terrestrial), of atmospheric constituents that have a role in controlling the global system, especially radiatively active trace gases, aerosols and reactive radicals.

- How will global changes affect terrestrial ecosystems? (Global Change and Terrestrial Ecosystems, GCTE). Priority issues: Responses of natural and managed ecosystems to changes in climate, atmospheric composition and land use, with emphasis on both impacts and feedback processes, investigated experimentally and through the development of dynamic vegetation models; the role of ecological complexity in the functioning of the global system.

- How does vegetation interact with the physical processes of the hydrological cycle? (Biospheric Aspects of the Hydrological Cycle, BAHC). Priority issues: The effect of land surface properties (soil, vegetation and topography) on water, carbon and energy fluxes; temporal and spatial integration of those processes, including improved modelling of complex landscapes; the down-scaling of climate information obtained from general circulation models.

- How will changes in land use, sea level rise and climate alter coastal ecosystems, and what are the wider consequences? (Land–Ocean Interactions in the Coastal Zone, LOICZ). Priority issues: The effects of changes in external forcing on coastal fluxes; coastal biogeomorphology and sea level rise; carbon fluxes and trace gas emissions; economic and social impacts of global change on coastal systems.

- How do ocean biogeochemical processes influence and respond to climate change? (Joint Global Ocean Flux Study, JGOFS). Priority issues: Processes controlling the fluxes of carbon and associated biogenic elements within the ocean, and their exchanges with the atmosphere, sea floor and continental boundaries; interpretation and application of remotely sensed ocean colour data.

• What significant climatic and environmental changes occurred in the past, and what were their causes? (Past Global Changes, PAGES). Priority issues: High resolution reconstruction, at the global scale, of the changes occurring in the past 2000 years; investigations of the more radical re-organizations of the global system during the most recent glacial/interglacial cycles.

Two other Projects are being developed for possible acceptance: Land Use/Cover Change (LUCC), and at an earlier stage of planning, the Global Ocean Euphotic Zone Study (GOEZS).

Two important and independently carried out directions of research (each embracing the needs of all CP) involve:

(1) Development of a Data and Information System (DIS) to ensure the archiving and broad access to the IGBP data for long periods of time.
(2) Creation of Regional Research Centres (RRCs) oriented towards stimulation and support of regional ecological research, especially in developing countries. The latter programme has been later transformed into a system of analysis, research and education in the area of global change (START) which is being accomplished at present very actively (see Report... (1992)).

A special place belongs to the problem of global modelling (IGBP, 1994b).

1.1.2 The US global change research programme

Of special interest is the development of the US Global Change Research Programme (USGCRP) which has been discussed in detail by Asrar and Dozier (1994). They have formulated relevant problems in the form of basic questions.

Physical climate subsystem:

• How might the roles of clouds, water vapour, and aerosols in the Earth's radiation and heat budgets change with increased atmospheric greenhouse gas concentrations? What other radiative feedback mechanisms lead or respond to changes in climate?
• How do the oceans interact with the atmosphere in the transport and uptake of heat, and what role do they play in global and regional climatic variability?
• How do atmospheric circulation and oceanic circulation affect the mass balance of ice sheets, glaciers, and ice caps, and what is the effect on sea level?
• How do land-surface properties (eg snow cover, evapotranspiration, land use, vegetation) influence circulation?
• How do changes in the energy output of the Sun influence climate?

Biogeochemical cycles:

• What roles do the oceanic and terrestrial components of the biosphere play in the changing global carbon budget? How are these roles shifting as atmospheric carbon dioxide increases?

- How do changes in the physical/chemical climate system link to changes in photosynthesis and evaporation? What are the principal natural and anthropogenic sources of carbon dioxide and methane, and what are the contributions from fossil fuels, biomass burning, and changes in land use versus natural sources?
- Is the changing chemical composition of the troposphere altering the atmospheric lifetimes of key radiatively and chemically active gases? What determines the oxidizing capacity of the troposphere, and how do biological and industrial processes affect it?
- What are the likely effects on natural and managed ecosystems of increased carbon dioxide, acid deposition, shifting patterns of precipitation, and changes in soil erosion, river chemistry, and atmospheric ozone concentrations?
- What are the feedback mechanisms and linkages between climate, atmospheric and river-borne geochemical loading to the ocean, and ecosystems?
- What are the mechanisms that determine magnitudes, locations, and frequencies of volcanic eruptions, and what are their effects on climate? How do changing patterns of land use affect the flux of aerosols and wind-borne dust into the atmosphere, and how might these processes affect the climate system?

Hydrologic cycle:

- How will atmospheric variability, human activities, and climate change affect patterns of humidity, precipitation, evapotranspiration, and soil moisture—as well as distributions of liquid water, snow, and ice—on the Earth's surface? How would any redistribution influence global sea level?
- What controls the mechanisms for the transfer of water among the hydrologic reservoirs, and what are the associated directions and magnitudes of transfer?
- How does soil moisture vary in time and space, and what are the mechanisms controlling rainfall in arid and semi-arid regions? How does this variability affect the hydrology, geomorphology, and ecology of such regions, and how do these variations translate into regional fields of carbon exchange?
- What is the role of climatic change in the cryosphere? The cryosphere has an internal system and a margin in which strong interactions occur with the physical and biogeochemical subsystems. How will the cryospheric system change internally, and how will these changes ripple through the global climate system?
- How well can we predict changes in the global hydrologic cycle using present and future observation systems and models? How can we best determine the interannual variability of global hydrologic processes, from natural variability and the seasonal cycle, to infer the mechanisms and magnitudes of climate change?

Asrar and Dozier (1994) have emphasized the three conceptual features relevant to global change:

(1) Global change research has reached the point where progress requires an integration of traditional disciplines, and many disciplines have reached the state of maturity where they are ready for that integration.
(2) The view of Earth from space has underscored the fact that the planet is a single, complex, integrated system.
(3) The growing awareness and apprehension about the effects of human-induced global change make a concerted scientific effort essential, and they increase the importance of reanalysing remote-sensing data acquired over the past two decades to understand and predict the evolution of the Earth system and our role in it.

Several central problems of global change deserve special attention (Asrar and Dozier, 1994):

• The greenhouse effect associated with increasing concentrations of carbon dioxide, methane, CFCs, and other radiatively active gases
• Ozone depletion in the stratosphere, resulting in a significant increase in ultraviolet radiation reaching the Earth's surface
• A diminishing supply of water suitable for human use
• Deforestation and other anthropogenic changes to the Earth's surface, potentially affecting the carbon budget, patterns of evaporation, precipitation, soil erosion, and other components of the system
• Changes in photosynthesis, respiration, transpiration, and trace gas exchange both on the land and in the ocean
• Decline in the health of vegetation caused by long-term changes in the chemistry of the atmosphere, precipitation, runoff, and groundwater.

1.1.3 Ecological monitoring
The exceptional complexity of modelling, and more so of forecasting global ecodynamics require creating an adequate system of ecological monitoring to be able to obtain sufficiently comprehensive observation data. The most promising research directly relevant to the above is being presently implemented in the USA within the programme "Mission to Planet Earth", whose observational component is the Earth Observing System (EOS). In what follows, we shall give a brief characterization of efforts being undertaken in this regard. Naturally, the substantiation of EOS must proceed from the analysis of the priorities of global and regional ecology. Although the subject has been treated in quite a few publications during recent years (see Kondratyev, 1990 a, d; Pokrovsky, 1981; Research Strategies..., 1990; The Spirit of Rio..., 1992), we shall examine some of its key aspects concerning the substantiation of priorities and requirements to observation data.

Moore (1984) has been absolutely right to say that, from the viewpoint of a researcher of the geosphere–biosphere, of special interest is study of biogeophysical cycles of carbon, nitrogen, phosphorus and sulphur, which are governed by both natural, and anthropogenic factors (see also Moore, 1994; Moore and Braswell, 1994). The latter ones are of particular significance for the carbon cycle, which has not been sufficiently investigated so far. The main sources of uncertainties are processes relevant to the contribution of the continental biomass dynamics (deforestation, etc.), and also to changes in the total productivity of ecosystems which are due to variations of other components' cycles (Kondratyev, 1990 a, d; Melack, 1984). This is what detemines the need for satellite monitoring of the biomass dynamics on a global scale with "telescopy" to obtain assessments of detailed spatial–temporal variability of the biomass in individual regions, which can be reliable only if there are adequate control data of direct ground-based measurements.

The key aspect of the carbon cycle relates to estimates of the contribution of the sea biota and the carbon exchange between the atmosphere and the ocean. Of principal significance is the accounting of the interaction between the cycles of carbon and nitrogen. The nitrogen cycle dynamics is determined by three processes with different time constants: long-term processes of the transport of nitrogen to and out of the atmosphere; a faster nitrogen exchange inside the biosphere; the growing income of anthropogenically induced nitrogen (due to high-temperature combustion processes alone, about 20 Mt of nitrogen per year is emitted into the atmosphere, and the utilization of fertilizers adds about 40 Mt of bound nitrogen per year to this amount). However, the global anthropogenic impact on the nitrogen cycle still remains negligible in comparison with the nitrogen reservoirs in the soil and in oceans. It may become substantial only over several decades (or in about a hundred years).

Unlike the cycles of carbon, nitrogen and sulphur, the phosphorus cycle is independent of processes in the atmosphere. In this case, the main processes are connected with dissolved and particle-shaped phosphorus that can be found in river waters, with soil weathering and biogenesis processes in sedimentary rocks. The important problems of the contribution of river-carried phosphorus, involved in the biological cycle, and the characteristic time scales of the transport of phosphorus to the ocean, have not been resolved so far. Among the basic aspects of studying the global phosphorus cycle there are: (1) mechanisms controlling the presence of phosphorus in soils, including the effect of anthropogenic factors (for instance, acid rains); (2) the transport of phosphorus to the ocean by river waters; (3) the relationship between the ocean bioproductivity and the phosphorus concentration (in particular, the influence of phosphorus income on the fixation of nitrogen in coastal zones).

The problem of anthropogenic impact on the sulphur cycle is of great interest. There are indirect assessments that indicate that by now the emissions of gas-phase sulphur to the atmosphere (due to fuel burning processes) have reached the order of magnitude of the contribution of natural factors. Of special interest are: (1) estimations of biologically induced gaseous compounds of reduced sulphur, studies of processes and anthropogenic impacts determining them; (2) study of the transformation of anthropogenic emissions of sulphur dioxide and transformations of gaseous sulphur compounds in the atmosphere in general, including gas-to-particle reactions of the formation of sulphate aerosol which may affect climate to a great extent (Kondratyev et al., 1992ab; Kondratyev and Grassl, 1996). Since processes of anthropogenic impact on biogeochemical cycles are slow and sluggish, it is urgently needed to be able to trace such dangerous tendencies well beforehand.

Delwiche (1984) has demonstrated that satellite remote sensing techniques form the most reliable basis for studying the peculiar features of the geographical distribution of ecosystems and boundaries between them, the scales and rates of anthropogenic impact on ecosystems, and the effect of climate and other factors on ecosystems. These techniques are especially important from the viewpoint of monitoring the variability of biogeochemical cycles, controlling the primary biomass dynamics and chlorophyll concentration. Table 1.1 presents a brief characterization of the requirements from observational data. Lidar sounding (mainly, employing the principle of differential absorption) appears to be the most promising method.

Table 1.1. Requirements from data of remote observations of biogeochemical sources, sinks and fluxes

Observed values	Observation target	Special region
Ecosystem boundary	Indicators of variations caused by environmental changes	Visible or near IR
Turbidity plumes in rivers	Indicators of erosion and eutrophication	Ditto
Chlorophyll content in the ocean	Indicators of primary productivity and its variations	Visible (including observations of forced fluorescence)
Atmospheric parameters: CH_4—total content in the troposphere CH_4—source intensity (and gradient) in individual regions	Intensity of biological and anthropogenic sources, lifetime	IR-absorption or lidar sounding
N_2O—total content in the atmosphere and (desirably) gradients over individual regions	Biological and anthropogenic (agricultural) sources	IR- or lidar sounding
CH_3Br—total content and (desirably) gradients $(CH_3)_2S$, $(CH_3)SH$, H_2S	Discrimination of assumed biological sources	IR-absorption or lidar sounding
Total content and (desirably) gradients	Discrimination of assumed biological sources and the duration of their functioning	IR-absorption or lidar sounding
NH_3—gradients in the troposphere over individual regions (forests, emission regions, etc.)	Intensity of biological sources	?
Non-methane hydrocarbons —gradients in the troposphere over individual regions	Discrimination of assumed biological sources and the duration of their functioning	?

The World Ocean (see Chase and McGoldrick, 1984) plays a key role in the formation of global cycles of biogenic components. With regard to biogeochemical cycles, the ocean functions as a huge reservoir of biogenic components. Component parts of crucial importance of the functioning of this reservoir are: the exchange of matter between the upper and deep oceanic layers, between ocean and land, between ocean and atmosphere. In many cases, the rates of this exchange are not reliably known. The ocean bioproductivity, low as it is per unit of area, totals to a considerable share of the biospheric productivity due to the greatness of the oceanic area, and it is closely connected with biogeochemical cycles. Thus, for instance, the rate of transformation of nitrate into organic compounds of nitrogen is dependent on the productivity of phytoplankton, which in turn is determined by the presence of nutrients.

In the sphere of studies of global biogeochemical cycles and ocean productivity, of special interest are: (1) mapping of the spatial–temporal variability of the biomass and phytoplankton productivity in the World Ocean; (2) interaction between biological and physical processes and its effect on the distribution and growth rate of the phytoplankton biomass. In this connection, of key importance are the following aspects: (1) detection of regions with marked mesoscale variability of productivity; (2) analysis of the influence of this kind of variability on global productivity and biogeochemical cycles; (3) "climatology", the seasonal and interannual variability of the biomass productivity; (4) contrasts between the oceans of the southern and northern hemispheres, the coastal and oceanic waters; (5) the vertical structure of the biomass and productivity, its temporal variations, the effect on the processes of horizontal redistribution.

In the investigation of the interaction between biological and physical processes, the priority issues are the following: (1) the relationship between mesoscale phenomena (vortices, meandering fronts, coastal jet stream current, etc.) and mesoscale distributions of biomass and productivity; (2) the effect of the bottom and coast topography on biological processes; (3) the connection between meso- and large-scale processes; (4) processes controlling the matter exchange between coastal and oceanic waters; (5) the influence of the general circulation of the ocean (including surface currents, return currents and long waves) on remote geographical regions of the World Ocean; (6) the effect of climate on biological processes; (7) the distribution of basic nutrients; (8) the income of nutrients from deep waters to surface ones; (9) the parameterization of mixing in the surface layer.

From the viewpoint of requirements to observational data, the main role belongs to information about the spatial–temporal variability of the phytoplankton biomass and primary productivity, which can be obtained with instrumentation of the type of the ocean colour scanner for the 350–800 nm region (with the 10 nm resolution), which ensures the obtainment of global information for 24 h with the spatial resolution of above 1 km in coastal zones, and 4 × 4 km in the open sea. To observe the chlorophyll fluorescence, data in the 600–750 nm with the 5 km resolution are required, and global mapping of bioluminescence will provide data in the 450–550 nm interval (the 10 nm resolution) with the spatial resolution of 5 × 5 km. Satellite observations should be accompanied by control ship and buoy observations.

It is a known fact that the World Ocean plays the key role in mitigating the Earth's climate owing to its gigantic inertia, the transport of heat to the poles, and the formation of cloud cover. Of equal importance is the contribution of the ocean to the global cycle of carbon, as well as the processes of transport and transformation of biogenic components governing the bioproductivity conditions (Chase and McGoldrick, 1984).

A classical picture of the oceanic general circulation built on the basis of the analysis of ship observational data cannot be absolutely reliable for the following two reasons: (1) the fields of oceanographic characteristics compiled from fragmentary (and time-differing) data of ship observations cannot be considered representative (although a relatively large amount of energy constitutes the share of low-frequency components of the transport, an essential role belongs to the dynamic and kinematic interaction between smaller and larger-scale motions); (2) the contribution of variations in the ocean surface level to the formation of the pressure field in the oceanic thickness remains unknown. Therefore, one of the most urgent problems is that of combined application of conventional and satellite observational means for more comprehensive studies of the dynamics and thermal regime of the World Ocean.

Table 1.2 shows the first-priority value of the physical characteristics of the ocean and requirements from relevant observational data. In addition, one should mention the possibility of finding the velocity vector of sea currents by following drifting buoys and acoustic generators from satellites. What is important in principle is the combination of the analysis of observational data and numerical simulation experiments.

Melack (1984) states that the central aspect of biospheric studies is reduced to finding to what extent the Earth's surface, atmosphere and hydrosphere are subject to the impact of biological, and not abiotic, processes. Considerable progress may be expected in this connection from the use of satellite observation means for monitoring the biological productivity and that part of biogeochemical cycles that is relevant to water systems.

So far we have not been able to obtain reliable quantitative estimates of the influence of living organisms on the atmospheric or hydrospheric composition, or sedimented rocks. Hence the necessity for estimating the role of diatomic algae and swamps in global biogeochemical cycles, which requires: (1) evaluation of the areals of these organisms or ecosystems; (2) measurements of the fixation of carbon, the rates of accumulation of deposits and gas formation.

In the light of large-scale anthropogenic impact on the carbon, nitrogen, sulphur and phosphorus cycles, there is an urgent need for measurements of natural and total fluxes of these elements on a global scale. This requires development of remote sensing of the biological productivity, as well as the fluxes of various components between inland waterbodies, ocean, land and atmosphere, taking account of a number of specific features of inland waterbodies: (1) a broad range of sizes (from 100 km to 1 km in length); (2) the wide territorial spread; (3) the extended boundary between water and land; (4) an extremely broad range of optical conditions (e.g. the chlorophyll concentration may vary from 0.01 to 100 mg/m^3); (5) rapid changes in

Table 1.2. Requirements from observational data relevant to physical oceanography

Observed values	Observation target	Observational data
Ocean surface topography	Oceanic circulation: geostrophic velocity near the surface, localization of mesoscale phenomena (fronts, vortices, rings); interaction between physical and biological processes.	Ratioaltimeter on satellite with orbit inclination angle 65° (non-helio-synchronous orbit with repetition of orbits 10–20 days): IR- and microwave radiometer for atmospheric correction.
Significant wave height ($H_{1/3}$)	Forecast of wind, waves and swelling sea.	Radioaltimeter, synthetic aperture radar (SAR).
Sea surface temperature	Interaction between atmosphere and ocean, and between physical and biological processes.	IR radiometers of the type used on meteorological satellites.
Wind stress near the ocean surface	Oceanic circulation (wind-induced, ageostrophysical component, upwellings), interaction between ocean and atmosphere.	Scatterometer in Ku band, measurements every 50 km in band $\pm 70°$ of latitude every two days.
Spectrum of surface water directions	Forecast of waves and wind, monitoring of storm movement.	SAR, scatterometer, scanning short-pulse radioaltimeter.

biological, chemical and physical conditions with time (with characteristic time variations from seconds to weeks, but for changes of special ecological significance— of the order of several days); (6) the importance of episodic and periodic fluctuations; (7) the presence of strong horizontal and vertical gradients of biological and physico-chemical characteristics.

Table 1.3 contains schematic requirements from observational data for inland waterbodies. The biological productivity can be found from the data of measurements of photosynthetic activity, which requires measuring the amount of photosynthetizing substance, the carbon fixation rate and determining the portion of fixed carbon consumed by other organisms or accumulated in precipitation. Fluxes of various components from land to inland waterbodies are mostly dependent on the manner of land use in the water catchment basin, and hydrological conditions. For instance, estimations of the income of nutrients to lakes from remote sensing data and information on the water catchment area, including land use and snow cover, have already become feasible.

Considering the important role of forests in the formation of biogeochemical cycles of carbon and nitrogen, and also the impact of forests on the energy and water budgets, Zinke (1984) mentions the necessity of solving the following problems: (1) the influence of forests (including the problem of deforestation) on the formation of precipitation on a large spatial scale; (2) the influence of forests on the local and regional energy budgets, and hence on climate; (3) the role of forests as a source or

Table 1.3. Requirements from observational data for inland waterbodies

Object of observation	Observation target	Instrumentation characterization
Regions of swamps and floods	Biological productivity, nitrogen fixation. Sources of reduced gases.	Multispectral images (including SAR), with resolution 30 m, once per day/twice per week.
Chlorophyll of phytoplankton and biomass	Spatial–temporal inhomegeneity of biological productivity.	Multispectral images (30 m), including spectrometric measurements of fluorescence.
Land use over water catchment area	Content of nutrients and suspended matter (as related to water quality and productivity).	Multispectral images (including SAR), 30 m, once per month/year.
Runoff and relevant hydrologic parameters	Content of nutrients and suspended matter.	Visible, IR, and microwave regions, once per day/week.
Surface temperature	Hydrography, evaporation and productivity.	IR images, 30 m, once per day/week.

sink of carbon dioxide; (4) the effect of such parameters of inland water quality as the temperature and turbidity of water in rivers and lakes, etc., on the practical aspects of land use resulting in variations in vegetation and forests in the water catchment basin.

Table 1.4 illustrates approximate requirements from observational data which can be obtained by remote sensing methods and are aimed at estimating the components of the hydrologic and energy budgets, and also biogeochemical cycles. One such example is the study of the contribution of tropical forests in the Amazon river basin as a source of water, which requires an analysis of the water balance of forests taking account of precipitation and evapotranspiration.

Data presented in Table 1.5, compiled by Kanemasu (1984), illustrate the requirements from observations of parameters characterizing biological processes on land. In this connection, one of the most important problems is the presence of water and the capability of plants to extract water from the soil, both of which strongly influence the processes of transpiration and photosynthesis. The key position belongs to studying the specific features of the energy balance of various ecosystems: deserts, forests, savannahs, agricultural areas, etc. The quantity and quality of vegetation in these systems are in a considerable interdependence with the character of processes taking place in neighbouring regions. For instance, it is obvious that deforestation and desertification heavily affect areas which are outside the limits of their direct influence, and lead to noticeable changes in CO_2 and water vapour fluxes, as well as nutrients fluxes over vast regions.

The river runoff and the motion of suspended matter introduce radical changes

Table 1.4. Requirements from date of observations of forests and natural vegetation

Observed values	Observation target	Observational data
Mass and energy fluxes incident and reflected shortwave radiation, relationship between fluxes of radiation, latent and sensible heat	Components of energy budget of forests and natural vegetation Effect of deforestation on microclimate and spread of diseases	Visible and IR spectral regions spatial resolution 50–60 m, at least once a month. Surface temperature, albedo, water vapour content, 50–60 m, once per month.
Hydrologic cycle components: precipitations, evapotranspiration, river runoff, moisture content of soil, snow content	Local and regional water budget for main rivers, and effect on it of land use and deforestation	Microwave measure ments of moisture content in soil (1 km^2) and in atmosphere; measurements of runoff and stagnant water surface; once per month
Density, structure and biomass of vegetation cover	Interrelationship between vegetation characteristics and energy and water budgets	Multispectral images (brightness fields), 60 m
Soil characteristics	Carbon and nitrogen content in soils	Regression relationship between multispectral satellite and ground-based data
State of vegetation	Assessment of state of vegetation, its classification and monitoring of seasonal dynamics	Multispectral images

into the water medium properties for downstream river currents. The surface albedo variation affects the thermal balance and climate. The interaction between the land surface, atmosphere and ocean present under such conditions is of primary interest, and for complete understanding of this interaction more comprehensive observational data are required. Data on the thermal balance of the Earth's surface which must be obtained from combined conventional and satellite observation means are certainly first-priority data. It can be seen from Table 1.5 that quite a number of biophysical characteristics (the leaf area index, phytomass, morphology and temperature) may be found by making use of remote sensing techniques.

On a time scale of a decade and more, the atmosphere, land and ocean function as an interdependent system with regard to not only physical, but also chemical and biological processes. In this connection, Mohnen (1984) analysed the role of the troposphere from the viewpoint of basic processes taking place there which govern

Table 1.5. Requirements from observations of biological processes on land

Observed values	Observation target	Observational data
Leaf area index, phytomass	Latent heat and CO_2 flux, phytomass of major ecosystems	Visible, IR and microwave regions, resolution 30 m, observations of individual regions at 13–15 h, every 3–5 days
Morphology of vegetation	Species discrimination, light absorption, withering determination. Spatial variability of vegetation characteristics	Ditto. Observations at three angles of vision Ditto. Resolution 10 m
Soil moisture	Latent heat, productivity, energy balance	Microwave radiometry (0–5 cm layer)
Surface temperature	Energy balance, drought, desertification	IR radiometry, 30 m, once per day, around noontime

the chemical composition and the cycles of various tropospheric components and determine its response to external impacts.

The following problems are of key importance: (1) the contribution of biological sources to the formation of the cycles of the compounds of carbon, sulphur, nitrogen and halogens (the most significant areas are the forests of medium and tropical latitudes, zones of grass cover, intensively cultivated regions, coastal waters and salted swamps, the continental shelf zones, as well as those of upwelling and tundra; the open ocean; regions of biomass burning); (2) the intensity of aerosol sources (dust, fuel combustion, etc.) on a regional and continental scale (the desert aerosol is of special interest); (3) the global distribution of basic gaseous and aerosol components taking part in chemical cycles, and the hydrological cycle components (water vapour, clouds, precipitation), with special reference to studying the photochemical processes, and dry and wet deposition of gases and particles (here, numerical simulation modelling becomes very important). Table 1.6 illustrates the approximate requirements to the data of remote sensing of the chemical composition of the troposphere.

The perspectives of further development of satellite remote sounding of the troposphere are mainly relevant to the solution of the problems of the global water cycle, cloud cover dynamics, interaction between the atmosphere and ocean, atmospheric circulation in the tropics and the changing gaseous composition of the troposphere. Relevant requirements to observational data are characterized in Table 1.7 (information on the gaseous composition is treated in a different section).

Although the most important aspects of the middle atmosphere have been fairly well investigated during recent years, quite a number of problems remain unsolved so far, and among these the problem of interaction between the troposphere and

Table 1.6. Requqirements to observational date relevant to the chemical composition of the troposphere

Observed values	Observational target	Observational data
CO_2, CO, CH_4	Understanding of biogeochemical cycles	Retrieval of gas content in three layers (0–15 km) with horizontal resolution 10 km and errors; ± 0.3 ppm (CO_2, 10 ppb + 3 ppm (CO), 100 ppb + 3 ppm (CH_4)
OH	Lifetime in the troposphere of such gases as CO and CH_4	Minimum detection limit $0.5 \cdot 10^4$ mol/cm^3
NO_2, NO, NH_3, N_2O	Nitrogen cycle	Detection limit 0.1 ppb
HNO_3, NO_3	Nitrogen cycle	Detection limit 0.05 ppb
SO_2, H_2S, COS and other sulphur compounds	Sulphur cycle	Detection limit 0.05 ppb
H_2, H_2O	Hydrogen cycle	Range to 0.02 ppm (H_2) and 1 ppm $\div$ $0.5 \cdot 10^3$ ppm (H_2O)
O_3	Oxygen and oxidant cycle	Range 2 ppb $\div$ 2000 ppb
Aerosol	Aerosol cycle (including sulphur and nitrogen	Range 0.1 mkg/m^3 $\div$ 100 mkg/m^3
Temperature, wind velocity, cloudiness, precipitation intensity, lightning	For interpretation of all cycles	Vertical resolution 1 km, wind velocity to 1 m/s

middle atmosphere (MA) expressed as an exchange of mass, energy and chemical components. As shown by Gille (1984), particularly important is the long-term evolution of the composition of the MA which is due, to a great extent, to anthropogenic impact. To understand this evolution, one must have data on all long-living basic components of the MA (including those that are sources of radicals, radicals themselves and molecules-"sinks" causing the removal of active components of the MA) during at least a single 11-year solar activity cycle.

Minimum requirements to observational data are presented in Table 1.8. These requirements have been mostly met by making use of instruments installed on the UARS satellite for the purpose of studying the upper atmosphere. The UARS satellite put up in 1991 in the circular orbit 600 km in apogee, at an inclination angle 57° (the planned lifetime of the satellite was 18 months) made it possible to perform the remote sounding of the atmosphere within an altitude of 0–150 km (UARS..., 1989). To retrieve the composition and temperature of the atmosphere, the satellite carried:

Table 1.7. Requirement to observational data for the troposphere

Observed values	Observation target	Requirements to observational data
Air humidity	Relationship between large-scale circulation with soil moisture and evapotranspiration	Microwave-, IR-radiometry, near IR region, lidar, not less than 3 levels below 500 with spatial averaging 2° latitude × 2° longitude, error ±20%, twice per day, global information
Moisture of upper soil layer (1 m)	—	Active and passive microwave instruments, IR-radiometry; resolution not worse than 2° × 2°, twice per day over continents
Evapotranspiration	—	The same instrumentation, estimates of moisture provision of vegetation cover
Precipitation over oceans	Annual and interannual variations of tropical oceanic moisture source	The same instrumentation, precipitation observations 4 times per day (ground-based control data are of crucial importance). To assess evaporation, data on humidity and wind profiles are required, as well as SST and cloudiness
Clouds (temperature and upper boundary height, thickness, albedo, moisture and water content), wind in tropics	Relationship between annual variation and interannual variability of climate (especially, effect of clouds on thermal budget)	Visible, near IR- and IR-spectral regions. Cloud amount (0–10) points; upper boundary height ±0.5 km 4 times per day, 2° × 2° grid.
	Study of circulation in tropics	Doppler lidar not less than 4 times per day, 100 × 100 km² grid, error ±2 m/s, at least at 3 levels

1. Cryogenic (on solid neon, −260°C) limb spectrometer based on Fabri–Perrot standard (CLAES) for the interval 3.5–12.7 μm. Spectrometric data have made it possible to retrieve the vertical profiles of the concentration of various components of the cycles of nitrogen and chlorine, ozone, water vapour, methane, and CO_2. The presence of 20 sensors determines the possibility of simultaneous measurements at 20 levels in the range 10–50 km.
2. An advanced sounder of the stratosphere and mesosphere (ISAMS), whose prototype had been carried by Nimbus-7, is a multichannel filter scanning IR

radiometer designed as a selective radiometer with gas cells, with 8 radiation sensors (cooled down to $-195°C$). The instrument covers the range 4.6–16.6 μm and enables one to retrieve the content of the compounds of nitrogen, ozone, water vapour, methane and carbon oxide.

3. Microwave limb sounder (MLS) to retrieve the vertical profiles of the concentration of chlorine oxide (this is made for the first time), hydrogen peroxide, water vapour and ozone from data on radio thermal emission at frequencies (wavelengths) 63 (4.8), 183 (1.64) and 205 GHz (1.46 nm).

4. Instruments for an occultation experiment to measure halogens (HALOE) based on measuring the absorption in the IR (2.43–10.25 μm) on "occultation" routes of solar radiation, to retrieve the content of HCl, HF, CH_4, CO_2, O_3, H_2O and various components of the family of nitrogen compounds. Like ISAMS, this 8-channel instrument is based on the principle of selective absorption (gas cells) and broad-band filters. Channel 8 ensured measurements of CO_2 absorption to retrieve atmospheric pressure.

5. A measuring complex for the satellite UARS has made it possible for the first time to obtain data on the global field of the horizontal component of winds in the upper atmosphere. The Doppler high-resolution video-spectrometer (HRDI) and video-interferometer to retrieve the wind field (WINDII) had the same aim. Both instruments scanned vertically and measured the Doppler shift of individual emission or absorption lines in two directions, which made it possible to retrieve the true wind speed, with the satellite's speed known. At altitudes below 45 km the HRDI, based on the triple Fabri–Perrot etalone, measured the Doppler shift of emission lines in the band of molecular oxygen, and estimated the wind speed with an accuracy, at least, of 5 m s^{-1}. At altitudes above 60 km, measurement will be made in the lines of neutral and ionized atomic oxygen in the visible and near-IR spectral regions, which made it possible to estimate the wind speed in the mesosphere and thermosphere with an accuracy, at least, of 15 m s^{-1}, with a vertical resolution of 4 km (the emission could be measured both at night- and in daytime).

6. The complex WINDII, being a video-interferometer, provides measurements of the Doppler shift of the emission lines. For this purpose, apart from the lines of neutral and ionized atomic oxygen, two lines of hydroxyl and one line of molecular oxygen were used. The high-resolution Fourier spectrometer served as a dispersing system for WINDII. Measurements were made simultaneously at angles of 45° and 135° with respect to the vector of the satellite's velocity. The vertical (horizontal) resolution was 4 (20) km, and the errors of the wind retrieval in the layer 80–300 km did not exceed 10 m s^{-1}. The complex UARS also included instruments to measure solar and ionizing radiation.

7. The solar spectral UV radiation monitor (SUSIM) measures extra-atmospheric insolation in the interval 120–400 nm with a resolution up to 0.1 nm, and with reliable absolute calibration. This complex consists of two spectrometers, seven radiation sensors, and four deuterium UV lamps (for calibration purposes). One spectrometer is designed to measure the solar UV radiation, the other the calibration lamps. Each day one of the four lamps was positioned before both

spectrometers to take another calibration, and its stability was controlled with the help of the remaining three lamps.

8. A special 3-channel spectrometer SOLSTICE to measure solar radiation (in daytime) and persistently bright blue stars (at night) in the interval 115–430 nm with a resolution of 0.12 nm (the stars' emission served as a standard for comparison). Each series of measurements could last from 1 s to 12 min, with the spectral transmission band varying from 0.1 to 5 nm.

9. The particles environmental monitor (PEM) provides measurements of charged particles (their type, amount and energy) including the thermosphere, the mesosphere, and the stratosphere. It consists of three units mounted on the sliding mast to measure electrons (energy 2 eV–5 eV), protons (1 eV–150 MeV), and magnetic field of the Earth. There is also a 16-element set of sensors to measure X-ray emission and to obtain X-ray images in the range 2–50 KeV.

Two most important problems arise in connection with the investigation of the role of polar glaciers in the formation of climate (see Research Strategies... (1990); The Noordwijk Declaration... (1989)): (1) assessment of the contribution of glaciers to the hydrological cycle in the "ocean–atmosphere–glaciers" system; (2) analysis of ice cores aimed at the retrieval of the palaeoclimate characteristics, as well as of variations of the concentration in the atmosphere of such components as CO_2, NO_x, SO_2, aerosols, etc., for the last 200 thousand years. Approximate estimates have

Table 1.8. Requirements to observational data relevant to the middle atmosphere

Observed values	Observation target	Requirements to observational data
Temperature	Chemistry, dynamics, transport, energetics of MA	Layer 0–150 km, with resolution 0.5 of height scale over vertical and errors not over ± 2 K (0–80
Wind		km), ± 5 K (80–120 km), ± 10 (120–150 km); errors or relative values—less by factor of 2.
Composition: molecules —sources of radicals 0_3, N_2O, CH_4, $CFCl_3$, CF_2Cl_2	Dynamics, transport	Layer 0–50 km (error ± 3 m/s); 50–150 km ± 10 m/s)
"reservoir" molecules HCl, HNO_3, H_2O_2 HNO_4, $ClONO_3$ radicals: ClO, NO, NO_2, OH, HO_2	Chemistry, transport	At various heights with error 10% (realistic) and 5% (desirable), vertical distribution 0.5 of height scale
Emissions: 0_2, $(^1\Delta g)$, OH bands, 1–4 μm, NO (2.8; 5.3 um); CO^2 (4.8; 10.4 μm)	Energetics of upper mesosphere–lower thermosphere (non-LTE)	Vertical resolution 0.5 of height scale, error $\pm 25\%$ (error of relative values $\pm 10\%$)

Table 1.9. Requirements to observational data relevant to polar glaciers

Observed values	Observation target	Requirements to observational data
Surface level height	Dynamics of glaciers	Profile measurements using a laser altimeter, with error 2 m on glacier and 0.2 m in shelf zone. Distance between profiles is 1 km
Level height variation	Dynamics and balance of glacier mass	Radioaltimeter observations for routes every 20 km, with interval 1–2 years. Error 0.1–1.0 m
Glacier boundary (from sea-side)	Speed of boundary displacement	Observations on shelf using SAR every 2 years (error 30 m) and inside glacier every 5 years (error 10 m)
Accumulation rate and surface temperature	Dynamics of glaciers	Area data about accumulation every 10–100 km (error 5 cm/year). Temperature every 100 km (data of microwave- and IR-radiometry with error 1°C/year)
Lateral stress on the surface	Modelling of ice dynamics	Localization of individual points from satellites with error 1 m and repetition rate 5–10 times per year (according to laser reflector)
Melting on the surface	Balance of mass and energy	Microwave radiometry in summer, 1–3 times around noon-time (interrogation of ground-based stations from satellite)
Breaking off of icebergs	Variations depending on hydrological conditions	Analysis of breaking off of icebergs: satellite SAR images. Estimation of regional production with error 10%.

revealed that the variability of glaciers caused by internal factors and the temperature and precipitation regime can heavily affect the climate and the World Ocean level over a time scale of one to several centuries. This shows that a study of the dynamics of glaciers based on numerical modelling and observational data is a task of primary importance.

Table 1.9 presents a summary of approximate requirements to observational data.

In the consideration of the problem of the influence of sea ice on climate, of special interest is the investigation of the interaction between ice cover and the atmosphere, particularly in the presence of polynyas and leads when this interaction is intensified in a radical way (Kondratyev, 1992). This kind of investigation should

Table 1.10. Requirements to observational data relevant to ice cover

Observed values	Observation target	Requirements to observational data
Position of ice cover boundaries	Study of ice cover characteristics, heat exchange between ocean and atmosphere	Microwave radiometers or SAR, radioaltimeter, daily, error 5–20 km
Ice concentration		The same instrumentation, daily for 10% of whole area, error about 10%.
Ice albedo		Averaged over area, with step 25–100 km and error 0.02
Ice motion		Displacement of fixed points with error 0.5 km/day, with spatial resolution 5–100 km, daily
Type and thickness of ice		Microwave radiometers, SAR, scatterometer, radioaltimeter, once per week
Ice hummocks		SAR, Landsat data, daily
Polynyas	Effect of thermal perturbations	The same instrumentation, daily
Ice field distribution		SAR, Landsat, etc., error in floe size about 10 m, once every 1–7 days
Surface melting		Microwave radiometry, daily in summer; in pack ice zone— throughout the year
Ice surface temperature		Microwave and IR radiometry, control data from buoys
Wind speed		Scatterometer, buoys, SAR
Sea surface temperature		Microwave and IR radiometry, error 1°C

be based on the employment of simulation interactive models of the "ocean–ice cover–atmosphere" system and the utilization of complex observational data for verification of the adequacy of the models. Table 1.10 shows the requirements to data of observations of the most essential values. Since the observations discussed are performed in remote regions, it is reasonable to use a special communication satellite for data transmission.

1.2 THE EARTH OBSERVATION SYSTEM (EOS)

The EOS is a multidisciplinary programme to study the Earth as a system of "atmosphere–hydrosphere–cryosphere–biosphere", planned for many years, based on the use of satellite observations made with a system of three satellites serviced (if necessary) by the personnel of a permanent orbital station (Graf, 1987). The EOS is a 15-year programme. For efficient processing and distribution of the data of satellite and conventional observations, a ground-based geoinformation system with a complex of computers will be created (later on the plans for the EOS have been substantially changed).

The satellites, twice as large as the previous Earth-resources satellites, must be put in the Sun-synchronous (inclination 98.7°) orbit 824 km high, for two satellites the time of crossing the equator being 13:30 (the ascending orbit), and for the third satellite 09:30 (the descending orbit). The orbital characteristics are chosen on the basis of a compromise in meeting the requirements put forward by various problems.

Two categories of space-borne instruments foresee: (i) obtaining the information for the global-scale mapping of the parameters of the environment and the biosphere every 2–3 days with a spatial resolution of several kilometres; (ii) obtaining data with a high resolution (tens of metres) but with a limited spatial coverage for a detailed monitoring of the processes in different regions. The developed complex should be installed on three satellites and includes 37 instruments. Table 1.11 contains a brief characteristic of the complex. It is important to emphasize, however, that financial limitations resulted in a number of changes during the course of preparations to the accomplishment of the EOS programme.

Asrar and Dozier (1994) have described an updated version of the EOS satellite series (Table 1.12).

Tables 1.13 and 1.14 contain updated information concerning the updated version of EOS instruments (Asrar and Dozier, 1994).

Asrar and Dozier (1994) have characterized the basic aims of various EOS missions in the following way:

- *EOS-AM Series*—Measurement of the diurnal properties of clouds and radiative fluxes and aerosols requires observations in morning and afternoon Sun-synchronous orbits, as well as the inclined orbits provided by TRMM and the EOS-AERO series. In addition, a group of instruments on the morning spacecraft will address issues related to land–atmosphere exchanges of energy, carbon, and water—a task that AVHRR and Landsat address now only qualitatively. Continued acquisition of Landsat data increases the likelihood of success for the EOS-AM series. EOS-AM1 will have an equatorial crossing time of 10:30, when daily cloud cover is typically at a minimum over land, so surface features can be more easily observed. The complement of instruments will obtain information about the physical and radiative properties of clouds (ASTER, CERES, MISR, MODIS); air–land and air–sea exchanges of energy, carbon, and water (ASTER, MISR, MODIS); total column measurements of methane (MOPITT); and the role of volcanoes in the climate system (ASTER, MISR, MODIS). The US provides CERES, MISR, and MODIS; Canada provides MOPITT; and Japan provides ASTER.

Table 1.11. EOS instruments

Instrument	Characteristics	Parameters
1	2	3

SISP—Surface Imaging and Sounding Package

Instrument	Characteristics	Parameters
Moderate-resolution slant-view imaging spectrometer (MODIS-T)	0.4–1.1 µm; 64 channels; spatial resolution 1 km	Biogeochemical cycles; ocean colour
Nadir-looking imaging spectrometer (MODIS-N)	0.4–1.1 µm; 36 channels; 0.5 km.	Biogeochemical cycles, temperature
High-resolution imaging spectrometer (HIRIS)	0.4–2.2 µm; 200 channels; 30 m.	Biogeochemical cycles; geology.
Thermal imaging spectrometer (TIMS)	3–6, 8–15 µm; 9 channels; 30 m	Same.
High-resolution multi-frequency microwave radiometer (HMMR)	1.4–91 GHz; 6 channels; 1.1 × 1.8 km at 91 GHz.	Brightness temperature of ocean and land surface.
Lidar atmospheric sounder and altimeter (LASA)	A set of wavelengths; receiving mirror 1.25 m in diameter	Atmospheric correction; aerosol and cloud sounding; altimetry.
Advanced automated data collection and location system (ADCLS)	Reference accuracy 2–5 km.	Mainly data from sea buoys.

SAM—Sensing with Active Microwaves

Instrument	Characteristics	Parameters
Synthetic-aperture radar (SAR)	C, L, X-bands at different polarizations; 30 m.	Characteristics of land, ice cover and vegetation.
Radar altimeter (ALT)	10-cm accuracy of height measurement.	Surface topography.
Scatterometer	Accuracy about ± 2 ms^{-1} of wind speed retrieval.	Wind shear near the ocean surface.

APACM—Atmospheric Physical and Chemical Monitor

Instrument	Characteristics	Parameters
Correlation radiometer		Retrieval of vertical profiles of CO, NH_3 concentrations
Nadir-looking Fourier spectrometer		NO_3, CH_4, H_2S retrieval.
Doppler lidar		Wind in the troposphere.
Lidar sounder, altimeter		Profiles of temperature, pressure, water vapour, ozone in the troposphere.

Table 1.11. (continued)

1	2	3
IR radiometer		Limb sounding of O_3, N_2O, etc.
Pressure-modulated radiometer		Limb sounding of $CFCl_3$, etc.
Sub-millimetre spectrometer		Limb sounding of OH, HCl, etc.
Microwave limb sounder		Atmospheric gas composition sounding.
Visible and UV spectrometer		Limb sounding of ClO, O_3, etc.
Fabri–Perrot interferometer		Wind and temperature profiles.
Cryogenic Fourier-spectrometer		Same.
	Monitors	
Solar constant monitor		
Particles and fields monitors		
Earth's radiation balance monitor		

- *EOS-COLOR Satellite*—The oceans' role in world climate is the second highest priority issue to be investigated by EOS. EOS-COLOR involves a one-time acquisition of observations of the oceans' primary productivity via a data purchase, like that for SeaWiFS scheduled for launch in early 1995. EOS-COLOR will observe ocean colour and productivity, with a specific focus on understanding the oceans' role in the global carbon cycle. This mission will provide data continuity until MODIS instruments are flying on both the EOS-AM and -PM series.

- *EOS-AERO Series*—Current plans call for the use of an internationally contributed spacecraft in a 57° inclined, 705-km (or slightly lower) orbit to optimize collection of occultation data in the equatorial and mid-latitude regions. At present, one US instrument makes up the payload—SAGE III, which measures aerosols, ozone, water vapour, and clouds from the middle troposphere through the stratosphere, all important parameters for radiative and atmospheric chemistry models.

- *EOS-PM Series*—This series' afternoon crossing time will enhance collection of meteorological data by the atmospheric sounders on board. The complement of instruments will provide information on cloud formation, precipitation, and radiative properties through AIRS, AMSU, CERES, MHS/AMSU-B, and MODIS. In concert with vector wind stress measurements from a scatterometer

Table 1.12. The EOS satellite series

Satellites (first launch)	Mission objectives
EOS-AM Series (1998) Earth Observing System Morning Crossing (Descending)	Clouds, aerosols and radiation balance, characterization of the terrestrial ecosystem; land use, soils, terrestrial energy/moisture, tropospheric chemical composition; contribution of volcanoes to climate; and ocean primary productivity (includes Canadian and Japanese instruments)
EOS-Colour (1998) EOS Ocean Colour Satellite	Ocean primary productivity
EOS-AERO Series (2000) EOS aerosol Mission	Distribution of aerosols and greenhouse gases in the stratosphere and upper troposphere (spacecraft to be provided through international cooperation)
EOS-PM Series (2001) Earth Observing System Afternoon Crossing (Ascending)	Cloud formation, precipitation, and radiative properties; atmospheric temperature and moisture profiles; air–sea fluxes of energy and moisture; sea–ice extent; and soil moisture and snow over land (includes European instruments).
EOS-ALT Series (2002) EOS Altimetry Mission	Ocean circulation and ice-sheet mass, balance (includes French instruments)
EOS-CHEM Series (2003) EOS Chemistry Mission	Atmospheric chemical composition and dynamics; chemistry–climate interactions; air–sea exchange of chemicals and energy (to include on as-yet-to-be determined Japanese instrument)

(e.g. SeaWinds on ADEOS II), AIRS/AMSU/MHS, MIMR, and MODIS will provide data for global-scale studies of air–sea fluxes of energy, moisture, and momentum. In addition, AIRS, MIMR, and MODIS will contribute to studies of sea-ice extent and heat exchange with the atmosphere. Flight of this platform during the operational lifetime of TRMM will allow assessment of the utility and accuracy of precipitation estimates, with MIMR and MODIS mapping the extent and properties of snow and its role in the climate and hydrological systems. The US provides AIRS, AMSU, CERES, and MODIS; the United Kingdom provides MHS/AMSU-B; and ESA provides MIMR.

- *EOS-ALT Series*—The EOS-ALT payload currently consists of GLAS, TMR, DORIS, and SSALT. GLAS and TMR are US instruments, and France supplies DORIS and SSALT. This payload grouping will ensure continuation of the valuable data set initiated by TOPEX/Poseidon. Investigation of ocean circulation and ice sheets (relevant to sea-level changes) requires accurate altimeter measurements. SSALT is a dual-frequency radar altimeter for the determination of ocean-surface topography, from which ocean circulation can be inferred; SSALT also measures wind speed and wave height. GLAS is a laser altimeter that will generate profiles of ice-sheet volume for Greenland and

Table 1.13. EOS instruments

Instruments in the early EOS period (1997-2001)

Atmospheric Infrared Sounder/Advanced Microwave Sounding Unit/Microwave Humidity Sounder (AIRS/AMSU/MHS)—Synergistic package that provides temperature and humidity sounding with much better accuracy than current sensors, with temperatures measured to 1 K accuracy at 1-km vertical resolution

Advanced Spaceborne Thermal Emission and Reflection Radiometer (ASTER)—Yields high-resolution images of land surface, water, and clouds from visible through thermal infrared wavelengths; one stereophotogrammetric band to enable production of digital elevation models

Clouds and Earth s Radiant Energy System (CERES)—Flies on multiple satellites in morning, afternoon, and inclined orbits to measure Earth s radiation balance

EOS Ocean Colour Satellite (EOS-COLOUR)—Observes afternoon ocean colour to provide continuity of SeaWiFS measurements of biological production; data purchase mission involving a single launch

Lightning Imaging Sensor (LIS)—Flies in an inclined orbit on TRMM in 1997, providing global observations of lightning distribution and its variability

Multifrequency Imaging Microwave Radiometer (MIMR)—Measures precipitation, cloud water, sea–surface temperature and winds, snow and ice extent, snow water equivalence, and soil moisture

Multi-Angle Imaging SpectroRadiometer (MISR)—Globally measures aerosol characteristics, bidirectional reflectances, and albedos at the top of the atmosphere and surface, cloud-top elevation and distribution, and vegetation properties; provides moderate-resolution topographic data through stereophotogrammetry

Moderate-Resolution Imaging Spectroradiometer (MODIS)—Flies in both morning and afternoon orbits to discern cloud cover, vegetation, ocean colour, surface temperatures, aerosols, and other global geophysical and biological processes for the land, ocean, and atmosphere

Measurements of Pollution in the Troposphere (MOPITT)—Measures carbon monoxide and methane

SeaWinds (NSCAT II)—Slated to fly on ADEOSII in 1999, provides all-weather measurements of near-surface and wind velocity and horizontal stress over the oceans

Stratospheric Aerosol and Gas Experiment III (SAGE III)—Generates global profiles of aerosols, clouds, ozone and related species, temperature, and pressure in the stratosphere

Antarctica. DORIS enables the precise positioning of the spacecraft (3 to 4 cm), and TMR correct the altimeter data for pulse delay propagated by water vapor. Plans are underway to separate the radar from the laser to allow flight on separate satellites to support different orbit altitude and inclination requirements.

- *EOS-CHEM Series*—EOS-CHEM instruments will provide measurements of solar energy flux (ACRIM), solar ultraviolet radiation (SOLSTICE II), and

Table 1.14. EOS instruments (continued)

Additional EOS instruments (Beyond 2001)

Active Cavity Radiometer Irradiance Monitor (ACRIM)—Measures solar irradiance reaching Earth

Doppler Orbitography and Radiopositioning Integrated by Satellite/Solid-sate Altimeter/ TOPEX Microwave Radiometer (DORIS/SSALT/TMR)—Synergistic package that provides ocean wave height and surface current velocity, sea-surface topography, wind speed, and atmospheric water vapour profiles

Earth Observing Scanning Polarimeter (EOSP)—Globally maps radiance and linear polarization of reflected sunlight to infer aerosol characteristics

Geoscience Laser Altimeter System (GLAS)—Measures the topography of land, glaciers, and ice sheets, and cloud and aerosol layer heights and thickness

High-Resolution Dynamics Limb Sounder (HIRDLS)—Globally measures temperatures; water vapour, and chemical species in the upper troposphere and stratosphere

Microwave Limb Sounder (MLS)—Globally measures parameters essential for assessing ozone depletion (radicals, reservoirs, source gases) and climate change (upper tropospheric water vapour and other greenhouse gases), with quality not degraded by aerosols or clouds

Solar Stellar Irradiance Comparison Experiment II (SOLSTICE II)—Measures ultraviolet solar irradiance

Tropospheric Emission Spectrometer (TES)—Provides global, three-dimensional profiles of virtually all infrared-active gases from the Earth s surface to the lower stratosphere

---

atmospheric temperature, aerosols, and gases (HIRDLS, MLS, SAGE III), including the greenhouse gases and the chemical radicals, reservoirs, and source gases that affect ozone depletion. HIRDLS, SAGE III, and MLS—along with MOPITT on EOS-AM1 and -AM2, and SAGE III on EOS-AERO—provide critical data related to tropospheric and lower stratospheric chemistry and dynamics, including troposphere–stratosphere exchanges.

- *Other EOS-Funded Instruments*—Other instruments funded through the EOS Programme receive their flight opportunities aboard international partner platforms. CERES and LIS on TRMM will improve diurnal coverage of the tropics, in conjunction with CERES on the EOS-AM and -PM satellites. SeaWinds has been selected as part of the ADEOS II payload; a to-be-determined Japanese instrument (presumably a TOMS-equivalent) will be carried on the EOS-CHEM series.

Important contributions will be made by Japanese and European Components of the International Earth Observing System (Tables 1.15 and 1.16).

In accordance with the data mentioned above, the EOS system is planned as a multipurpose information system; an analysis of its data will make it possible to understand the function of the Earth as a natural complex, to reveal the limits to variability of this complex, and to assess its evolution in the future (Dutton, 1989). It

Table 1.15. Japanese instruments planned as part of IEOS

	Instrument	Category	Measurement objective
ADEOS	AVNIR	VIS/IR Images	Solar light reflected by the Earth s surface
	OCTS	VIS/IR Images	Ocean colour and sea–surface temperature
	ILAS	Stratospheric chemistry	Stratospheric ozone and related species of high latitudes
	IMG	Tropospheric chemistry	Carbon dioxide, methane, and other greenhouse gases
	NSCAT	Active microwave	Wind speed and direction over the oceans
	POLDER	VIS/IR images and radiation budget	Atmospheric aerosols
	RIS	Atmospheric chemistry	Atmospheric trace gases
	TOMS	Stratospheric chemistry	Daily global ozone observations
TRIMM	CERES	Radiation budget	Radiation budget
	LIS	VIS/IR images	Distribution and variability of lightning over the Earth
	PR	Active Microwave	Three-dimensional profiles of rain rates in the tropics
	TMI	Passive microwave	Precipitation measurements
	VIRS	VIS/IR images	Variations of rainwater content with altitude
ADEOS II*	AMSR	Passive atmospheric sounding and passive microwave	Precipitation, water vapour distribution, cloud water, sea-surface temperature, sea ice, and sea-surface wind speed
	GLI	VIS/IR images	Biological/physical processes and stratospheric ozone
	IMG-2	Tropospheric chemistry	Carbon dioxide, methane, and other greenhouse gases
	Sea Winds	Active microwave	Ocean surface vector winds
Candidates for HIROS I	ADALT	Altimeter	Geoid, ocean waves, and polar ice
	AVNIR +	VIS/IR images	Upwelling radiance in multiple spectral bands
	E-LIDAR	Laser ranging and sounding	Aerosol and cloud vertical profiles of water vapour, and ice sheet and sea level
	IMB	VIS/IR Images	Ecological environment measurements with high spatial resolution
	PR-2	Active microwave	Three-dimensional measurement of global rain rate
	SLIES	Stratospheric chemistry	Infrared emissions of stratospheric and tropospheric minor species

Table 1.15. (continued)

	Instrument	Category	Measurement objective
	TERSE	Tropospheric chemistry	Global monitoring of tropospheric chemistry profiles
	TOMUIS	Stratospheric chemistry	Three-dimensional mapping of stratospheric ozone distribution
	SAR II	Active microwave	All-weather monitoring of land/water status

* HIRDLS, ILAS II, POLDER, and TOMS are also candidates for this mission.

Table 1.16. European instruments planned as part of IEOS

	Instrument	Category	Measurement objective
ENVISAT	ASAR	Active microwave	All-weather imaging of land surface, coastal zones, sea ice, and ice- and snow-covered surfaces
	GOMOS	Stratospheric chemistry	Global ozone monitoring
	MERIS	VIS/IR images	Ocean colour and biological components (carbon cycle)
	MIPAS	Stratospheric chemistry	Composition, dynamics, and radiation balance of the middle and upper troposphere
	RA-2	Altimeter	Significant wave height and sea-level determination, ocean circulation (dynamics), ice-sheet topography, and land mapping
	AATSR	VIS/IR images	Sea-surface temperature and land-surface measurements for ocean dynamics and radiation interaction studies
	MWR	Passive-atmospheric sounding	Corrects the radar altimeter height error caused by water vapour
	SCARAB	Radiation budget	Global measurements of the radiation budget
	SCIA-MACHY	Stratospheric and tropospheric chemistry	Total concentration and vertical distribution of atmospheric trace gas species, temperature, and aerosols in the troposphere and stratosphere
METOP	AMSU-A1/2	Passive-atmospheric sounding	Global temperature profiles from ground level to 45 km
	AVHRR-3	VIS/IR images	Global monitoring of clouds, sea-surface temperature, vegetation, and ice
	DCS	Data relay (ARGOS+)	Relays data from over 4000 collection platforms worldwide

Table 1.16. (continued)

Instrument	Category	Measurement objective
HIRS-3	Passive atmospheric sounding	Global atmospheric temperature profiles, atmospheric water content, and cloud properties
IASI	Passive atmospheric sounding	Atmospheric temperature and humidity profiles, and continuous monitoring of global radiation, dynamics, and energy flux
MHS	Passive atmospheric sounding	Precipitation and water vapour profiles
ASCAT	Active microwave	Ocean surface wind speed and direction, and ocean circulation and dynamics
AATSR	VIS/IR images	Sea-surface temperature and land-surface measurements for ocean dynamics and radiation interaction studies
GOMI	Stratospheric chemistry	Global ozone distributions from both solar radiation backscatter and differential optical absorption spectroscopy
MCP	Data relay	Direct data handling and broadcast of operational instrument data streams to ground stations
MIMR	Passive microwave	Precipitation rate, cloud water, water vapour, sea-surface roughness, sea-surface temperature, ice, snow, and soil moisture
S&R	Data relay	Receives beacon signals, and transmits in real-time to ground stations around the world
SCARAB	Radiation budget	Global measurements of the radiation budget
SEM	Other	Monitors particles and field to measure/predict solar events

means that an EOS should provide global-scale synchronous observations of all characteristics of the environment and the biosphere needed for an interactive analysis of the dynamics of the components of the Earth as a single system.

Being an information system, the EOS includes three components: (i) complexes of scientific instruments on satellites put in Sun-synchronous polar orbits; (ii) complexes to control the satellites' functioning; (iii) a system for data transmission to ground-based stations, data processing to obtain physical parameters to be used for further analysis and data distribution.

With an account of the combined use of conventional and satellite data, the EOS will make it possible: (i) to obtain data on a set of interacting processes which determine the evolution of the Earth as a system on different spatial and temporal scales; (ii) to improve simulation numerical modelling and prognostic models by specifying the parameterization techniques for different processes based on comparison with observational data; (iii) to develop empirical models of the components and processes still without theoretical substantiation; (iv) to undertake studies of various concrete situations of high priorities; (v) to reveal long-term trends and scales of global changes, bearing in mind the results of numerical modelling that show the priority of various processes and regions. The unprecedented volume and variety of the EOS data determine a much higher complexity of the problems of processing, archiving and analysis of data compared to the construction of the observational system.

Now we shall move on to a brief characteristic of the scientific complex for the EOS system (it must be mentioned again that it is not the final choice of instrumentation).

High-resolution videospectrometer (HIRIS) (Goetz and Herring, 1989)

Designed on the basis of the experience gained from the use of multispectral prototypes, the HIRIS was meant to obtain images in 192 channels, covering the wavelength range 0.4–2.5 μm at a high spatial resolution (the diameter of an instant FOV in nadir is about 30 m), within the swath width of about 30 km. This is a complex of the point-by-point and not survey type, with the viewing direction able to vary between $-30°$ and $+60°$ along the subsatellite trajectory and in the interval $\pm 30°$ across the orbital plane. The unprocessed information flow constitutes 512 Mbytes s^{-1}.

The high spectral resolution opens up wide perspectives for identification of vegetation and rocks. Laboratory data on spectral brightness show that more than 100 minerals containing Fe^{2+}, Fe^{3+}, OH, H_2O and CO_2 are characterized by unique signatures in the visible and near-IR spectral regions. However, this is not so for the principal components of rocks, such as quartz and feldspar (in this case data are needed for the interval 8–12 μm).

Studies of bare rocks and soils (they constitute about 30% of land surface) open up two directions of developments: (i) description of and mapping the sediments and volcanic rocks affected by tectonic processes and subsequent erosion; (ii) description of and mapping the surface rocks and various formations on land, which reflect the geological processes both in the past and now.

Numerous channels and high spectral resolution (~ 10 nm) of HIRIS also create a reliable informative basis for: (i) retrieving the content of phytoplankton and mineral suspensions in the surface layer of homogeneous waters with an appropriate atmospheric correction; (ii) analysis of biogeochemical processes (including biogeochemical cycles) from the data on such characteristics of vegetation cover as biomass, primary productivity, photosynthetic activity, transpiration, etc. Of particular interest are recognition and quantitative estimation of the oppressed state of vegetation determined by either excess or deficient moisture and by the effect of toxicants (i.e. heavy metals). In this connection it is possible, in particular, to estimate the ratio of the contents of lignin and nitrogen in plants.

Multichannel scanning radiometer (MODIS) (Salomonson et al., 1989)

Based on experience from using the multichannel scanning instruments for the visible and IR spectral regions on the satellites Landsat, NOAA and Nimbus-7, the MODIS complex has been designed to ensure the global long-term and regular monitoring of the processes in the environment (on land, in the atmosphere and in the ocean) through obtaining the quantitative multispectral information withing the dynamic range 2×10^{12}.

The requirements for information are as follows: (i) a two-day repeatability of the global data basis with spatial resolutions of 250, 500, and 1000 m (this is provided with the Sun-synchronous orbit with an angle of inclination 98.7° and height 824 km); (ii) continuous nadir viewing and excluded contribution of the sun glint (specular reflection), which determines the necessity of simultaneous functioning of independent complexes MODIS-T (slant sounding) and MODIS-N (nadir viewing).

The 64-channel (wavelength range 0.4–1.04 μm; channel width 10 nm) MODIS-T, whose viewing direction can vary within $\pm 50°$ with respect to nadir (in the plane normal to the orbit), provides a 2-day global data base with a spatial resolution of 1 km (the swath width is 1890 km). The MODIS-N complex is aimed at obtaining multispectral information in 40 channels (wavelength range 0.4–14.2 μm) within the swath width 1780 km).

It is supposed that based on the multispectral data, various problems can be solved of the remote sounding of the atmosphere, the ocean, and the surface. The research studies plan also observations of polarization near the wavelength 0.7 μm, and differential absorption in the oxygen band A (0.754–0.7663 μm) to retrieve the cloud cover top height.

Multi-angle imaging spectroradiometer (MISR) (Diner et al., 1989)

The comb-like system of the multi-angle spectroradiometer (MISR) has been aimed at continuous obtaining of images of the illuminated part of the Earth at four viewing angles with respect to the local normal 25.8°, 45.6°, 60.0°, and 72.5°, both forward and backward, making use of eight cameras, each having a "comb" in the form of 2048 sensors 15 μm in size.

To provide these viewing angles, pairs of cameras A, B, C, D with viewing angles 27.4°, 22.3°, 17.5° and 13° are inclined, respectively, at angles 22.7°, 39.3°, 50.1° and 57.6° (the instantaneous fields of view are 0.9°, 0.7°, 0.5°, and 0.3°). The time of viewing a fixed site of the Earth's surface with all the eight cameras constitutes 8 minutes.

The global data base is divided into groups of 32 images (eight viewing directions by four spectral channels). The complex functions in the regimes of regional and global survey. In the second case an averaging is made over 8×8 pixels. Such a technique will make it possible to obtain global information (without gaps) in the form of multispectral images at various viewing angles with a homogeneous resolution of 216 m for individual scenes and 1.73 km for a global survey.

The problems of thematic interpretation of the data have determined the choice of four spectral channels at wavelengths 440, 550, 670, and 860 nm (the widths of the channels are, respectively, 35, 20, 25, and 60 nm). With a swath width of 210 km (443 km near the equator for individual cameras) the repeatability of obtaining the global data base will be 16 days.

The main scientific problems are connected with studies of the problem of atmospheric correction for the visible and near-IR spectral regions. As for the aerosol, the observations are aimed at obtaining the data on its content and optical characteristics needed to assess the effect of aerosols (layers of haze and dust, aerosol plumes) on the shortwave radiation transfer, bearing in mind, in particular, the monitoring of the long-term trends of the aerosol content on regional and global scales. The optical aerosol characteristics to be retrieved are as follows: optical thickness (depth), single scattering albedo, and the parameters of size distribution (e.g. Junge distribution).

To solve the problem of atmospheric correction, of importance are multispectral and multi-angle observations, which should take into account the effect of radiation non-orthotropically reflected from the surface as well as horizontal inhomogeneity of the surface creating the effect of "lighting-up" (Kondratyev et al., 1992). The MISR data have similar advantages from the viewpoint of studies of the optical characteristics of clouds and the effect of their 3-D spatial inhomogeneity on radiation transfer. These data open up possibilities of a more reliable recognition of cloud types.

As for the land ecosystems, here we speak about recognition of natural landscapes and revealing the ecophysiological changes in order to assess: (i) the level of anthropogenic impacts on land biota; (ii) the "drifting" of the species composition of ecosystems under the impact of both natural and anthropogenic changes of the environment; (iii) the parameters of the architecture of vegetation cover. In this connection one can solve the problems of retrieving the evapotranspiration, biomass, primary production, photosynthesis, breathing and solar radiation absorption.

The MISR data can be used for a more reliable retrieval of the surface radiation budget components (this information can be used in climate models for the more adequate formulation of boundary conditions).

Satellite lidar (Curran, 1989)

The main stimuli for the development of satellite lidar sounding are possibilities to reach a very high vertical resolution when determining the vertical profiles of the concentration of minor gaseous components using the differential absorption technique (DIAL), as well as when retrieving the wind profile from the data of the Doppler observations. Three types of lidars have been developed.

To estimate the wind speed with an error from 1 m s^{-1} in the troposphere to 9 m s^{-1} in the upper troposphere and the lower stratosphere (the altitude range 1–15 km, vertical resolution 1 km, horizontal resolution 100 km), the complex LAWS has been developed with the CO_2 laser ($\lambda = 10.6 \mu m$) based on measuring the Doppler shift of the backscattering signal by aerosol, which is an indication of atmospheric motions. Naturally, in this case it is possible to retrieve only the wind speed vector component along the viewing line, which determines the need for data combination for two viewing directions (such a technique has been tested successfully on aircraft).

The diameter of the LAWS telescope is 1.5 m, the pulse power is 10 J, the pulse frequency is 1–10 Hz (the pulse duration is 3 μm). In case of scanning over the cone with a frequency of 6 rev. min^{-1}, the swath width can be 2800 km (with the height of the orbit 827 km). This complex is planned to be mounted on the Japanese polar platform.

The lidar atmospheric sounder and altimeter (LASA) is designed to solve problems enumerated in Table 1.17.

To retrieve the total moisture content and the water vapour profile, one can use wavelengths of 0.723 and 0.94 μm. For retrieval with an accuracy of not less than 10% with a vertical resolution of 500 m over the grid with a 100-km step can be made using a lidar with the following characteristics: pulse power 2 J, frequency 20 Hz, mirror diameter 1.25 m. As for retrieving the temperature and pressure, it can be based on the 2-channel data in band A for oxygen (0.76 μm) and on the data in the 0.31 μm ozone band.

The data of atmospheric lidar ATLID based on the principle of backscattering will make it possible to retrieve the following parameters: the ABL height near the tropopause and cloud top; recognition, optical thickness and height of cirrus clouds; recognition, optical thickness and height of aerosol layer.

Table 1.17. Scientific problems solved using the LASA complex

Problems	Parameters to be retrieved	Methodic basis
Deeper insight into the impact of aerosol and clouds on the processes in the surface–atmosphere system	Total aerosol optical thickness	Backscattering
	Aerosol concentration profile in the troposphere	Same
	Aerosol concentration profile in the stratosphere	Same
	ABL height	Same
	The height and other characteristics of cloud top	Same
Study of global water cycle from water vapour content observation data	Total water content in the atmosphere	Same
	Water vapour concentration profile	Same
Obtaining global data base on the structural parameters and ozone content in the atmosphere	Surface atmospheric pressure	Same
	Pressure profile	Same
	Total ozone content	Same
	Ozone concentration profile	Same
	Temperature profile	Same

Table 1.18. Parameters observed with ATLID and requirements for retrieval accuracy

Parameters	Acceptable retrieval errors
ABL height	50–100 m (height); 10 km (horizontal averaging)
Height of tropopause	1–2 km (height); 100–200 km (horizontal averaging)
Cloud top height	1–2 km (height); 100–200 km (horizontal averaging)
Height and optical thickness of cirrus clouds	100–500 m (height); 10–100 km (horizontal averaging); 10% (optical thickness)
Height and optical thickness of aerosol layers	100 m (height); 100 km (horizontal averaging); 0.01 (optical thickness)

The data of Table 1.18 characterize the requirements for observation errors. Two types of Nd:YAG lasers are considered, with a mirror 0.5 m in diameter: (i) pulse power 50 mJ, pulse frequency 100 Hz; (ii) pulse power 500 mJ, pulse frequency 10 Hz. Apparently, the second type of laser is preferred. The first test of a satellite lidar (LITE) took place during the Shuttle flight in 1994.

Multifrequency microwave radiometer (Le Vine et al., 1989)

The complex of high-resolution multifrequency microwave radiometer (HMMR) developed to be used on a polar platform of the EOS system consists of three components: advanced microwave sounder unit AMSU, the satellite prototypes of which have been used earlier (mainly, for the remote sounding of the atmosphere), as well as two new devices—advanced mechanically scanning radiometer (AMSR) and electronically scanning radiometer (ESTAR).

The 20-channel AMSU will make it possible to retrieve vertical profiles of temperature (from the data for the O_2 resonance band 50–60 GHz) and water vapour (the resonance line at 183 GHz). The 15-channel sub-system AMSU-A has 12 channels operating in the band 60–70 GHz. Five channels of the sub-system AMSU-B include channels at frequencies 99 and 160 GHz. The spatial resolution for these sub-systems will constitute, respectively, 50 and 15 km. The temperature profile can be retrieved up to altitudes of about 40 km with an error of 1–1.5 K (except for the surface layer). The error for humidity retrieval is 5–15%.

The AMSR complex is designed to obtain images at frequencies 6, 10, 18, 21, 37, and 90 GHz (at both polarizations). A combined interpretation of data for various frequencies and polarizations will make it possible to obtain, first of all, abundant information about the global water cycle characteristics, including such parameters as soil moisture, rain rate, the extent and water equivalent of snow cover, moisture and water content of the atmosphere, evaporation (from the oceans), evapotranspiration (on land). Supplied with 25 antennas 20 m by 11 cm (real-aperture observations) ESTAR is designed to obtain images at a frequency of 1.4 GHz (21.23 cm), which will enable one to accomplish the global mapping of the upper soil layer moisture with a spatial resolution of about 10 km (the swath width is 1400 km).

Table 1.19. Possibilities of thematic interpretation of microwave data

Observed characteristics	Frequency, GHz									
	1.4	6	10	18	21	37	50–60	90	160	183
Soil moisture	1	3								
Snow cover		3	3	1		1		2		
Precipitation										
over the ocean			2	1	3	2				
over land				2		1		1		2
SST	1		2	2	2	3				
Ice cover										
extent				1		1		3		
type	3		2	1		1		2		
Wind speed near the										
ocean surface			1	2	3	3				
Atmospheric moisture										
content										
total (over the ocean)				1	1	2				
vertical profile					2	3	2	3	2	1
Water content of clouds over						2	1		2	
the ocean										
Temperature profile					3	3	1	3		

The data in Table 1.19 illustrate the possibilities of thematic interpretation of the observation results for different channels and the information content of the channels (1—data needed, 2—important data, 3—useful data). A set of parameters characterizing the atmosphere and the ocean enables one to study the interaction of the atmosphere and the ocean.

The requirements for the observation data interpretation determine the necessity to reach the radiometric precision within 0.5–2.0 K with an absolute accuracy of 1.0–2.0 K and a spatial resolution of about 10 km. The repeatability for obtaining the global data base should not be below 3 days.

Advanced microwave scanning radiometer—AMSR (Tachi et al., 1989)
The multi-year successful experience from using microwave remote sounding to assess such parameters as SST, soil moisture, sea-surface wind, humidity and water content of the atmosphere, sea water salinity, etc. has determined the decision of the Japan National Space Agency (NASDA) to develop an advanced multi-channel microwave scanning radiometer (AMSR) to be carried by the Japan polar platform of the EOS system.

The data in Table 1.20 characterize the requirements for information which show the necessity to use the radiometer with not less than five channels and orthogonal polarizations.

The radiometer should provide a 10-km spatial resolution, radiometric accuracy

Table 1.20. Requirements for the microwave remote sounding complex

Observed parameter	Sphere of application	Frequency Ghz	Spatial resolution	Calibration accuracy km	Repeatability days K	Swath width km
Snow cover characteristics	Forestry, agriculture	37, 10, 21	1–2	5	10–14	200
Sea ice characteristics	Meteorology	31, 37, 10	5	5	3	1000
Cloud water content	Meteorology	19, 23, 31, 37	10–20	1		
Atmospheric moisture content	Meteorology	23	10–20	1		
Sea-surface wind	Meteorology Oceanology	19	10–20	1		
SST	Fishery Meteorology	6.5	20	0.5		1500
Soil moisture	Meteorology Forestry Agriculture	2.7, 1.4	20			
Atmospheric pressure	Meteorology	31, 50				
Sea water salinity	Fishery Oceanology	1.4				

of 0.5 K and, at least, a 3-day repeatability of data (at the orbit's height 824 km it means the need for a swath width of more than 1200 km). With account of such requirements, preliminary characteristics of the microwave complex were chosen; they are shown in Table 1.21. The main objective of the AMSR data interpretation (the Japan platform is planned to be launched by the end of the century) will be studies of the global water cycle.

Microwave complex to estimate soil moisture (Jackson and Schmugge, 1989)
The search for optimal conditions of the soil moisture retrieval from the data of space-borne microwave remote sounding has led to the conclusion that the most informative are data in the wavelength interval 20–30 cm (L-band) at horizontal polarization, with viewing angles close to nadir. Here the volume liquid water content of the upper 5-cm soil layer is retrieved from the radiobrightness temperature (RBT). Theoretical estimates and analysis of observational data have shown that with the use of the L-band the characteristic thickness of the efficiently emitting layer constitutes about 5 cm (except for very dry soils in arid conditions). The dry soil emittance is 0.95, and for wet soil it is 0.7, this illustrates that the RBT is very sensitive to the soil moisture content.

Table 1.21. Proposed characteristics of the AMSR complex

Parameter	Characteristics of the complex				
Frequency, GHz	6.6	10.65	18.7	23.8	36.5
Bandwidth, GHz	400	100	200	400	1000
Polarization		Vertical and horizontal			
Sensitivity, K	0.3	0.5	0.6	0.5	0.6
Absolute accuracy, K			0.5		
Dynamic range, K			10–350		
Integration time, ms	125				62
Viewing angle (with respect to nadir), deg	55	58.4		52.7	51.2
Instant FOV at land surface level, km	26×50	20×48	11×18	10×16	8×13

The retrieval of soil moisture is hindered by the necessity to filter out the dependence of RBT on soil properties, surface roughness and vegetation cover. The problem of soil properties is connected with the fact that the soil consists of three major components with substantially different dielectric constants (in brackets): air (1), soil particles (4), and water (80). These differences determine the possibility of the remote sounding of soil moisture.

The presence of free and bound water is also important. The dielectric constant of bound water is much less, and its amount is determined by the specific surface of soil particles and average density of soil, whose characteristic values vary within 10–150 $m^2 \, g^{-1}$ and 1–1.5 g cm^{-3}, respectively. The *a priori* taken values of these parameters for different typical regions are satisfactory.

The effect of surface roughness on emittance I_{surf} can approximately be parameterized with the following relationship:

$$I_{surf} = 1 + (I_{soil} - 1)e^h$$

where I_{soil} is the emittance of a smooth soil surface; h is an empirical parameter of roughness depending on the dispersion of the surface level with respect to the level $h = 0$. In the case of dry soil, when $I_{soil} > 0.9$, the effect of roughness is negligible, but it grows when the soil gets moist.

An approximate parameterization of the effect of vegetation cover consists in the possibility of its presentation as an efficient layer of water or wet biomass, since the water content of vegetation can be remotely sounded from the data for the visible, near-IR and microwave ranges. Naturally, with thick vegetation (e.g. forest) the soil moisture cannot be retrieved.

The main difficulty with the practical use of the data of the microwave remote sounding of soil moisture consists in their low spatial resolution, whereas the field of soil moisture is characterized by a very strong horizontal inhomogeneity. Therefore it is very important that the ESTAR complex now under development will make it possible to obtain global data on soil moisture (from observations in L-band with a spatial resolution of about 5–10 km).

Synthetic aperture radar (Huneycutt, 1989)
The space-borne imaging radar SIR-C has been designed to be carried by the Shuttle to obtain images of the surface at various frequencies and polarizations. It is supposed to be a direct prototype (earlier prototypes had been tested on satellites Seasat and Shuttle) of a similar complex carried by polar platforms of the EOS system. The SIR-C functions in bands L (centred at 1248.75 MHz, bandwidth 10.20 MHz) and C (5298.75 MHz, 10.20 MHz) at different polarizations (HH, HV, VV, VH), being equipped with antennas 12.08×2.95 m^2 and 12.08×0.75 m^2, respectively, which can turn within 15–55° with respect to nadir. The pulse is 4300 and 2250 W, and the pulse width can be (in both cases) 8.4, 16.9, and 33.8 μm. With the circular orbit's inclination of 57° and height of orbit 225 km, the azimuthal spatial resolution constitutes 30 m, and the range resolution varies within 10–60 m.

Within the programme "Mission to Planet Earth" the NASA (USA) is preparing a permanent manned orbital station (MOS) which, presumably, will consist of three components: (i) the MOS itself out in a low orbit with an inclination of 28.5°; (ii) a module near the MOS in the same orbit to accomplish experiments on data processing and for other operations; (iii) a polar platform (PP) maintained by astronauts and put in a very high quasi-polar Sun-synchronous orbit. These initial plans were significantly changed later on. The agreement has been signed concerning the combined use (at the first stage) of the Russian "MIR" station and Shuttles (the first experience of docking took place in 1995).

McElroy and Schneider (1985 a,b) substantiated the necessity to use the PP for an operational solution of numerous problems connected with studies of the environment and natural resources, with the simultaneous utilization of the instruments of meteorological, oceanographic and Earth's resources satellites, both available and under development, aimed at the realization of the PP project in the early 1990s. The scientific PP programme can be divided into three stages (these stages are largely overlapping).

(1) The atmosphere and meteorology
In this case the instruments for advanced satellites of the TIROS-N type (ATN) serve the basis for the instrumental complex. This complex includes scanning multi-channel radiometers (SMR) to obtain data on brightness fields at different wavelengths and multi-spectral images (at a resolution of about 0.5 km), which enables one to solve the following problems: weather forecasts; assessing precipitation; ERB studies; mapping the global distributions of snow and ice cover and SST, of ocean currents and total ozone; monitoring hydrological phenomena assessing the state of vegetation cover. Major requirements for the SMR consist in provision for precise radiometric calibration and a daily global data base. A separate complex consists of instruments for remote sounding of the atmosphere (an operational vertical sounder of the ATN satellites can serve as the prototype), which

must twice a day give the information needed for numerical weather forecasts on a grid with a step from 10–15 to 250 km.

Asrar and Dozier (1994) have formulated in this case the following principal questions:

- How will clouds influence the Earth's radiation budget, and modulate or enhance tropospheric warming caused by increasing concentrations of greenhouse gases, especially water vapour?
- How will tropospheric warming from increasing greenhouse gases affect atmospheric circulation patterns and regional precipitation patterns?
- How do increasing concentrations of atmospheric trace gases affect the global and regional balances of precipitation, evaporation and transpiration, and runoff?
- What are the feedback and interactions between the atmosphere, oceans, and land-surface hydrology?
- How do surface fluxes and large-scale atmospheric motions transport moisture and partition energy among their various sinks and sources, and what are the effects of these transport processes on regional climate fluctuations?
- Does the variation of solar irradiance during the solar cycle modulate greenhouse forcing, and is there a systematic long-term variation in solar irradiance leading to different climate regimes like the "Little Ice Age"?

A special place belongs to the problem of greenhouse gases and tropospheric chemistry:

- What are the source distributions of radiatively active gases with natural and anthropogenic origins? What is the natural and anthropogenic variability in ecosystems that results from changes in temperature, acid deposition, rainfall, and ultraviolet radiation?
- What is the natural variability in tropospheric ozone? Is tropospheric ozone increasing? Are its precursors (carbon monoxide, nitrogen oxides, and hydrocarbons) increasing? What are the roles of convection, stratosphere–troposphere exchange, and long-range transport in ozone formation? What are the magnitudes of ozone production from industrial activity and biomass burning? What are the effects of ozone changes on forests, agriculture, and ecosystems?
- What are the spatial distributions of the hydroxyl radical and hydrogen peroxide in the troposphere? What is the total abundance of the hydroxyl radical, and is it changing?
- What are the terrestrial and oceanic contributions to the global carbon cycle? What are the anthropogenic contributions to these trace gases, and how are they distributed? Are there trends in the emissions of radiatively and photo-active gases, both natural and anthropogenic? Are there large-scale interactions of clouds and precipitation with trace gases?

A number of important questions are connected with the field of ozone and stratospheric chemistry studies (Asrar and Dozier, 1994):

- Do we understand the evolution of the compositions of stratospheric trace gases during a period of large anthropogenic changes in the stratosphere?
- Can we clearly separate human-induced from natural change?
- How strongly will chlorine affect the stratosphere during the EOS period?
- How will changes in greenhouse gas concentrations (e.g. methane, carbon dioxide, and nitrous oxide) affect the chemistry and dynamics of the stratosphere?
- How will aircraft emissions of nitrogen oxides in the lower stratosphere affect stratospheric ozone?

The questions relevant to the climatic impact of volcanic eruptions and dust storms are very important:

- What are the temperatures and morphologies of lavas and plumes?
- What is the rate at which solid and gaseous materials erupt, and what altitudes do they reach?
- What is the rate of conversion of sulphur dioxide to sulphate aerosols?
- What is the residence time in the atmosphere of volcanic aerosols that affect climate?
- What are the interactions between wind-blown mineral and soil dust and the climate system, and how will these interactions change in the future?

(2) Ocean and ice
Here major problems are connected with increasing reliability and providing for synoptic global scale of the following information: SST and water mass characteristics (including the chlorophyll content); sea state, currents and gyres; concentration and properties of ice cover; wind speed, wind shear and SST. The following types of SMR are good examples: (i) advanced 7-channel (4.3, 5.1, 6.6, 10.65, 18.7, 21.9, 36.5 GHz) microwave radiometer with orthogonal polarizations (AMR) with an antenna 4 m in diameter, rotating at a speed of 60 rotations per minute. This device will enable one to retrieve: SST at a resolution of 25 km and accuracy 1.5 K over the scanning band 1350 km wide; wind speed ($0–50$ m s^{-1}) with an error of 2 m s^{-1} (or 10%) at a resolution of 17 km; ice cover concentration with a 15% uncertainty, 9 km resolution and simultaneous classification into one-year and multi-year ice; total water content in the atmosphere with a 0.2 g cm^{-2} uncertainty, 9 km resolution; (ii) IR radiometer scanning along the sub-satellite trajectory—ATSR (SST retrievals with a 0.3 K accuracy); (iii) a specialized 4-channel (19.3–85.5 GHz) scanning microwave radiometer SSM/I to equip the US Defence meteorological satellites and the US Navy oceanographic satellites N-ROSS; (iv) a 9-channel scanning complex to determine the colour of the ocean (OCI) like the OZCS on Nimbus-7 (retrieving the chlorophyll content between 0.05 and 100 mg m^{-3} to an accuracy of a factor of 2, at a spatial resolution of 500–800 m, as well as the suspended matter content to the same accuracy). A very important component must be the following active-sounding means: (i) radioaltimeter at 13.5 GHz, similar to that developed within the programme N-ROSS (the error in estimating the height of satellite 8 cm; wave height 0.5 m; wind speed 2 m s^{-1}); (ii) a 6-beam 13.5 GHz

scatterometer of the same origin; (iii) a synthetic-aperture radar (SEASAR) with horizontal polarization in the L band.

According to Asrar and Dozier (1994) the following questions are of the first priority:

- What are the large-scale transports of heat and water within the upper ocean, and how do they control air–sea exchange and vertical ocean circulation?
- What dynamic balances control upper ocean circulation, and how will the circulation change in response to changing surface fluxes?
- What are the oceanic biogeochemical cycles for climate-sensitive (chemical) species, and how sensitive are these cycles to changes in physical climate?
- What are the mechanisms for, and present magnitudes of, air–sea exchanges of climate-sensitive chemical species?
- What are the rate, geographical distribution, and controlling factors for oceanic primary production and new production?
- How does the ecosystem structure control the rate of organic matter transport to deep oceans?
- How are oceanic ecosystems changing in structure and species makeup?

(3) Land

The Earth's resources complex consists of advanced high-resolution scanners used on Landsat. A multi-channel scanner MLA is now being developed with a varied (using the on-board processor) number of channels (8 to 32) in the wavelength interval 0.45–12.5 μm at a spectral (spatial) resolution of 20 nm (10 m). Scanning can be made in both the orbital plane (to obtain stereoscopic images) and the perpendicular plane, with a scanning band 185 cm wide.

The GEOSAR complex, similar to the SEASAR, is characterized by a specific set of frequencies, polarization and viewing geometry, which provides the remote sensing of land (cartography, geology, hydrology, glaciology, agriculture, and forestry, as well as other fields of data interpretation). Apparently, a system of two PPs in the morning and afternoon orbits 900–1000 km high, visited by cosmonauts (to examine and repair the instruments, if necessary), is optimal.

McElroy and Schneider (1985a) emphasize the exceptional importance of a powerful ground-based data-processing centre for collective use. The instruments are developed by joint efforts of the USA, west-European countries, and Canada. So, for instance, Great Britain developed an instrument unit to sound the stratosphere and takes part in the development of a microwave complex. French specialists developed a system, ARGOS, to collect and transmit information from ground-based platforms. Canada has an interest in developing instruments for global monitoring of atmospheric ozone. Following an agreement between Great Britain, Italy, Canada, USA, France, Germany, Japan, and the European Economic Community, an International Committee on Earth Resource Satellites (IERSC), responsible for coordination of the development of satellites to study the environment and natural resources, and an International Working Group on Polar-Orbiting Meteorological Satellites (IPOMS), were organized.

The following important questions have to be answered (Asrar and Dozier, 1994):

- How will the land surface's biophysical controls on the carbon, energy, and water cycles respond to and feed back on climate change?
- How will climate change affect the respiration component of the carbon cycle, particularly decomposition?
- How will ecosystems respond to climate change and anthropogenic pressure, particularly through feedback into the climate system and cycling and storage of carbon and trace constituents?
- What are the global distributions changing over time?
- How do land-cover changes and management practices caused by climate change affect the water and energy balances of the land surface?
- How do we best parameterize the heterogeneous biological, biophysical, and biogeochemical processes occurring at large grid scales?

A number of important questions have to be addressed to cryospheric studies:

- What are the current mass balances of the polar ice sheets?
- Through what processes are these ice sheets growing or thinning?
- What are the rates of snow accumulation, melting, and iceberg calving, and how do these reveal the key dynamics of ice flow?
- How will the climate system and its changes affect the mass balances of alpine glaciers and ice sheets, and what is the resulting effect on sea level?
- Will changes in the mass balances of ice sheets and glaciers cause a significant rise in sea level in the next century?
- How will snow cover change as the climate warms; in particular, will a greater fraction of the winter snowfall occur as rain?

1.3 THE INTERNATIONAL SPACE YEAR

The 1992 International Space Year (ISY) confirmed an urgency for space research and illustrated wide prospects of its further development. No doubt, the 1992 ISY became the culminating point in the most urgent areas of space research. It goes without saying that in the late twentieth century the ecological problem is the most vital one. The acuteness of the situation is confirmed by a wide scope of problems: from the problems of everyday life (first of all, environmental pollution) to ecology of the planet as a whole.

The development of space ecology (within the ISY) is based on the accomplishment of a long-term international programme of Earth observations from space, with an efficient coordination of processing and standardization (unification, compatibility, etc.) of the information obtained. The accomplishment of such missions as European (ERS-1) and Japan (JERS-1) Earth's resources satellites, further development in Russia of the systems "Meteor", "Meteor-Priroda", "Resurs" favour the solution of this problem, as well as the Earth's resources module of the "Mir" orbital station, the Russian–French cooperation to measure the Earth's radiation budget (SCaRaB) and to perform lidar sounding of the atmosphere (the programme "Alice"), as well as the Russian–American studies of the ozone layer (using the American TOMS instrumentation carried by Russian satellites). An advancement in measuring complexes carried by satellites NOAA, SPOT, Landsat, the launching of the Indian ERS-1, further development of meteorological and Earth-resources satellites in China, developments within the French–American programme TOPEX/POSEIDON, the launching of the American satellite UARS to study the upper atmosphere, the launchings of satellites ADEOS (Japan) and MECB (Brazil), etc. open up wide perspectives.

All this makes it possible to obtain various pieces of information which characterizes: spectral and total solar constants, the structure of the Earth's magnetic and electrical fields, the input of particles to the atmosphere, winds in the thermosphere, mesosphere and stratosphere, the composition and the temperature of the troposphere, stratosphere and mesosphere (including the total content and vertical profile of ozone concentration); cloud cover and atmospheric aerosol, ERB components, snow and sea ice covers, the ocean colour (the phytoplankton content), vegetation cover, wetlands, mineral composition and surface temperature, roughness and wind speed near the ocean surface, sea currents, topography of land and ocean surfaces, volcanic eruptions, Earth crust dynamics, etc.

Techniques have been developed or require a substantial improvement in retrieving the parameters which characterize: the concentration fields in the stratosphere and mesosphere of such minor gaseous components as HO_x, HCl, CO, NO_x, HFC and many others, as well as aerosols; the vertical temperature profile, with a vertical resolution of about 1 km (at a retrieval accuracy of about 1°C); the wind field in the troposphere; precipitation, water and ice content of clouds; the height of the atmospheric boundary layer; the species diversity of phytoplankton and the biology of lakes; snow cover properties; the physiological properties of vegetation; types of soils and the mineral composition of rocks; sea-roughness spectra; soil moisture, processes of mesoscale geodynamics; the gravitation field, etc.

This and other information enabled one to start solving a wide variety of problems connnected with studies of regional- and global-scale dynamics of natural processes. It should be borne in mind, however, that in all cases the sub-satellite complex observations were necessary at key sites (KS) characterizing typical natural systems (river systems, lake-watershed systems, various ecosystems).

Priorities
As for priorities, it went without question that of the first priority was the problem of the global biosphere dynamics—a key aspect of global-scale ecological problems.

A very important problem was the mapping (on global scales) of primary production and biomass, the first stage being an assessment of net primary production and biomass in boreal and tropical forests. The latter contribute most to the biospheric biodiversity and, on the other hand, play an important role in the formation of global biogeochemical cycles, studies of which were a key aspect of the IGBP. Immediately followed the problem of desertification.

Studies of global 3-D fields of chemically and (or) optically active minor gaseous components of the atmosphere and of aerosols were very interesting from the viewpoint of both the biospheric dynamics and analysis of the factors of formation and possible variability of the atmospheric greenhouse effect affecting the climate. The global dynamics of the ozone layer was one more aspect of these problems. Studies of global cycles of water and energy were closely connected with these interrelated problems. A detailed analysis of this aspect of global ecology can be found in the programme of Global Energy and Water Cycles Experiment (GEWEX), which is part of the World Climate Research Programme (WCRP).

In the context of atmospheric sciences, of interest are recommendations of the Long-range Planning Committee on the development of atmospheric sciences created by the US National Science Foundation (NSF) and by the University Corporation of Atmospheric Research (UCAR), which determined the first priority for the period 1989–1994 of the following four directions to study global changes in the atmosphere (Taylor and Eyre, 1989): (i) Programme on Global Tropospheric Chemistry (PGTC); (ii) Meso-meteorological Investigations (MMI); (iii) Programme to study tropical ocean and global atmosphere (TOGA); (iv) Processes of interaction of the energetics and dynamics between individual atmospheric regions (EDIP).

As for the PGTC, its principal objective (during the first decade of the programme realization) is to substantiate the forecast of possible changes in the chemistry of global atmosphere during the century to come, especially from the viewpoint of the contribution of the atmosphere to the formation of biogeochemical cycles, as well as to assess the factors affecting the oxidizing and radiative properties of the atmosphere. Of primary importance are the following five interrelated issues: global distributions and trends of the atmospheric composition components; the role of biological processes and interaction with the surface; gas-phase photochemical reactions; multi-phase processes; theoretical studies. The most urgent directions of studies have the following order of priority: interacting components of the climatic system; sudden climate changes; monitoring the climate system; solar–terrestrial relationships; physics of clouds and precipitation; numerical long-range weather forecasts; physics of the Sun.

The key aspects of MMI are: (i) understanding the nature of convection in cumulus clouds and of mesoscale convective systems, as well as their interaction with large-scale processes; (ii) the effect of mesoscale fluxes of energy, moisture and momentum on synoptic processes and climate change; (iii) the interaction of mesoscale systems with topography, ecosystems, processes in the boundary layer, radiation fluxes, evaporation and condensation, the effect of scale processes on atmospheric chemistry on regional and global scales as well as on local climate.

The principal objective of TOGA is a study of the nature and predictability of the interaction between tropical oceans and atmospheric general circulation on time scales from weeks to several years, as well as the use of results from such studies to obtain short-term climate forecasts. An analysis of the processes of interaction between the energetics and dynamics of neutral and ionized upper atmosphere— from mesosphere to exobase (50–500 km)—constitutes the principal objective of EDIP, which includes a consideration of the mechanisms for solar–terrestrial relationships.

Table 1.22. A summary of the existing and perspective possibilities to use the aerospace data in hydrologic modelling

Factor	Possibilities to use the data of space-based remote sounding		
	Existing	Immediate perspective	Future perspectives
1	2	3	4
Precipitation	Areal extent of zones and rain duration; approximate estimates of rain rate from cloud cover characteristics.	Use of satellite data on rain rate to extrapolate ground-based point rain gauge data.	Use of satellite radars to obtain data on the spatial and temporal variability of precipitation.
	Ground-based radars enable one to monitor the rainfall distribution and to estimate rain rates.	Combined satellite and radar data give information to forecast floods.	Putting into practice the ground-based automatic polarization and Doppler radar to more accurately estimate rain rates.
Snow cover	Snow cover extent mapping hindered by difficulties in distinguishing between snow and clouds, as well as assessing the snow cover in forests.	Use of the channel 1.55–1.75 μm to raise the resolution and to improve the distinguishing between snow and clouds when drawing mean monthly maps of snow cover.	Use of microwave and IR sensors to estimate snow cover thickness (water equivalent). An account of the effect of topography and vegetation cover.
	Monitoring the lake ice melting.	Regional distribution of snow cover, estimation of water equivalent and the onset of snow melting from microwave data.	Use of multitemporal and multispectral data to map various characteristics of snow cover.
Cloud cover	Reliable information about the extent and the types of cloud cover.	Automatic mapping of cloud conditions with the use of multispectral data.	Use of lidar sounding to estimate the cloud top height and use of multi-channel microwave instruments to determine the moisture and water content.
Land cover	Spatially averaged information on land use to limit the number of categories.	Detailed recognition of categories and mapping of land use.	Improving the observational means and accumulating geosystem data.

Table 1.22 (continued)

1	2	3	4
	Aircraft survey as a control of the quality of mapping from satellite data.	Automatic classification of natural formations.	Operative high-resolution satellite data will provide information about variations in watershed basins in a real time scale and renew the geosystem data bases.
Hydro-geometry of rivers and valleys	Obtaining data in forestless (photogrammetry) and forested (aircraft laser systems) regions.	Improving aircraft instruments to draw topographic maps.	Aircraft laser systems to map a 3-D relief, including river-valley sections.
Soil moisture	Qualitative assessment of the soil surface moisture.	Operative mapping of soil moisture from microwave aircraft and satellite data.	A detailed mapping of soil moisture almost in a real time scale with the use of satellite passive and active radar technique.
Surface waters	Operational mapping of water basins–land boundaries (forests is a complicating factor).	An increase in spatial resolution of satellite data enables higher accuracy to be obtained. SAR data for 21–25 cm wavelengths are especially perspective.	Mapping inundation consequences in almost real time is possible on the basis of active and passive microwave remote sensing.
Evapo-transpiration	Very approximate assessments on the basis of data on cloudiness and vegetation.	More reliable estimates with the use of multispectral data and conventional meteorological information.	Computer mapping of evapotranspiration in almost real time with the use of multichannel data on atmospheric and soil properties.

Link (1984) based his analysis on various hydrologic models and discussed the possibilities to use data of aerospace remote sounding in the hydrologic modelling. Table 1.22 contains a summary of the available possibilities to obtain data for hydrologic modelling as well as the nearest and farthest perspectives in this field. In this connection of the first priority is an improvement in the techniques to retrieve rain rates and snow cover characteristics (extent, thickness, density, water equivalent).

The most substantial advantage of the satellite-derived information consists in a possibility to have the spatial distribution of parameters (types of natural formations and of land use, hydrogeometry of rivers and valleys, drainage network). The primary-importance parameters are soil moisture and evapotranspiration. So far, the use of satellite information has not ensured a marked progress in the reliability of hydrologic modelling in view of insufficient spatial resolution of satellite data, but, no doubt, an improvement in space-borne instruments will lead to a radical change in this situation. However, it is important to develop hydrologic models which will ensure the compatibility of the models with specific features of satellite information.

A separate section is studies of the World Ocean, including both the processes in the ocean itself (dynamics, thermal state, chemistry and biology of the ocean) and the processes of ocean–atmosphere interaction (first of all, from the viewpoint of the contribution of this interaction to the formation of global biogeochemical cycles). Naturally, in this connection, the emphasis must be placed on such programmes under realization as, for example, TOGA and WOCE.

The variety and diversity of problems, the huge volume and high cost of satellite information necessitated a system approach to planning the ISY. First of all, an integrated programme of studies, with clear-cut priorities, had been worked out (results of Kondratyev and Pokrovski, 1989; Kondratyev 1990 a, b, c) may be considered only as an initial approach). This programme has formed the basis for planning an optimal global system of satellite ecological observations, with an account of the information content of various types of observations, according to priorities.

Not only the choice of a set of parameters to be measured but also requirements for the spatial and temporal resolution had been substantiated. Simulation numerical models of the processes and phenomena studied served the basis for the substantiation required.

One more problem of exclusive importance was the provision of standardization, archiving and accessibility of all observational data, which required the development of regional and global geo-ecoinformation systems.

Preparation for the ISY programme accomplishment
The International Conference held in Durham (New Hampshire, USA) from 18 April to 1 May 1988 decided to form the Space Agency Forum on International Space Year (SAFISY), including two committees: (i) on Earth Sciences and Technologies (ESTC); (ii) on the problems of education and application of satellite information. From 27 February to 1 March 1989, by the NASA initiative and sponsored by the British National Space Centre, the first ESTC session was held in Abingdon (Great Britain), and was aimed at developing programmes to use data obtained during the ISY. The respective suggestions were then discussed at a Plenary SAFISY Session held on 2–3 May 1989 in Frascati (Italy), where the Information Center for European Space Studies is located.

The ESTC decided to divide its activity into three categories and organized the respective working groups (WG): (i) Satellite data for analysis of global changes of the environment and the biosphere (WG-1); (ii) testing global information system (WG-2); (iii) propagation of knowledge about global changes (WG-3).

The WG-1 objective consisted in revealing (on concrete examples) the significance of satellite ecological information for assessing the long-term changes of the environment and the biosphere, bearing in mind the following problems of the first priority: (i) global consequences of changes in the land vegetation cover (it concerns, mainly, deforestation); (ii) atmospheric greenhouse effect; (iii) ocean–climate interactions; (iv) polar "ozone holes" (Kondratyev, 1987a).

Global dynamics of vegetation cover
As for deforestation, a major objective here was to assess the trends of variability for various global regions and their significance from the viewpoint of the impact on global climate, biogeochemical cycles, ecosystems' dynamics and biodiversity. With this purpose, data were used from satellites SPOT, Landsat, Meteor, Kosmos, orbital station "Mir", NOAA AVHRR, for individual KS. In this connection, of great importance was a provision for ground-based calibration of the on-board instruments and observational data comparability, accumulation of long (at least, for 10 years) data series, development of algorithms for retrievals and numerical simulation models. The principal result consisted of drawing annual thematic maps for the chosen regions during the period 1975–1992, characterizing the changes in the land properties as well as accumulating a digital data base.

Greenhouse effect
The principal objective of studies on the greenhouse effect problem was to develop a programme of the International Greenhouse Effect Detection Experiment (GEDEX), bearing in mind a reliable identification of manifestations of its intensification (first of all, from the viewpoint of the impact on global climate).

Though an analysis of the SAT observational data for the last century has not given any evidence of the contribution of the greenhouse effect in increasing mean global temperature, the growth of concentrations of such greenhouse gases as CO_2, methane and chlorofluorocarbons raises no doubts. The strategy for detecting the manifestations of the greenhouse effect was based on a combined analysis of the numerical modelling results, which enabled one to substantiate the most representative signatures, and observational data. Of course, the solution of the problem of CO_2 signal recognition required, in particular, the filtering out of the contributions into temperature changes of such factors as solar activity and volcanic eruptions. An annual symposium held in April 1991 discussed possible approaches to detecting the CO_2 signal and substantiated the requirements for respective observational data. The objective of the 1991 Symposium was to develop the programme for an International Greenhouse Effect Detection Experiment (GEDEX) planned for 1992 (after the third symposium).

The ocean–atmosphere interaction
In this case a major objective was to use satellite information to study the climatic impact of the processes taking place in the ocean and in the cryosphere, as well as to analyse the adequacy (from this point of view) of the information obtained by the year 1992. Of particular concern were the zones of transition from the stable polar

ice cover to the open surface of the ocean; the distribution of SST in the tropics; the atmosphere–ocean interaction in the energy-active zones; the bioproductivity of the World Ocean.

The "ozone holes" in polar regions
They were studied based on the joint analysis of the data of conventional and satellite observations to calibrate and assess the reliability of space-borne instruments, as well as to study the processes in the high-latitude stratosphere. The international expeditions were accomplished in 1992–1993 in the Arctic and in the Antarctic with the use of ground, aircraft and balloon observational means. Of great importance for the realization of this programme was a broad accessibility of the data of the UARS satellite launched in 1991.

The effort of WG-2 connected with testing the global information system (GIST) was focused on the solution of the problems: the bioproductivity of the World Ocean; the rate of deforestation; the change of the World Ocean's surface temperature; the dynamics of the polar ice cover. In all these cases of great importance was the use of combined conventional and satellite information, bearing in mind an accumulation, calibration, qualitative analysis, and recognition of data.

The GIST objectives were: stimulating the international cooperation for the combined analysis of observational data; creating conditions for an easy access to data archives; informing a wide sphere of users about available data that can be used not only in scientific developments but also in solutions of various socioeconomic problems. The WG-2 accomplished four projects dedicated to the solution of the problems mentioned above.

Bioproductivity of the World Ocean
Studies in this direction were focused on: (i) obtaining, archiving and analysis of global information about the chlorophyll content (phytoplankton) in the upper layer of the World Ocean obtained from data of the Nimbus-7 CZCS and other similar instruments; (ii) substantiating the retrieval algorithms for the chlorophyll content and their subsequent application to processing of the data from Landsat-6, SeaWiFS and other similar space-borne instruments. Wide-angle instruments for multichannel measurements of the water basins' surface brightness (SeaWiFS) with a high spatial (1 km) and temporal resolution were designed to obtain data on the field of the phytoplankton content. This complex has a greater number of channels compared to CZCS, which made it possible to perform a reliable atmospheric correction simultaneously. The correct interpretation of the SeaWiFS data required various additional pieces of information, especially about wind speed near the ocean surface, roughness and sea currents, obtained with the help of the ERS-1 scatterometer and radioaltimeter (this satellite was launched in late 1990). A number of working meetings made it possible to solve the problem of retrieving algorithms and, by the year 1992, to obtain a first representative global data base on the phytoplankton content, and on the wind and sea roughness fields.

The rate of deforestation
In this case the principal objective was a global-scale inventory of forests and tracing their dynamics from the data of both existing and planned satellites. In this connection, it was important that starting from 1982, the NASA experts have been accumulating a global base of monthly mean estimates of the normalized differential vegetation index (NDVI), which made it possible to have a 10-year observational series (of particular concern were the problems of the tropical forest clearing and forest fires).

Sea-surface temperature (SST)
Obtaining and accumulating the SST data were determined by their important role in the solution of the problems of numerical modelling of global circulations of the atmosphere and the ocean. In this connection, the objective was: (i) to raise the reliability and representativity of SST data; (ii) to realize a technique for substantiating the complex SST data archive with their ensured mutual calibration; (iii) to accumulate regional-scale highly reliable data bases; (iv) to improve the SST retrieval algorithms. The final objective was to accumulate by the year 1992 a representative global data base on SST.

The polar ice cover dynamics
This direction foresaw obtaining the satellite information (first of all, from data of ERS-1 and JERS-1; the latter was launched in early 1992) to analyse the laws of the annual change of the ice cover extent in the Arctic and in the Antarctic, as well as the large-scale dynamics of the ice cover manifested, in particular, through drifting ice and icebergs. The principal contribution to obtaining such information was made by passive and active radar techniques. The formation of a representative global data base had been completed by the year 1992.

The WG-3 experts were aimed at representing global satellite information in the form accessible for a wide sphere of users. With this in mind, an "encyclopaedia" and an atlas that described global changes of the environment and the biosphere were prepared. These publications contained information about changes in land surface and marine biota both on regional and on global scales.

In connection with the problems discussed, of extreme importance was a provision for comparable, universal formats and easy data access. This required respective recommendations and publications of data catalogues, which determined the development of a project dedicated to the problem of accumulating a global-scale reference data base which contained information about vegetation cover; the state of land and ocean surface; air humidity near the surface and in a free atmpsphere; the World Ocean's level; ice and snow cover; ocean colour; atmospheric characteristics, etc.

1.4 THE GEWEX PROGRAMME

In connection with the further development of studies within the WCRP and planning the IGBP, a Global Energy and Water Cycles Experiment (GEWEX) has been proposed aimed at: (i) describing and analysing the laws of transport of water (vapours, liquid and solid) as well as energy fluxes in the global atmosphere and at the surface level; (ii) developing techniques to forecast natural and anthropogenic changes in the distribution of water in all the three phases in the atmosphere and at the surface level. Meeting these objectives requires various advanced observational means, space-borne instruments included.

The completion of GEWEX will make it possible to make the first step in studies of global changes taking place in the environment, based on an improvement of the global system of observations. The choice of the period 1995–2000 to realize the GEWEX is determined by the following circumstances: (i) an increasing urgency of the problem of global changes, whose key aspects are studies of biogeochemical cycles, general circulation of the atmosphere and ocean, energy and mass exchange; (ii) availability of new space-borne means of observations of the atmosphere and ocean by the years 1995–2000 (it particularly refers to active lidar and radar sounding); (iii) expected serious progress in computer potential.

The existing observational system has a number of shortcomings, including: (i) insufficient representativity of the global data base on the 3-D wind field (over the Indian Ocean, in particular); (ii) serious uncertainties of data on precipitation over land and practical lack of such data over the ocean; (iii) substantial inadequacy of global data bases on 3-D fields of water content and cloudiness; (iv) a very limited volume of information on the radiation budget and optical properties of surface on global scales; (v) scanty quantitative geographical information on land use, types and properties of vegetation cover, etc.

Requirements of data of satellite observations necessitate the use of geostationary and low-orbit satellites. In particullar, five geostationary satellites are necessary which would carry: (i) multispectral instruments for the visible and IR spectral regions to obtain both high-resolution images and quantitative data on the brightness fields at various wavelengths; (ii) medium-resolution sensors for the IR and microwave intervals to retrieve 3-D fields of temperature, water and moisture content, as well as other parameters.

As far as low-orbit satellites are concerned, at least, two polar-orbit (nearly 800 km) Sun-synchronous satellites are needed, and the launch of an orbital station with individual platforms in an almost equatorial (30°) orbit is being planned. The equipment for low-orbit satellites includes: (i) an operational meteorological unit to obtain images, to perform remote sounding, to collect information from various automated platforms; (ii) a unit to obtain data on the cloud cover structure and on the wind field (lidar altimeter); a multi-spectral radiometer to obtain stereographic images of clouds; a scatterometer to retrieve winds and wind shear near the ocean surface; the Doppler lidar to obtain data on the wind in the cloudless atmosphere; (iii) a microwave unit to obtain data on precipitation (multi-channel scanning microwave radiometer with a broad spatial coverage, including a low-frequency channel in the S-band to retrieve soil moisture); radar at frequencies 10–15 and 35 GHz to measure rain rate with a high spatial resolution; two types of radar are recommended: a large-antenna radar on an orbital station providing a 200-km swath width, with a high vertical resolution (0.5 km), and a compact radar on polar-orbit satellites to identify the zones of precipitating clouds); (iv) a unit to measure the ERB components, including advanced ERB sensors, narrow-band (in the bands of H_2O, CO_2, etc.) radiometers to assess the effect of cloudiness and greenhouse gases on the ERB, a lidar to retrieve the heights of cloud tops and atmospheric boundary layer, a multi-spectral radiometer to obtain medium-resolution images, a multi-channel IR radiometer with several FOVs (along the route of the satellite) to retrieve the SST.

Also, important information has been obtained from the satellite GEOSAT (launched in 1985) and meteorological satellite DMSP SSM/I(AF) (launched in mid-1986). Operational NOAA meteorological satellites provide the almost-real-time information about the fields of wind, sea roughness, SST, sea currents, sea and lake ice cover.

Information from various launched and planned satellitees will also be used, in order of priority of their launchings: TOPEX/POSEIDON, Japanese oceanographic satellite MOS-1, Canadian satellite RADARSCAT.

Geostationary satellites METEOSAT are an important component of the European Space Agency (ESA) Programme aimed at using space-based observational means to study the environment and Earth's resources. Three-channel (0.5–0.8; 10.5–12.5; 5.7–7.1 μm) scanning radiometers carried by these satellites provide a 5-km nadir spatial resolution, and with the use of duplicated sensors in the visible—2.5 km (one of these sensors operates with the sensor using the 5.7–7.1—μm channel).

Processing the data from METEOSAT-1 (launched in November 1977 and from late 1979 it only collected and transmitted data because of the scanning radiometer's malfunction) and METEOSAT-2 (launched in June 1981) has made it possible to obtain the following information: cloud cover distribution; ocean surface and cloud top temperature; water content of the upper troposphere; Earth's radiation budget; wind field (from the motion of clouds). In the period 1986–1994, three or four satellites have been planned for launch, and starting from 1992, the use of the Italian satellite SIRIO-2 to collect and transmit meteorological information.

Two SKYLAB experiments have been accomplished based on the use of: (i) a metric camera to obtain images over the area 188.5 × 188.5 km (a 23 × 23-cm square, the film 120–150 m long), with a resolution of 10–20 m, which will allow a thematic mapping on a scale of $1:10^5$ to be conducted; (ii) SAR—microwave radiometer operating in various regimes (40° to the vertical). In the SAR regime, images with an area 9 × 2500 km, with a resolution of 25 × 25 m, are obtained, and in the radiometer regime—SST is retrieved with an error of ± 1°C.

Table 1.23 gives the ERS-1 characteristics, whose development started in 1982 and whose launch in the 675-km Sun-synchronous orbit was realized on 17 June 1991. As seen from the Table, the programme of the satellite has been focused, first of all, on monitoring the ocean and ice cover.

The S-band radar is a combination of SAR and scatterometers to retrieve the characteristics of sea state and wind vector. The measuring complex also includes the IR radiometer scanning along the orbit of the satellite, which must provide SST retrievals with an accuracy of 0.5 K.

The Earth-resources information can be obtained from the ground network

Table 1.23. The ERS-1 radar complex

Parameters	Range	Error	Horizontal resolution	Coverage and repeatability	Instrument
Wind:					
Speed	4–24 m s^{-1}	± 2 m s^{-1}; $\pm 10\%$	50×50 km	Global; 3 days	Scatterometer
Direction	0–360°	± 20	20×20 km	Global; 3 days	Radioaltimeter
Sea state spectrum:					
Direction	0–180°	$\pm 7°$; 30%		Discrete	Scatterometer
Spectral				measurements	(2-D roughness
accuracy			10 km^2	in grid knots	spectrum)
Wavelength	30–480 m	Spectral resolution 30 m		with a step of 900 km in longitude at the equator; 3 days	
Ice cover thickness		± 2 m	10×10 km	Global; 3 days	Radioaltimeter
Significant wave height	1–20 m	± 0.5 m; $\pm 10\%$	10×10 km	Discrete measurements	Radioaltimeter
High resolution images		Resolution 1 dB by the brightness levels	100×100 m 30×30 m 15×15 m	in grid knots Band 80 km wide; 3 days; global monitoring for 35 days	SAR

EARTHNET of four stations, launched in 1978 to receive, process and distribute data from different satellites (given in brackets): Fuccino in Italy (Landsat-1, 2, 3), Kiruna in Sweden (Landsat), Lanion in France (Nimbus-7 and a satellite for mapping the soil heat capacity, HCMM), Maspalomas on Canary Islands (Nimbus-7). Also, two centres have been formed for satellite SAR data in Farnborough (England) and Oberpfaffenhoffen (FRG), as well as the EARTHNET Programme Office in Frascatti (Italy).

By the 1990s eight satellites had carried 19 new types of instrumentation (mainly, for the microwave region): three or four scatterometers, four radioaltimeters, three SARs, five microwave radiometers, one low-frequency sensor, two IR radiometers, one multi-channel visible radiometer.

The daily data base on the World Ocean included 2–4 thousand reports from ships and buoys, 30–70 thousand retrieved SST values. By the years 1991–1992 the volume of combined conventional and satellite information had increased in the following way (in thousands of reports per day, Table 1.24).

The NNEE-DD system would have made it possible to provide information on the ocean in the 1990s, it being not so costly. The use of data from satellites of the ERS-1 type via NESDIS is vital for the system. The launching of the first of these

Table 1.24. Increase in the volume of combined conventional and satellite information

Parameter	Years					
	1984	1985	1986	1987	1988	1989–1990
Wind speed	2–4	60	1000	2000	2000	4000
Wind direction	2–4	2–4	2–4	1–4	2–4	40–910
SST	30–40	30–70	30–70	30–70	30–70	950
Sea-surface roughness	2–4	60	60	60	60	120

satellites in the 833-km Sun-synchronous orbit (inclination 98.7°) had been planned for 1989 to obtain global information about the World Ocean for 36–42 hours with the help of the following instruments: (i) the 13.999 GHz 6-antenna scatterometer to estimate wind speed (error 1.3 m s^{-1}) and direction (16°) near the ocean surface with a spatial resolution of 50 (or 25) km and swath width 600 km; (ii) nadir-viewing 13.5 GHz radioaltimeter to measure the relative sea surface height 3.5 (or 18) cm, significant wave height (0.5 m or 10%) and wind speed (2 m s^{-1} in the range 1–68 m s^{-1}); (iii) four-frequency (19.3, 22.2, 27.0, and 85.5 GHz) 7-channel (only for the second frequency, measurements are made at vertical polarization, and for the remaining frequencies—at two orthogonal polarizations) cone-scanning (45°—nadir angle) microwave radiometer with the 1394-km swath width to retrieve wind speed (± 2 m s^{-1} in the range 3–35 m s^{-1} with 25-km resolution), ice concentration and location of the ice edge ($\pm 12\%$ in the interval 0–100%; ± 12.5 km, 25-km resolution), rain rate (± 5 mm h^{-1} in the interval 0– 25mm h^{-1}, 25-km resolution), cloud water content (0.1 kg m^{-2}, 0–1 kg m^{-2}), atmospheric water content (2.0 kgm^{-2}, 0–6 kg m^{-2}), qualitative assessment of soil moisture (dry–wet, wet–oversaturated); (iv) scanning (cone, 45°) 2-channel (5.2, 10.4 GHz) low-frequency microwave radiometer for all-weather SST retrievals with an error of 0.5 K, resolution 10 km and 1.0 K, resolution 25 km (swath width 1400 km). This programme has not been realized, however.

As has been mentioned above, the ERS-1 scientific complex consists, mainly, of the instruments for active and passive microwave sounding that are able to provide the most adequate information on the sea-surface wind field and sea roughness. The on-board radar complex (OBRC) includes: (i) the 5.3 GHz S-band SAR at horizontal–horizontal polarization (the size of the antenna 10 × 10 m) to obtain images with a 30-m spatial resolution, within the 80-km viewing belt; (ii) scatterometer to retrieve sea roughness (12 wavelength intervals, 100 to 1000 m) for 100-km bands along the satellite's track (resolution 5 km^2) at an angle of about 23° to the vertical; (iii) scatterometer to retrieve wind speed (error 20°), at a spatial resolution of 50 × 50 km within the 500-km band (25–55° from nadir). In the last case, three antennas have been used, directed forward, downward and backward, 3.6 × 0.3 m (two antennas) and 2.5 × 0.3 m in size.

The OBRC also includes the 13.5 GHz Ku-band radioaltimeter (antenna 1 m in diameter), with a measurement accuracy of not less than 10 cm (5 cm in the future), to retrieve the significant wave height within 1–20 m (error 0.5 m), as well as a laser retroreflector (to track the satellite from the ground). A 3-channel cone-scanning radiometer has been designed (3.7, 11, and 12 μm; resolution 1 km; coverage 500 km) to retrieve SST (expected error 0.5 K for areas 50 × 50 km, 8-point cloudiness) from data of 2-angle measurements, as well as a 2-channel (23.8, 36.5 GHz) microwave radiometer to retrieve the total water content in the atmosphere (two additional channels can be used at 90 and 150 GHz).

In Japan, an oceanographic satellite MOS-1 was put in a circular (909 km) Sun-synchronous orbit, with an inclination of 99.1°, carrying: (i) 4-channel (0.51–0.59; 0.61–0.69; 0.72–0.80; 0.80–1.10 μm) self-scanning radiometer with an instant FOV of 54.7 $\pm$ 5.0 mrad 100-km scanning width; (ii) 4-channel scanning visible and IR radiometer (0.5–0.7; 6.0–7.0; 10.5–11.5; 11.5–12.5 μm), with instant FOVs 1 mrad (visible) and 3 mrad (IR), scanning bandwidth 1500 km; (iii) 2-channel (23.8 $\pm$0.2; 31.4 $\pm$0.25 GHz) microwave scanning radiometer at horizontal (23.8 GHz) and vertical (31.4 GHz) polarizations with the beam width, respectively, 1.9° and 1.3° and scanning bandwidth 317 km (the dynamic range 30–300 K, error 1 K at 300 K).

The use of MOS-1 data makes it possible to solve problems of retrieving SST, sea-surface wind speed, atmospheric water content and other parameters. In Japan the launch was realized of the Earth-resources satellite JERS-1 in the 570-km 99° circular Sun-synchronous orbit, whose measuring complex includes: (i) the SAR at 127 GHz frequency at HH polarization, with the swath width 75 km (nadir angle 33°) and spatial resolution 25 × 25 m; (ii) 4-channel scanning radiometer for the visible and near-IR spectral regions (0.45–0.52; 0.52–0.60; 0.63–0.69; 0.76–0.95 μm), with an instant FOV of 43.9 mrad and swath width of 150 km. This satellite is aimed at studying the sea-surface state, in particular.

A possibility has been considered to launch the MOS-2 satellite, for which the following instruments are being improved: (i) ocean colour and SST scanner (0.43–0.45; 0.50–0.53; 0.54–0.58; 0.65–0.67; 0.75–0.79; 3.7; 10.5–11.5; 11.5–12.5 μm), with a swath width of 1400 km; (ii) the 14 GHz radioaltimeter (error $\pm$10 cm for the ocean level and 0.5 for the significant wave height) with a spatial resolution of 2 km, together with a laser retro-reflector; (iii) an advanced 4-channel (31.4, 23.8, 10.7, 6.6 GHz) scanning microwave radiometer with a 50-km spatial resolution (temperature resolution 1 K, swath width 1400 km); (iv) the 14 GHz scatterometer (VH polarizations), with a spatial resolution 50 km and swath width 500 km (errors in retrieving the wind speed and direction, respectively, 2 m s^{-1} and less than 20°).

To understand the causes of present climate change, of great importance are data on precipitation (it refers particularly to the tropical convective precipitation characterizing the latent heat release in the middle troposphere) presented in the form of global fields (in regular grid knots) of the rain rate monthly means. From the viewpoint of climate change in time scales from one month to one decade, the requirements for accuracy of monthly mean precipitation one the 500-km-resolution grid are determined by the need to estimate 1°C variations in surface air temperature

(SAT), which is equivalent to a regional anomaly of about 10 W m^{-3} of heat flux divergence (BEST..., 1988; Browning, 1987).

The global mean precipitation constitutes 1 m y^{-1}, which corresponds to a latent heat release of 80 W m^{-2}. With 1 cm month-1 as an acceptable uncertainty of regional monthly mean precipitation, it is equivalent to an error in the heat flux divergence of 10 W m^{-2}. However, the accuracy can be reduced to 25 W m^{-2} (3 cm month-1). At present the World Weather Watch (WWW) system carries out an exchange of global data from approximately 3500 raingauge stations (on a regional basis—up to 7000–8000 stations), though national networks have up to 140 thousand points of raingauge measurements.

Analysis of the data of the frequenced raingauge network in Texas (USA) has shown that to estimate the summertime rains on the grid with a 410-km step with an error of 1 cm month^{-1}, the data from about 14 stations are needed (this is equivalent to 20 stations on a grid with a step of 500 km). With an error assumed to be 25 W m^{-2}, in this case to draw the field of precipitation on a 500-km grid, data from five stations are needed for each of the grid cells. But, with the possibility of using satellite data on precipitation over land, with a 10 W m^{-2} error, 10–15 stations are enough for a 500-km grid.

The simplest satellite technique of rain rate retrieval consists in the use of the precipitation index GPI determined from the GOES data on the amount of clouds with a temperature below 235 K. Over the land the coefficient of correlation between GPI and observed monthly mean precipitation varies in summer (winter) within 0.7–0.8 (0.4–0.6), but in the case of tropical convective precipitation over the ocean it rises to 0.8–0.9. More complicated techniques to consider the characteristics of isolated clouds on satellite images can be applied only to summertime convective clouds. The best results have been obtained with the GIST technique based on consideration of the evolution of convective clouds from the data of geostationary satellites. Naturally, the most promising is the combined use of the data of surface and satellite observations. The problem-oriented field experiments are needed to calibrate the satellite data.

From the viewpoint of climate studies, it is important to measure precipitation with an accuracy of at least 20% over a 2° lat. × 2° long. grid (this is equivalent to a maximum permissible error of ±1 cm day^{-1}). Naturally, the prospects for obtaining the global data base on precipitation are connected mainly with observations from satellites in a wide wavelength range, from the visible and IR (estimates of precipitation from cloud brightness and cloud top height) to microwave (passive and active radar measurements). As Browning (1987) notes, the main difficulty of rain rate retrieval is determined by its indirect relation to cloud properties depending substantially on special features of synoptic situation.

However, there are general laws determining the need for accounting for: (i) non-precipitating clouds with a cold top boundary (cirrus clouds); (ii) precipitating clouds with their warm top (sometimes without ice phase); (iii) situations with a large vertical gradient of rain rate determined by the level of relative humidity in the lower layers of the atmosphere; (iv) horizontal inhomogeneity of the distribution of precipitation appearing with the simultaneous precipitation from both stratus and cumulus clouds as well as under the influence of orographic factors. The only technique able to overcome the enumerated complications is the satellite radar sounding, which makes it possible to retrieve the vertical distribution of precipitation.

There are different possibilities to raise the reliability of retrieval of rain rate from satellite observations in the visible and IR spectral regions making use of: (i) data on the rate of change of the cloud top area as an indicator of the intensity of the upward motions; (ii) estimates of cloud thickness; (iii) information on the spatial structure and texture of clouds; (iv) data for a "split" transparency window (to retrieve the water vapour content and to estimate evaporation); (v) results of 4-D assimilation (to estimate precipitation and evaporation under clouds); (vi) conclusions from the numerical simulation modelling. The enumerated information can be used most efficiently in the case of using passive and active radar techniques. In this case the global survey is possible only on the basis of the combined polar-orbit and geostationary satellites as well as a satellite in the orbit with a small angle of inclination (to sound the clouds in low latitudes).

Based on the use of the data of the remote sounding of precipitation in the tropics from the proposed satellite TRMM, the American–Japan programme foresees a regular obtaining of information characterizing the tropical precipitation as one of the leading weather- and climate-forming factors (TRMM..., 1988). The TRMM satellite was planned for launch in 1994 (since been postponed), and it will be one of the first major components in the system of means of observation combined by a space station to be (possibly) launched in the late 1990s.

The importance of the problem of the cycle and phase conversions of water in the atmosphere is determined by the leading role of the respective processes as factors of weather and climate variability as well as by great practical importance of water resources. The later heat release due to water vapour condensation playing the key role in atmospheric energetics is realized, first of all, in low latitudes and, mainly, in an ITCZ band where precipitation falls out from about 30 cloud clusters, each about several hundred kilometres in diameter.

The vertical energy transport and about 60% of the precipitation are concentrated within varying cloud clusters and about 2000 cumulo-nimbus clouds of penetrative convection (they are often called "hot towers").

The vertical velocities of the upward motions in the "towers" vary within 5–30 m s^{-1}, and the rain rate within 4×4 km^2 squares can exceed 100 mm h^{-1}. The remaining part of precipitation falls out more gradually from large "anvils" or stratified branches of "hot towers" (the share of such precipitation increases as the cloud system grows older). The interannual variability of the latent heat release by cloud clusters is the major cause of interannual variations in global climate, especially those observed in the form of ENSO (El Niño/Southern Oscillation).

The following problems connected with studies of the interactive "atmosphere–ocean" system are most interesting: (i) the 4-D structure of latent heat in the tropical atmosphere, its diurnal and annual change, the intraseasonal and interannual variability; (ii) the role of latent heat released in the tropics in the formation of tropical and extra-tropical circulation; (iii) monthly mean precipitation over the tropical oceans averaged over the area 10^5 km^2 and their effect on the structure and circulation of the oceans; (iv) relationship between precipitation and variations in boundary conditions on the Earth's surface (SST, soil moisture, vegetation cover); (v) the diurnal course of precipitation in the tropics and its spatial variability; (vi) the relative contribution of precipitation from convective and stratus clouds, its geographical variability and annual change; (vii) the role of more reliable information about precipitation for a better understanding of the hydrological cycle in the tropics.

The following requirements for observation data from the viewpoint of their spatial and temporal resolution and retrieval errors determine the need to solve various problems: climate modelling (10^5 km^2, monthly mean, 1 mm day^{-1} or 10% in the case of heavy rains); analysis of intraseasonal variability (10^6 km^2, 15 days, 20% or 0.8 mm day^{-1}) of the drought in the Sahel (2° lat. × 10° long.; monthly means, 20%); monsoons (10^6 km^2, 1 month, 10%); the diurnal change over the ocean (20° lat. × 5° long., 2 months, 10% for amplitude and 20% for the second harmonic).

The vertical resolution, in the case of using the meteorological radar sounding, should reach 500 m (swath width 60 km) from the viewpoint of AGCM (Atmospheric General Circulation Model) requirements and 250 m (in nadir) when analysing cloud statistics. When studying the structure and dynamics of tropical precipitation, the horizontal (vertical) resolution of 20 km (500–4 km), temporal resolution of 12 h and error about 30–50% are needed.

These circumstances have stimulated the development of the TRMM satellite, to be launched in a circular orbit with an inclination of 35° and altitude of 350 km, bearing in mind the obtaining of monthly mean precipitation over the 5° lat. × 5° long. grid, as well as assessing the vertical profile of the latent heat release during a period ot not less than 3 years. With this in view, three types of scientific complexes are being developed. The major component of the complexes is the MR developed by Japanese specialists for the retrieval of rain rate in the atmospheric layer 0–15 km; it functions at a frequency of 14 GHz and should provide a retrieval of minimum rain rate 0.5 mm h^{-1}, with the horizontal (vertical) resolution in nadir not less than 5 km (250 m), with a minimum swath width of about 200 km.

The complex of microwave passive sounding includes the electronically scanning microwave radiometer ESMR (frequency 19.35 GHz, horizontal polarization, resolution in nadir 9 km, swath width 700 km) and radiometer SSM/I (channels 19.36, 22.235, 37, and 8.5 GHz horizontal and vertical polarizations, resolution in nadir from 4–5 km for channel 8.5 GHz to 16–23 km for 19-GHz, the channel swath width 520 km).

One more component is the 6-channel (0.665, 0.650, 1.61, 6.72, 10.7, and 12.0 μm) advanced radiometer AVHRR-3 for the visible and IR spectral regions, with a spatial resolution of from 1 to 2–3 km for the swath width of 1100 km (the number of channels will be reduced).

The data for the optical range will be used: (i) to assess the cloud conditions; (ii) to measure the parameters needed for the algorithms to be used to retrieve the rain rate from the data of microwave radiometer and meteorological radar; (iii) as a "bridge" to transfer from the data of microwave soundings to the data of optical sounding of precipitation obtained from operational (geostationary and polar-orbit) meteorological satellites (the TRMM data can be used for calibration purposes).

The programme BEST developed under the auspices of CNES (France) is dedicated to a study (first of all, based on analysis of satellite information) of the energetics of weather- and climate-forming systems in the tropics (BEST..., 1988). Thir programme was to combine the interests of: (i) the WCRP with its components, such as TOGA, WOCE and GEWEX; (ii) the IGBP.

The fundamental considerations for the programme BEST are connected with the inadequately studied global cycle of water and, specifically, with such a powerful source of energy for the atmosphere as latent heat released when the cloud cover develops. In the balance of energy in the troposphere, latent heat constitutes more than one third (37.5%), whereas the shares of other sources of energy are as follows: 34.5% (absorbed solar radiation); 20.3% (absorbed longwave radiation); 7.8% (heat flux divergence due to turbulent heat exchange between the surface and the atmosphere).

The moisture convergence in the tropical atmospheric boundary layer (ABL) is one of the major sources of energy for the atmospheric general circulation, which stimulates the penetrating moist convection, leading to the transformation of latent and sensible heat into potential energy with its subsequent transport to the subtropics by the upper branch of the Hadley cell. Also, of importance is a combination of convergence zones from the region of Indonesia to the Central Pacific, leading to the Walker cell transformation characteristic of the ENSO events.

These and other circumstances determine the key role of satellite information about the 3-D wind field and water cycle, taking into account the inadequacy and the insufficient reliability of data available. The estimates have shown that it is necessary to retrieve the vertical profile of wind speed with an error of not more than $1–2 \text{ m s}^{-1}$ with a vertical resolution of about 1 km in the troposphere and 300–500 m in the ABL. In this connection there is a need for improved instruments of remote sounding, such as satellite MR, which would make it possible to retrieve rain rate, as well as lidars, based on the principle of differential absorption (retrieval of the ABL water content), etc.

Of principal value is an account of the interrelationship between water- and energy-cycles manifesting itself particularly strongly in the processes of cloud–radiation interaction as well as the relationship between the tropical convection and wind field. The convergence in ABL in the tropics, stimulating the process of penetrative wet convection, affects substantially the generation of super-long waves of Madden-Julian propagating eastward (apparently, they are Kelvin waves caused by convection determined by convective instability of the second kind—CISK), which, in turn, affects the wind field in the whole tropical belt and causes a modulation of monsoon circulation.

All this determines the critically important role of data on the 3-D wind field to solve the problems of the GEWEX programme. Especially it refers to the tropics, where the wind field cannot be retrieved from the data on the mass field in view of the broken geospheric balance. Other information needed is images of cloud cover and data on the ERB.

Thus, to achieve the GEWEX objectives, a satellite launched in a low orbit with a small inclination angle is needed in addition to the polar-orbit platforms planned earlier; it should include the following kinds of on-board scientific instruments: scanning radiometers to obtain cloud cover images in the visible and IR spectral regions; instruments to retrieve the 3-D wind field (including the Doppler lidar); means of passive (microwave radiometers) and active (MR) sounding in the radio-range to retrieve the rain rate; the ERB sensors. The programme BEST has been aimed at achieving these objectives.

The scientific complex of a satellite planned to be launched in a circular orbit with an inclination angle of 28.5° and height 500 km (this makes it possible to repeat a 24-hour cycle of observations over a 250 × 250-km grid for each point every 24 days) will include, first of all, the Doppler lidar (DL) and MR. The CO_2 lidar (pulse power 3 J, pulse frequency 2–10 Hz) has four longwave (9.1 μm) telescopes, mounted orthogonally at an angle of 45° with respect to nadir, which will provide a retrieval of the vertical wind profile with a resolution of about 50 km within a 400-km sub-satellite band. With only one telescope, a conical scanning is expedient. If the radius of the circle of scanning is 625 km (which corresponds to half of the distance between two successive sub-satellite trajectories), the whole tropical band is scanned over 12 h. The data thus obtained will make it possible to calculate the fields of vortices and wind-speed vector divergence.

The one-frequency pulse (13.75 and 13.76 GHz) MR with a pulse power of 1 kW and real aperture (with the beam width 0.18 × 0.18°), scanning across the orbit plane (the frequency of double pulses is 3500 Hz) can ensure the retrieval of rain rate in a 20-km atmospheric layer and with the horizontal resolution in nadir 1.6 km and vertical resolution about 400 m, with swath width 100 km (it is possible to recognize the homogeneous layers of precipitation up to 5 km thick with a rain rate of 60 mm h^{-1}).

A comparatively narrow swath width of MR which can shift to both sides of the sub-satellite trajectory determines the necessity for the simultaneous use of a wide-angle passive microwave radiometer with a broad swath width. The 4-channel radiometer SSM/I used on the American DMSP satellite, with characteristics given in Table 1.25, can serve as a prototype.

Another possible prototype is the AMSR complex developed for polar platforms (channels 6.6, 10.6, 18.7, 23.8, 31.5 GHz). Apparently, the second prototype is more appropriate for achieving the objectives of the programme BEST. The use of the complexes described above will make it possible to solve a key problem of the programme—to obtain information about precipitation averaged over one month for 5° × 5° squares.

As has been mentioned earlier, the scientific complex is planned to also include a lidar functioning at a wavelength near 730 nm based on the principle of differential absorption (DIAL) coordinated in the viewing direction with DL and designed to obtain information on the vertical humidity profile. Possibilities have been discussed to use a scanning radiometer to obtain stereoimages of cloud cover in the visible and IR spectral regions, to retrieve the wind field from cloud motion (the system WINDMATIC) as well as the ERB sensors of the type developed within the project

Table 1.25. Characteristics of the 4-channel radiometer SSM/1

Characteristics	Channels			
Central frequency, Ghz	19.35	122.24	37	85.5
Polarization (vertical—V, horizontal—H)	V/H	V	V/H	V/H
Radiometric resolution, K	0.8	0.8	0.6	1.1
Spatial resolution, km with the height of the orbit 833 km	70×45	60×40	38×30	16×14

SCaRaB. It is important to provide a synchronization of observations with the data of geostationary satellites. The processing of data whose volume is expressed in terrabites is a great problem.

As Chahine (1992) noted, the 25-year development of the technique of remote sounding of the atmosphere resulted in achieving a 2.0°C global mean standard error of retrieved temperature with respect to the radiosonde data. The MSD of retrieved absolute (relative) SST with respect to the data from the buoys is 1.5°C (0.5°C). The error in retrieving the total water content of the atmosphere over the ocean (from microwave data) is about 0.1 cm, but over land this error is much greater. The error in retrieving the vertical profile of the water content from the data for the 6.3 μm band reaches 30–50% and more (up to 100% near the surface).

The accuracy of remote sounding can be raised by the combined use of microwave and IR data (with a high spectral resolution). For the lower troposphere, most perspective are data for the Q-branch, 4.3-μm CO_2 band, whereas above the level 300 hPa the microwave data, which can also be used to filter out the effect of clouds when processing the data for the 4.3 μm band, give the most reliable results.

The combined use of IR and microwave data can ensure the retrieval of the temperature profile with an error of 1.5°C under any cloud conditions (with a cloud amount of up to 80%). To retrieve the surface temperature with an error of about 1 K, one can use 3-channel data in H_2O continuum near 3.7 μm, which makes it possible to estimate even the land surface emissivity and the contribution of reflected solar radiation (in the daytime). Besides, the data in channels 11 μm and 8 μm of the transparency window can serve as a source of information about SST. The perspective of raising the accuracy of the moisture profile retrieval is connected with the use of data for the 183-GHz channel (this problem requires, however, further study), with the use of lidar sounding.

Staelin (1987) discussed the possibilities of the remote sounding of the atmosphere and obtaining the hydrological, oceanographic and other information making use of an advanced scanning ($\pm 47.85°$ during 8 s) microwave sounding unit (AMSU) developed to be carried by the operational meteorological satellites. This complex has a 15-channel unit A (bandwidth, in MHz, is given in brackets): 23800 (270); 31400 (180); 50300 (1); 52800 (1); 53596 ± 115 (2); 54400 (1); 54940 (1); 55500 (1); I_{L_0} = 57290.344 (1); $I_{L_0} \pm 217$ (2); $I_{L_0} \pm 322.2$ (4) ± 48; $I_{L_0} \pm 322.2$ (4) ± 10; $I_{L_0} \pm 322.2$

(4) ± 4.5 MHz; 89 GHz (1) and 5-channel unit B (GHz); 89.0 (1); 166.0 (1); 183.31 ± 1.00 (2); 183.31 ± 3.00 (2); 183.31 ± 7.00 (2).

The enumerated units provide continuous scanning within a broad swath width with resolutions in sub-satellite points 50 and 15 km, respectively. The swath width is such that it makes a complete coverage possible of the global surface in latitudinal zones more than 30° every 12 h. The data of unit A permit mapping of the global fields of moisture and water content (channels 1–3, 15), air temperature at altitudes 0–40 km (channels 4–14) and some surface parameters (ice cover, specifically)—channels 1–3, 14.

Channels of unit B include the transparency window (89 GHz) and water-vapour band-wing 183 GHz (the remaining four channels). In this case a higher spatial resolution permits a detailed analysis of the spatial structure of precipitation cells, plus an increased humidity near the fronts, sea ice and continental snow cover, etc. as well as ensuring an analysis of cloud conditions in the FOV of unit A when the temperature profile is retrieved. During each scan all channels are calibrated against the blackbody. Apparently, in the future, the AMSU will be the major component of a scientific complex for the atmospheric sounding carried by the operational meteorological satellites.

As Hamada (1987) pointed out, one of the most important requirements of the GEWEX programme for the observation data is to obtain a representative information volume characterizing the interdiurnal variability of atmospheric general circulation, especially in the tropics, which requires the solution of the problem of retrieving the wind vector by making use of various satellite data. The most substantial information of the kind has been obtained from the data of geostationary satellites on cloud motions (during the FGGE period, five geostationary satellites functioned), but this information suffers from some serious shortcomings: (i) it can be obtained only for the regions with clouds; (ii) the wind vector can be retrieved at no more than two levels; (iii) the wind retrieved is inaccurately referenced to a fixed level (especially in the case of cirrus clouds); (iv) it is difficult to estimate the drifting speed of rapidly moving cirrus clouds.

The enumerated shortcomings can be overcome, in particular, by: (i) tracing the drift of water vapour inhomogeneities (in cloud-free zones); (ii) using data for channel 6.8 μm (H_2O-band) to retrieve the wind at intermediate levels near 500 hPa (these data can also serve to specify the height of the reference level), to make stereo-observations, to obtain images of rapidly moving clouds with a frequented repeatability. Data from scatterometric and DL observations planned for the near future will become an important source of information about winds (or wind shear) near the ocean surface.

Platt (1987) described a satellite Doppler lidar to be used on the Space Shuttle or polar-orbit satellite to perform the wind sounding of the atmosphere within the programme WINDSAT. Use of the Doppler shift of the signal of backscattering by aerosol depending on the projection of the wind vector onto the viewing direction (obtaining data for several directions by conical scanning enables one to retrieve the wind vector) constitutes the physical basis of retrieval.

Examination of the possibilities of sounding at different wavelengths between 0.35

and 10.6 μm has led to the conclusion (with account of the harmful effect of lasers on the eyes in the visible and near-IR spectral regions) that the choice of the 9.11-μm CO_2 laser is the most promising, but, probably, the choice of a solid-state laser at $\lambda = 1.5$ μm or exymer laser (0.35 μm) will also be worth-while. Development of a CO_2 coherent lidar for the interval 9–11 μm has resulted in successful ground-based and aircraft tests in the field conditions.

Interpretation of observational data needs a numerical modelling of the interaction between light pulse and the atmosphere, including the effect of turbulence, backscattering by aerosol, and other processes. Most difficult is an account of aerosol backscattering for very transparent layers of the upper troposphere in the far oceanic regions, where data on winds are particularly important. Simulation numerical experiments have been carried out for a two-satellite system consisting of Shuttle spacecraft in circular orbits at altitude 300 km and operational meteorological satellites (800 km).

From conical scanning over a period of 7 or 11 s, with varying repeatability of pulses, one can obtain uniformly distributed global data with a horizontal resolution of 300 km and a vertical resolution of 1 km for the lower 20-km atmospheric layer. The pulse power (duration) constitutes 10 J (6.7 μs) and the diameter of the telescope is 1.25 m. If the height of the orbit is 300 km, then it is possible to retrieve wind speed at every altitude with an error of 0.7 ± 0.5 m s^{-1}. With the height increasing to 500 km the error grows sharply at altitudes above 10 km from 1 m s^{-1} (at $h = 11$ km) to 5 m s^{-1} (14 km) and more. A lidar is being developed for the Shuttle, which will provide a retrieval of wind speed with an error of 1 m s^{-1} (the weight of the measuring complex is 830 kg). A lidar weighting 470 kg is also under development for the polar-orbit satellites (power supply 559 W).

Chedin (1987) described the WINDMATIC complex designed to retrieve the wind speed making use of pairs of images obtained with scanning radiometers in the visible (500–700 nm) and IR (10.5–12.5 μm) spectral regions for the areas in front of and behind the sub-satellite point. Pairs of images of cloud cover areas obtained with a time interval of 1 minute enable one to estimate the speed and direction of winds from cloud drift through a correlation analysis of the areas of successive images 15×15 km^2 in size.

An objective is to retrieve the wind speed in the range 1 m s^{-1} (in the visible) or 4 m s^{-1} (IR) to 60 m s^{-1}. The vertical referencing of wind speed with an error of 100 m is made with a lidar altimeter—part of the complex (the Nd:YAG pulse laser at $\lambda = 530$ nm, pulse power 0.5 J and pulse duration 10 ns, the diameter of the receiving mirror 0.6 m). The IR radiometer with a radiometric accuracy of about 1 K is a component of the IR complex, designed to measure the cloud top brightness temperature. There is an on-board computer for data processing (correlation analysis of the pairs of images), though the recorded images should also be transmitted to the ground-based receiving centre.

The high requirements of the GEWEX for the accuracy of satellite ERB observations are determined, in particular, by the circumstance that the forecasted doubled-CO_2-induced global mean climate warming within 1.5–4.5°C is possible, provided the ERB disturbance reaches only 2– 3W m^{-2} (in this case variations in

Table 1.26. Spheres of application and requirements for the ERB data

Application	ERB components	Spatial resolution km	Temporal resolution		Error $W\,m^{-2}$
			Period of averaging	Repeatability	
1. Input information for monitoring and numerical modelling of climate.	Solar constant	—	1 month	Daily	0.2–1
	OLR, global means	—	1 month	1–3 h	0.2–1
	OSR, zonal means	—	1 month	1–3 h	1–3
	SRB, regional means	100–200	1 month to 1 day	1–3 h	2–5
	OLR, daily means	100–250	1 month	1–3 h	2–5
	OSR, synoptic			Synoptic periods	
	SRB, studies	100–250	No averaging		10
	SRB, components	100–250	1 month	1–3 h	10
2. Input data and validation of numerical weather forecasts.	OLR, OSR, SRB: Regional means	100–250	No averaging	1–3 h	10

each of the ERB components reach approximately 4–6 W m^{-2}), and regional anomalies vary from 20 W m^{-2} in the tropics to 100 W m^{-2} near the poles (the latter figure refers to the absorbed solar radiation variability). Hence, data from long-term (decades) ERB observations can be a very important source of information for the detection of anthropogenic climate changes.

Table 1.26 contains a summary of the basic requirements for the ERB observational data (OLR–outgoing longwave radiation; OSR—outgoing shortwave radiation). No agreement has been reached, so far, with respect to the choice of an optimal ERB measuring complex, but the following requirements must be mentioned: (i) active thermal control of the sensors; (ii) their "smooth" spectral sensitivity (without selectivity); (iii) possibility of the computer modelling of the instruments; (iv) provision for in-flight and pre-flight calibrations; (v) lack of sensitivity to polarization. The combined use of scanning and non-scanning instruments or (in priority) the use of either of them raises no doubts.

1.5 THE GLOBAL CLIMATE OBSERVING SYSTEM (GCOS)

A substantiation of an optimal global system of climate observations requires, first of all, an analysis of priorities. Analysis of the data from the Meteorological Services of 50 countries sent at WMO's request suggested the following order of priorities for the factors of the interannual climate variability (Kondratyev, 1987a): (i) the atmosphere–ocean interaction; (ii) deforestation; solar activity; (iii) the variability of the snow and ice cover extent; (iv) other factors (urbanization, CO_2, aerosol, desertification, stratospheric aerosol, soil moisture). On a time scale of decades, the priority may be the following: (i) CO_2; (ii) forest clearing; (iii) urbanization, ocean–atmosphere interaction; (iv) other factors (aerosol, solar activity, desertification, volcanic eruptions, stratospheric ozone, anthropogenic heat releases, snow and ice cover).

Atmospheric parameters of the first priority, which must be presented in the form of global fields, are the following: surface air temperature (absolute and anomalous), atmospheric pressure at sea level (anomalous), precipitation (absolute and anomalous), fields of winds or stream lines near the surface (in the tropics), cloud distribution, heights of 500 and 200 hPa levels (anomalous), relative topography 500/1000 hPa (anomalous), fields of winds or stream lines at 200 hPa level (in the tropics).

The first-priority oceanic parameters presented as time series are: SST (anomalous), wind speed near the surface (averaged vector of wind stress), heat content of the ocean surface layer (in definite regions). Observations of the OLR and OSR (ERB) are of vital importance. The most important characteristics of the cryosphere are the extent of continental snow and ice cover and fluctuations of glaciers.

Data on global mean concentrations of optically active atmospheric minor gaseous components (MGC) (ozone, CO_2, nitrogen oxides, freons, methane, etc.), extra-atmospheric solar radiation, ocean surface level (in definite regions) as well as on such indices of the climate system as the Southern Oscillation index; the oscillation characteristics of the Atlantic and Pacific Oceans in the northern hemisphere; the indices of zonal transport, blocking and trade winds; the amplitude and phase of the quasi-biennial oscillations in the stratosphere, and various indices describing the teleconnections in the troposphere are also important.

The emphasis must be placed on the following typical features of climate: jet streams, prevailing trajectories of cyclones, trade-wind systems, intertropical convergence zone, centres of action (the Aleutian and Icelandic minima, the sub-tropical high-pressure bands). Considerable progress in the development of satellite remote sensing techniques gives perspectives on the monitoring of vegetation cover, precipitation zones, stratospheric aerosols (of volcanic origin, in particular), polar ice thickness, oceanic currents, surface albedo, and insolation.

From the viewpoint of the physical properties of climate, the transport of latent and sensible heat at the surface–atmosphere interface, the latent heat release in precipitation zones, radiation-cloud interaction and interactions between the optically active MGCs and aerosols, the moisture cycle, atmospheric turbidity, etc., are of primary importance.

Table 1.27 gives the regions of the globe that are important from the viewpoint of monitoring the parameters and factors of climate.

The WCRP Joint Scientific Committee recommends that three classes of observational programme be distinguished, to which three classes of data on climate correspond. These data must be used: (i) to study the climate-forming processes and to develop techniques for their parameterization (the data of class P must be complex, detailed, but can be confined to one or several small regions and short time intervals from several weeks to several years); (ii) to test the adequacy of

Table 1.27. The first-priority key global regions with respect to monitoring the parameters and factors of climate

Climate system's components and climatic parameters	Key regions, first-priority processes and parameters
Atmosphere	1. Regions of the most frequent formation of the blocking cyclones: 160°W–120°W; 40°W–70°W; East Siberia–the Sea of Okhotsk along 60pi1 > 8N. 2. Zones of jet streams. 3. Regions of teleconnections: western Pacific Ocean, western Atlantic Ocean. 4. Location of ridges and troughs of superlong waves: Greenland, Taimyr, Alaska, Aleut Islands. 5. Sub-tropic high-pressure bands: eastern and western Pacific and Atlantic Oceans. 6. The Tibet maximum: from Central Asia to east Asia in summer. 7. The wind field in the tropics, including flows across the equator over Africa, the Atlantic and Pacific Oceans. 8. The South Pacific maximum, the Australian–Indonesian minimum. 9. Studies on atmospheric compositions at background stations (CO_2, etc.); lidar observations at individual locations.
Ocean	1. The Equatorial Eastern Pacific (El Nio): 180–90°W; 0–°8S. 2. SST along 137°E in January and July, especially in 0–7°N band. 3. The Somali current in the Indian Ocean. 4. The Kuroshio and Oyashio currents in the north-western Pacific Ocean. 5. The Central Pacific in the northern hemisphere.
Cryosphere	1. The Tibet plateau. 2. Siberia. 3. North America. 4, 5. The ice cover in the Sea of Okhotsk and Arctic seas.

theoretical climate models (the data of class A require global-scale observations during long time periods and must contain information about numerous characteristics of the climate system); (iii) to perform a long-term monitoring of slowly varying components of the climate system (class M), which is important for assessing the present global climate, understanding natural factors of the formation and variation of climate as well as to study the possibilities for climate forecasts.

Table 1.28 gives a preliminary list of climatic parameters and indicates the requirements for the spatial and temporal resolution, and measurement errors. These requirements are formulated, first of all, with the needs of climate numerical modelling taken into account, and, therefore, they are correlated, in particular, with the spatial grid step of climate models.

Table 1.28. Requirements for observations of the climate system parameters

Type of observations	Climate system parameter	Class of data	Spatial resolution km	Temporal resolution days	Error
1	2	3	4	5	6
Basic meteorological parameters according to GARP requirements	Temperature	P, A, M	500 100–200 hPa	To be specified	1°C
	Wind speed	P, A, M	500 100–200 hPa	To be specified	1–3 m s^{-1}
	Relative humidity	P, A, M	500 200–300 hPa	To be specified	7–30%
	Surface pressure	P, A, M	500	To be specified	1–3 hPa
	SST	P, A, M	500	To be specified	1°C
Radiation budget and its components, cloudiness	Solar constant	M	—	1 month	1–5 W m^{-2}
	Extra-atmospheric UV solar radiation	P, M	—	P—1 day M—to be specified	P—10% M—to be specified
	Earth's radiation budget	A, M	500	15–30	2–5 W m^{-2}
	Cloudiness	A	500	5–15 (vertically)	5% total 1°—top boundary temperature
	Global radiation	P, A	To be specified	5	1–3%

Oceanic parameters	Net longwave radiation	P, A		5	1–3%
	Surface albedo	A	To be specified	5–15	0.01–0.03
	SST	A, M	500	A—5-10 M—30	0.5-1.5°C
	Upper-layer heat content (200 m)	A	500	5–10	1–3 Kcal cm^{-2}
	Wind stress	A	200	5–10	0.1–0.4 dyn cm^{-2}
	Ocean surface level (to determine the speed of currents)	A	200	5–10	2–10 cm (dynamic topography)
	Surface currents	A, M	only critical regions	30	2–10 cm s^{-1}
	Deep water circulation	A, M	1000	5 years	0.1–0.5 sm s^{-1}
Precipitation and hydrology	Precipitation over the ocean	A	500	5–10	4 levels (1 mm day^{-1})
	River runoff	A	Major river basins	15–30	To be specified
	Soil moisture	A		15	10% field water stress, 2 levels
Cryosphere	Snow cover extent	A, M	50–100	5–15	Presence/absence
	Sea ice extent	A, M	50–100	5–15	Presence/absence
	Ice thickness	A, M	200	15–30	10–20%
	Sea ice melting	P	50	5 days	Yes/no
	Thickness of glaciers	M	200	1 year	0.1–1 m
	Deformation of glaciers	M	200	1 year	2–10 m

Table 1.28 (continued)

1	2	3	4	5	6
Atmospheric composition	CO_2	M, A	2 background and 10 regional stations	15 weeks	±1 ppm
	Vertical profile of ozone concentration	P, A	10 stations over the globe	1 week	±1 ppm
	Total ozone content	M	WMO network	1	1–5%
	Global distribution of ozone	M	500 km; 2 km (vertically)	—	—
	Tropospheric aerosol	M	Background WMO stations	—	—
	Atmospheric turbidity	M	Background WMO stations	1 week	1%
	Stratospheric aerosol	M	2–4 background stations	—	—

The least substantiated requirement for the observational data is a considerable arbitrariness in determining acceptable errors in the measurements. This is difficult to avoid because it is impossible to formulate universal requirements of accuracy, since they depend on the specific character of the problems to be solved. The use of correlations among various parameters of the climate system is of great importance for optimization of the accuracy requirements. One efficient way of raising the accuracy is an averaging over the data of frequented measurements (especially where they refer to observations from satellites).

In testing the adequacy of climate models by comparing with observational data, the problem of objective analysis deserves serious attention. Experience has shown that application of various techniques for objective analysis gives (with identical input data) substantially different results. Apparently, to check the adequacy, it is sufficient to have monthly averaged data bases.

Requirements of the accuracy of the ERB measurements are formulated with a view that an instrumentation for the ERB experiment must provide an accuracy not worse than ± 5 W m^{-2}, which will make it possible to analyse the climatically substantial ERB variations on regional scales.

The problem of obtaining the data on the 3-D cloud field remains unsolved. Information on cloud cover climatology must include the following data: global distribution of total cloud cover; types of clouds and the height of their upper boundary; interannual and seasonal variabilities of cloud cover; the diurnal change of low-level clouds and convective clouds; statistical characteristics of cloud size. An improvement in the SST retrieval accuracy (bearing in mind the prevailing contribution of the ocean to the formation of climate and its changes) is a serious problem. The present retrieval accuracy of about 1–2 K permits neither reliable determination of the SST nor diagnostic studies.

The uncertainty of such a critically substantial parameter as wind stress (0.1–0.4 dyn cm^{-2}) is equivalent to that in wind speed of 3–6 m s^{-1}, which can be reached, since the error in scatterometric measurements from the SEASAT satellite did not exceed ± 2 m s^{-1}. There is a need for an extensive programme of numerical simulation experiments to substantiate more reliably a set of parameters and requirements to the accuracy of their measurements, as applied to various problems.

The existing and planned satellites make it possible to realize the remote sensing of the characteristics enumerated in Table 1.29, with the requirements for spatial and temporal resolution and the accuracy ensured. The meteorological satellites of the TIROS-N type, first launched in 1978, make it possible to raise the accuracy of estimation of SST from a level of 1.5–2°C (for a spatial grid step of 160 km) to 1°C, using the AVHRR, thereby ensuring the mapping over the spatial grid with a step of 50 km. In this case the third of the requirements listed in Table 1.29 will be satisfied with an AVHRR FOV ensuring a resolution of about 1 km.

A 5-channel microwave radiometer developed for Nimbus-7 and Seasat-1 satellites enabled one (for a grid step of 100 km) to reach an accuracy in SST retrieval of about 1.5°C, with measurements made in all kinds of weather. The IR instruments used earlier meet the requirements for measurements of the temperature of snow, ice, and land surface. The presence in the last case of a strong diurnal

Table 1.29. Requirements for surface characteristics measured using the technique of remote sensing from space, from the viewpoint of WCRP

Parameter	Spatial resolution km	Temporal resolution (repeatability days)	Accuracy
SST	200	5–10	0.5–1.5°C
	500	5–10	0.5–1.5°C
	Maximum possible	30	0.5–1.5°C
Land surface ice	100	5	1.0°C
cover temperature	500	5	0.1–3.0°C
Wind stress near	200	5–10	0.1–0.4 dyn cm^{-2}
the ocean surface			
Sea currents and	200	5–10	2–10 cm
vortices			(topography)
Ice cover extent	100	5	Presence/absence
	150	5–10	Presence/absence
	50	5–10	Presence/absence
Ice cover thickness	200	13–30	10–20%
Ice cover melting	50	5	Yes–No
Ice cover drift	400	1	5 km
Snow cover extent	100	5	Presence/absence
	50	5–15	Presence/absence
Soil moisture	100	5	10% field moisture content
	500	15	2 gradations
Surface albedo	100	5	0.1–0.3
	500	5–15	?

change necessitates the use of geostationary satellites.

Use of microwave radiometers and radars of Nimbus-7 and Seasat-1 has opened up wide possibilities to estimate the wind speed near the ocean surface with an accuracy of 2 m s^{-1} (with a grid step of 50 km and 36-h repeatability). Averaging over an area of 200 × 200 km for 5–10 days ensures meeting the requirements mentioned in Table 1.29. Later on, the accuracy of estimating the wind speed up to 1 m s^{-1} (with a grid step of 25 km) can be reached.

The existing IR radiometers enable one to identify the boundaries of the sea currents and vortices, with temperature contrasts of about 2°C. The GEOS-3 radiometer permitted an accuracy of sea level measurements which meets the WCRP requirements. The 10 cm accuracy needed (the 20-km grid step, over 5–10 days) was reached with the altimeter carried by the oceanographic satellite Seasat-1. Apparently, this accuracy can be raised further to 2–10cm.

At present, the technique for analysing the space-derived imagery has been developed thoroughly to study the spatial structure of ice cover (with clouds filtered out). Microwave remote sensing has made this technique all-weather and opened up possibilities to distinguish reliably between open water, one-year and multi-year ice, as well as to assess the ice cover thickness (Kondratyev, 1987a). Identification of the types of ice and subsequent assessment of their thickness can be made from scatterometer data. Side-looking radars (SLR) are an important means for monitoring the ice cover. The synthetic-aperture radar (SAR) of very high resolution (about 25 km) was carried by Seasat-1 and later by satellites of the type "Kosmos", "Almaz" and ERS-1.

The brightness contrasts in the visible recorded with AVHRR and multichannel scanning radiometers on satellites Landsat and SPOT make it possible to identify the zones of melting snow and ice cover. Microwave measurement data can also be used for this purpose owing to a strong contrast between the emissivities of water and ice (or snow).

However, radiothermal images have a very low spatial resolution (20–30 km) to monitor the ice drift (icebergs, in particular). For this purpose, the SLR data are more useful. Another possibility is to monitor the drift of sea buoys.

The requirements for the monitoring of the snow cover extent can be met with available data. The combined use of the visible and near-IR imagery provides information on variations in the structure of snow cover and, in particular, snow melting. Previous results have revealed a good correlation between the snow cover extent dynamics and river runoff. So far, no remote sensing technique has been developed to assess the snow cover thickness. Techniques for the remote sensing of soil moisture are at the initial stage of development. To solve this problem, data of multichannel microwave measurements are most useful. Techniques to estimate surface albedo from satellite data must be improved. Of principal importance is that possibilities to process all data are efficiently obtained.

WCRP satellite data reguirements have been recently updated (Tables 1.30 and 1.31) by a group of the WMO/ICSU Joint Scientific Committee (Report of the Fifteenth Session..., 1994).

In connection with the climate problem, monitoring of the sea ice cover is of particular importance. The WMO-organized working meeting of experts on the effect of sea ice on global climate discussed three problems (Kondratyev, 1990d): (i) available data on the ice cover; (ii) natural climate change and the role of sea ice; (iii) possible impact of human activity on climate and the consequences for the ice cover dynamics. In this connection it has been emphasized that both ice and snow cover are the most sensitive indicators of climate change. It is manifested, in particular, through a strong annual change of surface albedo in latitudinal bands 55–80 °N and 60–70 °S, which in the northern hemisphere is largely determined by variations of the continental snow cover, and in the southern hemisphere by the seasonal variability of sea ice.

Regular observations of the global cryosphere were started only in 1966, with an appearance of meteorological satellites put in polar orbits. Available data are, so far, irregular, inadequate, and for periods longer than 100 years have been obtained, as a rule, from different indirect indicators.

The principal difficulty in the numerical modelling of the atmosphere–ocean–cryosphere system consists in a parameterization of sub-grid processes, especially those connected with the existence of sea ice. Therefore, further studies are needed of

Table 1.30. WCRP satellite data requirements—upper-air

Parameter	Regional/ global	Horizontal resolution	Vertical resolution	Frequency	Accuracy	Use
1	2	3	4	5	6	7
Wind vector profile	Global troposphere	500 km	2 km	12 h	1 m s^{-1}	B
	Global stratosphere	500 km	5 km	12 h	1 m s^{-1}	B
Temperature profile	Global troposphere	500 km	2 km	12 h	1 K	B
	Global stratosphere	500 km	5 km	12 h	1 K	B
Humidity profile	Global lower troposphere	100 km	1 km	12 h	5%	B, D
	Global upper stratosphere	100 km	3 km	12 h	10%	B, D
	Global stratosphere	500 km	5 km	12 h	20%	B, D
Liquid water or ice	Global	100 km	3 km	3 h	5%	B, D
Cloud amount	Global	100 km	Total column	3 h	10%	B, D
Cloud top temperature	Global	100 km		3 h	3 K	B, D
Cloud top albedo	Global	100 km		3 h	1%	B, D
Cloud water profile	Global	100 km	1 km	3 h	10%	B, D
Cloud base height	Global	100 km		3 h	500 m	B, D
Radiation fluxes at TOA (SW & LW)	Global	200 km		3 h (or non-sun synchronous sampling	1 W m^{-2} (bias) 10 W m^{-2} (RMS)	B, D
Aerosol	Global troposphere	100 km	3 km	6 h	10%	B, D
	Global stratosphere	500 km	5 km	12 h	10%	D

Note: Atmospheric chemistry monitoring requirements for research are not finalized yet.

Table 1.31. WCRP satellite data requirements—surface

Parameter	Regional/ global	Horizontal resolution	Frequency	Accuracy	Use
1	2	3	4	5	6
Wind vector	Global ocean	200 km	12 h	1 m s^{-1}	B
Temperature	Global ocean	100 km	5–10 days	0.2 K	B, D
	Global land	100 km	3 h	1 K	D
Multispectral albedo	Global	100 km	5–10 days	1%	D
Radiation fluxes[1]	Global	100 km	5–10 days[2]	5 W m^{-2}	D
Precipitation totals[1]	Global	100 km	5–10 days	0.5 mm day^{-1}	B, D
Snow cover	Global land and ice	10 km	5–10 days		B,D
Snow water equivalent soil moisture[1]	Global land and ice	100 km	5–10 days	1 mm	D
Significant wave height	Global ocean	500 km	12 h	10 cm	D
Mean sea level dynamic height	Global ocean	100 km	5 days	3 cm	D
Ocean colour	Global ocean	100 km	1 day		D
Sea ice concentration	Polar ocean	100 km	1 day	1–5%	B, D
Sea ice edge	Polar ocean	10 km	1 day		B, D
Sea ice motion	Polar ocean	100 km	1 day	1 cm s^{-1}	
Ice-sheet and ice-stream topography	Polar region	10 km	1 year	3 cm	D
Iceberg extent	Polar ocean	1 km	1 year		D
Iceberg topography	Polar ocean	1 km	1 year	10 cm	D

[1] Parameters to be inferred from more basic quantities obtained from a combination of remote sensing data and surface-based measurements (instantaneous or statistics)
[2] If possible, resolving the mean diurnal cycle over the period (data in eight 3-hour bins)

the sea ice dynamics and the development of the respective parameterization technique, with an account of processes taking place in the ice cover and in the atmospheric and oceanic boundary layers, variability of the oceanic salinity regime, albedo and thickness of the ice cover and other factors.

A principally important problem is the monitoring of ice and snow cover with an account of meeting the requirements enumerated in Table 1.32. Here the AVHRR stands for Advanced Very-High-Resolution Radiometer, IRSR and VISR for Infrared Scanning Radiometer and Visible-Infrared Scanning Radiometer, respectively, MSR for Multizonal Scanning Radiometer, ESMR for Electrical-Scanning Microwave Radiometer.

Hooper and Sherman (1986) analysed the requirements for satellite oceanographic information determined by the needs of the problem's solution, which covers the problems of governmental interest, as well as of interest for scientific and commercial organizations. Data in Table 1.33 characterize general requirements which form the basis for the development of a scientific complex for the US National system of oceanographic satellites in order to obtain operational geophysical information about special requirements for the spatial and temporal resolution of various parameters for various fields of observational data interpretation.

For most of the users, in 70% of the cases, 6-h data repeatability is enough. The requirements of spatial resolution are rather diverse. It is shown that, to obtain a global data base on the wind field every six hours, it is necessary to have an instrumental complex containing two types of scatterometer as well as three scanning multichannel microwave radiometers. The monitoring of natural water quality can be made with two ocean colour spectrometers. Global-scale information on the ice cover can be obtained with the use of one SAR. Apparently, about 70% of the oceanographic information needed can be obtained from the satellites ERS-1, DMSP, and NOAA.

A minimum programme of climate monitoring should include the obtaining of the following information (Hooper and Sherman, 1986): (i) weekly microwave images of both polar regions, similar to those obtained with Nimbus-5 (19 GHz) and Nimbus-6 (37 GHz) ESMR; (ii) daily global images in the visible and IR spectral regions; (iii) data of global-scale objective analysis of the fields of wind, pressure, air humidity and temperature every 12 hs; (iv) daily information about the global distribution of cloud cover; (v) all available data of measurements of the ERB components with the instruments carried by polar satellites; (vi) selected data on the surface and aircraft meteorological observations in polar regions.

NASA (USA) has undertaken the development of a 10-year programme of climate studies based on preparation and realization of the systems of monitoring the climatic parameters and further improvement of techniques for numerical modelling of climate and its changes, in accordance with the American general programme of climate studies aimed at foreseeing climate change and its national and international aspects, as well as revealing possible impacts of man on climate on regional and global scales.

The climate is determined here as the state of weather near the Earth's surface averaged over time periods of one month or longer. Depending on the time scales,

Table 1.32. Observation requirements: Sea ice and snow cover

Parameter	Coverage	Type of observations	Resolution Temporal days	Resolution Spatial km	Accuracy	Duration	Priority	Technique	Remarks
1	2	3	4	5	6	7	8	9	10
ICE									
1. Location of boundaries	Global	Contours	3	20	20	Continuous	1	AVHRR, IRSR, VISR	Applicable only in regions with clear ice edge.
2. Concentration	Global	Part of area	3	100	20% if C > 0.8, 8% if C < 0.8	Continuous	1	AVHRR, SAR	Correlation with albedo is possible.
3. Trajectory of motion	Arctic basin and chosen antarctic regions	Shift in some areas of ice	1–3	500	2 km	Several years	1	AVHRR, MSR dropped sea buoys	Monitoring ice drift in the Greenland Sea using buoys with a grid step 100–200 km
4. Albedo	Global	Areal characteristics	3	100	0.03	Several years from late spring to early autumn	2	Multispectral satellite radiometry and aircraft observations.	Correlation with ice concentration is possible.
5. Surface temperature	Global	Areal characteristics or point-to-point data	3	100	1°C	Several years	2	IR space-based radiometry	

Table 1.32 (continued)

1	2	3	4	5	6	7	8	9	10
6. One-year/ multi-year ice	Global	Areal characteristics	15	100	Presence/ absence	Several years	2	ESMR, MSR	
7. Ice cover thickness	Global	Areal or profile characteristics	15	100	0.5–1.0 cm thick; 2% of area	Several years	2	Space lidars (surface topography), sub surface lidar	
SNOW									
8. Extent	Global	Part of area	3	100	10%	Continuous	1	AVHRR	
9. Albedo	Global	Areal characteristics	3	100	±0.03	Several years	2	Satellite multi-spectral radiometry	3-day temporal resolution only in periods of rapid snow cover variability.
10. Water content	Global	Areal characteristics	During winter maximum	100	10%	Several years	2		

Table 1.33. Requirements for operational oceanographic information

Parameter	Error	Resolution Spatial km	Temporal	Delay in obtaining information
Winds				
Speed	2 m s^{-1}	25	12 h	3 h
Direction	10	25	12 h	3 h
SST				
Global	1.0°C	25	3 days	12 h
Local	0.5°C	10	1 day	12 h
Roughness				
Significant wave height	0.3 m	25	12 h	3 h
Direction	10°	25	12 h	3 h
Ice cover				
Extent	15%	20	3 days	12 h
Thickness	2 m	50	3 days	12 h
Age	Fresh, 1-year multi-year	20	3 days	12 h
Height of glaciers	0.5-m variation	10	1 year	1 month
Water masses				
Chlorophyll content	100%	0.4	2 days	8 h
Turbidity	Low, middle, high	0.4	1 day	10 h
Sub-surface currents				
Velocity	5 cm s^{-1}	20	1 day	1 day
Direction	10°	20	1 day	1 day

four aspects of the problem have been considered. Climate A is defined as the present state of the climate, and the respective developments are aimed at obtaining actual data on the present climate and its analysis (for example, assessing water resources from the snow cover data). The principal objective of observations is, first of all, to obtain information on the parameters deemed important from the viewpoint of production of food and fibre, assessment of water resources and solution of the problem of energy production.

Climate B is a regional climate on characteristic time scales of more than a month and less than a decade. The principal objective here is the forecast of natural variability (characteristic scales—hundreds of kilometres) of regional and global climates, with an account of previously obtained and continuously accumulated data, bearing in mind modelling of climate changes caused by some slowly varying characteristics, such as: SST, snow and ice cover extent, soil moisture, etc. An initial problem is to understand the nature of annual change and interannual variability as well as studies of such regional-scale phenomena as monsoons.

Climate C is characterized by time scales of more than a decade. The eventual objective is to understand the causes of natural variability of global climate, whereas initial stages are studies of the factors affecting the radiation budget (e.g. volcanic eruptions, solar activity, etc.); of the interaction between radiation and processes of cloud formation; of the heat transport by sea currents; of ice cover physics, etc.

It should be emphasized that to determine a number of characteristics (precipitation, properties of clouds, evapotranspiration and water stress of vegetation, sea currents, ocean–atmosphere interaction, aerosol, cryosphere and solar–terrestrial relationships), particularly important are Sun-synchronous satellites, aircraft and ground-based measurements, in view of the ambiguity of remote sensing data (Kondratyev, 1982).

Principal initial problems in the numerical modelling of atmospheric general circulation (AGC) and climate, solved with the use of climate monitoring data, are the following studies of: (i) major persistent features of AGC in middle and high latitudes (e.g. prevailing trajectories of cyclones and anticyclones); (ii) persistent features of AGC in the tropics (ITCZ, large-scale convection, SST anomalies, oscillation of the Walker circulation in the southern hemisphere, tropical cyclones, Asiatic monsoon); (iii) large-scale interaction between circulations in the tropics, middle and high latitudes. Studies of climate on other planets (Venus, Mars, Jupiter) are very important in solving problems of the Earth's climate studies.

The urgency of assessing the anthropogenic impact on climate puts forward numerous requirements for the monitoring of atmospheric pollutants (minor gases). In this connection, an informative overview has been made (The International..., 1989) of the present and perspective possibilities to detect and monitor the environmental pollution based on the use of technique of remote sensing from space. Table 1.34 characterizes the atmospheric pollutants, objectives and requirements for measurement accuracy in the cases when the effect of pollutants on the environment has been established more or less reliably. Table 1.35 gives summaries of the components whose effect on the environment has been studied insufficiently.

One of major sources of information to monitor the atmosphere, ocean and land pollutants is multispectral images like those obtained with the MKF-6 camera on Soyuz and Salyut manned orbital stations, as well as with multispectral instruments carried by Landsat, SPOT and Skylab.

Important data have been accumulated on the basis of the application of spectroscopic techniques used on the MOS Soyuz, Salyut, Mir, as well as Nimbus-7 and SAGE satellites. In this connection, the development of techniques for correlation and interferometric spectroscopy is very important. Such techniques were used during Shuttle flights to measure concentrations of such atmospheric components as CO, NH_3, H_2O, NO_2, CH_4, NO_x and SO_2. Techniques of the remote sensing of the oceanic pollution from space must be thoroughly developed. In this connection the colour of the ocean is the most important characteristic.

Numerous and complicated chemical processes taking place in the troposphere have determined the necessity to use the space-borne observation means for their

Table 1.34. Requirements for measurements of atmospheric pollutants whose effect on the environment has been established more or less reliably

Component and atmospheric region	Objective and importance of measurements	Accuracy
1	2	3
	GLOBAL PROCESSES	
CO_2 troposphere and stratosphere	Changes in increasing concentration affecting the climate.	0.5 ppm
O_2 upper troposphere and stratosphere	Formation of aerosol particles from SO_2 coming from the troposphere and influenced by volcanoes and supersonic aviation.	0.5 ppb
O_3 stratosphere	Study of the long-term trend to reveal its causes, the correlation with solar activity, in particular.	Total content 1%. Vertical profile of concentration 10%.
H_2O stratosphere	Study of the effect on: (1) Concentration of ozone; (2) Stratospheric radiation budget; (3) Aerosol particles size distribution in the sulphate layer.	Total content 20% for (1) and lower accuracy for (2). Vertical profile 0.5 ppm for (3).
NO_x stratosphere	Study of the effect on the ozone concentration	NO_2 and NO 10 ppb
	REGIONAL PROCESSES	
SO_2	(1) Damage to vegetation (2) Formation of aerosol particles affecting the precipitation acidity.	10 ppb
H_2S	(1) It is oxidited to give SO_2. (2) Natural sources are uncertain.	0.1 ppb
NO_x	(1) Damage to vegetation and toxicity at high concentrations. (2) Photooxidation of hydrocarbons and the formation of particles. (3) Precursors of PAN.	0.1 ppm for (1); 10 ppb for (2), (3).
\<HC\>	(1) Leads to the formation of particles due to photochemical processes; (2) Determines the formation of toxic substances.	1 ppb (?)

Table 1.34. (continued)

1	2	3
O_3	Irritating and destructive effects; product of photochemical processes with the participation of and NO_x	10 ppb
PAN	Toxic products of photochemical reactions.	2–10 ppb
Hg	Study of the transfer in the atmosphere and accumulation in the biosphere.	10^{-2} ppb
Thermal pollutants	Factor of regional climate changes.	

Table 1.35. Requirements for measurements of atmospheric pollutants whose effect on the environment has been studied insufficiently

Component and atmospheric region	Objective and importance of measurements	Accuracy
1	2	3
	GLOBAL PROCESSES	
CO troposphere stratosphere	1. The effect of fuel burning on CO concentrations. 2. Study of the effect on the stratosphere.	10 ppb
HNO_3 stratosphere	The effect on ozone concentration and aerosol formation.	1 ppb
<HC> stratosphere	The effect on aerosol formation.	?
CH_4 troposphere and stratosphere	(1) Formation of particles due to photochemical reactions in the troposphere. (2) The effect on the distribution of water vapour and ozone in the stratosphere.	Troposphere 0.5 ppm Stratosphere 0.2 ppm
Chlorofluoromethanes. Troposphere, stratosphere	An accumulation due to anthropogenic releases.	0.001 ppb (?)
N_2O stratosphere	Photodissociation in the stratosphere.	50 ppb

Table 1.35. (continued)

1	2	3
CO	(1) Revealing the sources, sinks and lifetime in the lower atmosphere. (2) Formation of particles due to photochemical reactions. (3) All indicator of processes in the oceans.	10 ppb
H_2CO	(1) Formation of particles due to photochemical reactions. (2) The irritating factor for concentrations of about 1 ppm.	1 ppb
Halogens	(1) Toxicity and the destructive effect. (2) Bromine as an indicator of oceanic bioproductivity.	1 ppb
NH_3	Reacts with H_2SO_4 giving $(NH_4)_2SO_4$ particles.	10 ppb

investigations, bearing in mind first of all, an assessment of the content of optically active minor gaseous and aerosol components (MGAC). Natural and anthropogenic surface sources of MGAC are as follows: volcanoes, biogenic processes in soil and oceans, burning of fossil fuel and plant residuals, functioning of internal-combustion engines, etc. Tropospheric sources of MGC involve: lightning, photochemical reactions induced by UV solar radiation, numerous chemical reactions which transform the atmospheric properties. The urgency of adequate information about MGC is determined by their important role as factors of air quality, visibility, acid rains, ozone layer depletion, climate formation.

Experience in applying the techniques of classical and correlation spectroscopy, spectral radiometry and lidar sounding testifies to the usefulness of the remote sounding of MGAC based on satellite observations. Therefore, at a Workshop in New York on 9–13 September 1985 the scientific and technical aspects of the remote sounding of the atmospheric composition have been discussed in detail. Practically, the results obtained include: (i) retrieving the aerosol optical thickness of the atmosphere from measurements of the surface–atmosphere system brightness in the visible and near-IR spectral regions made from operational (polar-orbiting NOAA and geostationary GOES) meteorological satellites and Earth's resources Landsat satellites; (ii) assessing the content of aerosol, water vapour, ozone, and some other MGC in the middle and upper troposphere from data of occultation sounding (SAGE, Nimbus-7, ERBS, orbital station Spacelab-3, Shuttle).

Of particular interest is the successful testing of the interferometer spectrometer within the ATMOS programme (Spacelab-3, April–May 1985) and correlation gas-filter nadir-viewing radiometer (MAPS programme, Shuttle, 1981 and 1984). These instruments have been used, first of all, to estimate the content of carbon monoxide and methane in the troposphere.

Studies of the chemical composition of the troposphere from satellite observations are aimed at (in priority): (i) determination of continental and oceanic sources and sinks of several optically and chemically active MGC, such as CO_2, CO, CH_4 and other hydrocarbon compounds, N_2O, NH_3, $(CH_3)_2S$, H_2S, COS, and SO_2; (ii) analysis of spatial and temporal variability (in particular, annual and latitudinal change, regionally and globally averaged trends) of various MGACs, in particular, H_2O, CO, O_3, NO_2, SO_2, acid and soot aerosols.

In this connection, it is important to emphasize that all first-priority components (H_2O, O_3, CO and CH_4) participate in chemical and photochemical reactions of the formation and destruction of hydroxyl OH. Thus, OH turns out to be the key chemically active component of the troposphere taking part in reactions with almost all the other components and governing their residence time in the troposphere (nitrogen oxide whose lifetime is controlled by ozone is the only important exception). A very short lifetime of OH (about a second) and its very low concentration (about 10^5–10^6 mol cm^{-3}) exclude any possibility of reliable direct measurements of its content in the troposphere, determined by the reaction

$$O('D) + H_2O \rightarrow 2OH$$

with excited atoms of oxygen resulting from ozone photolysis

$$O_3 + h\nu \rightarrow O('D) + O_2.$$

The destruction of hydroxyl is controlled by two reactions:

$$OH + CO \rightarrow CO_2 + H; \; OH + CH_4 \rightarrow CH_3 + H_2O.$$

Thus, H_2O and O_3 are responsible for the photochemical formation of OH, whereas CO and CH_4 cause the chemical destruction of OH.

Four principal projects have been described in detail (Space Opportunities..., 1987) connected with the use of spectrometry, correlation radiometry, and lidar sounding. Based on this discussion, plans have been formulated of studies and developments both for the time period (1986–1992) and in perspective (1992–2000), including the programme of supportive investigations.

The first programme mentioned foresees the use of correlation radiometers to retrieve CO (three layers in the troposphere) and CH_4 (lower and upper troposphere), interferometer spectrometer (Michelson's interferometer) recording the outgoing thermal emission spectrum (the content of several MGCs in the lower, middle and upper troposphere), and lidar (aerosol sounding). In perspective, lidar soundings are to provide information not only about aerosols but also about several MGCs (water vapour, ozone, carbon monoxide, methane, and, probably, ammonia).

Numerous climatic parameters to be monitored and the difficulty in the realization of a complete system of satellites for climate monitoring bring forth an urgent problem of determining a minimum data base needed to solve the first-priority problems of studying the climate and its changes.

The report (Status..., 1978) prepared by the COSPAR Working Group-6 contains results of discussions of the available possibilities and prospects for satellite observations to study the physical processes that determine the climate. The discussion took place at the meeting of experts in NCAR (Boulder, CO, USA, July, 1976) convened by the COSPAR WG-6 on the recommendation of the GARP Organising Committee. The problems discussed have been grouped in the following way: (i) interaction of cloudiness and radiation; (ii) the effect of land surface processes; (iii) radiatively active MGACs of the atmosphere; (iv) ocean–atmosphere interaction; (v) cryosphere and hydrosphere and processes taking place in them.

The main objective was to determine a set of climatic parameters and factors which could be remotely sensed from space, as well as to choose adequate observational means. Table 1.36 contains a brief characteristic of the results of discussions. Since, so far, it is impossible to accurately substantiate the requirements for a satellite system of climatic observations, the related considerations and recommendations are strictly preliminary. This particularly concerns studies of the processes in the ocean, since recent studies have put forward many new and, so far, unsolved problems (the role of mesoscale vortices, upwellings, large-scale SST anomalies, etc.).

A set of stratospheric MGCs must be specified, which, apart from three basic components (water vapour, carbon dioxide, and ozone), includes numerous compounds of nitrogen (N_2O, NH_3, NO_2, NO, HNO_2, HNO_3), carbon (CH_4, CO), hydrogen (OH, HO_2), sulphur (SO_2, H_2SO_4, H_2S, CS_2, COS), and halogens ($CFCl_3$, CCl_4, CF_2Cl_2, HCl).

Since there are data on an increasing content of water vapour in the stratosphere, special emphasis must be placed on studies of the processes of water vapour formation due to methane oxidation.

The global nature of the processes in the atmosphere, ocean and on land determines the necessity to consider the Earth as a single interactive system in order to understand and forecast the state of this system. On the other hand, the complexity of the internal processes taking place in each of the system's components necessitates their individual study. From the viewpoint of creating an observational system, the final objective is the development (with an account of the circumstances described above) of such a system, which would be able to provide information about the planet, on the whole, and about its components, using both conventional and satellite observational means.

In connection with the development of satellite remote-sensing techniques, the use of various techniques based on data for different spectral regions, as well as a combined processing of the conventional and satellite information (4-D assimilation), plays an important role as factors of raising the accuracy of retrieval of the parameters sought.

Of critical importance is the provision of calibration techniques which would guarantee the long-term stability of both the observational data and the retrieved geophysical parameters. This, particularly, concerns the "solar" channels of diverse space-borne instruments. Still urgent is the accomplishment of complex programmes of sub-satellite control observations. In this connection it is worthwhile, in particular, to realise in thez future a programme like FGGE.

Table 1.36. Possibilities to study the climate-forming factors and processes using observations from space

Factors and processes	Effect on climate	Estimated parameter	Measured parameter	Techniques to process and analyse	Accuracy and spatial and temporal resolution	Remarks	Observation technique
1	2	3	4	5	6	7	8
			1. RADIATION AND CLIMATE				
Incoming solar radiation	Original source of energy for climate system	Total insolation at the level of orbit and surface, from UV to IR	Same	Non-specific	Desired absolute accuracy 0.1% but not below 0.7%, daily observations, at present several times per year	Satellite and rocket-borne instruments are available. Instruments for shuttles and automated satellites must be developed further.	Cavity radiometers calibrated against secondary electrical references.
		Insolation variability.	Same	Same	Accuracy 0.1 for a period of sun rotation; daily.	Instruments like those of Nimbus-6, 7 can be used.	Radiometers with a flat receiving surface calibrated against the sun.
Heating and photo-dissociation in the stratosphere and mesosphere	Controls the thermal regime, dynamics and photochemical processes	UV solar radiation flux in the range 180–310 nm with resolution 5 nm.	Same	Same	Absolute accuracy 10%, relative accuracy 1% for 5-nm intervals daily.	Accuracy is determined by reliability of references.	UV radiometer, spectrometer.

Parameter	Variable to be observed	Measured characteristic	Method	Accuracy	Status / remarks	Instruments
Atmospheric heating due to radiatively active gases	IR radiation flux in the range 0.8–4 μm for ten intervals.	Same	Same	1% or better.	None, so far.	IR filter radiometers.
Earth's radiation budget and its components	Global distribution of OLR and OSR.	Outgoing radiation flux.	Schemes of intensity-to-flux transition and account of diurnal change.	Desired accuracy 1% but 5% acceptable for shortwave and 10% for longwave radiation; not less than 4 times a day.	High-priority observations.	Radiometers.
Synoptic-scale cloudiness in connection with radiation balance	Type, amount, height of boundaries of cloud cover	Brightness in the visible and IR.	Retrieval of the sought-after parameters from the brightness field.	5%—cloud amount; 1% —height of boundaries.	Observations of clouds and radiation must be synchronous.	Radiometers; stereoimages or lidar.
Components of atmospheric energy balance.						

2. SURFACE

Parameter	Variable to be observed	Measured characteristic	Method	Accuracy	Status / remarks	Instruments
Evaporation sensible heat exchange	Effective albedos of different types of surface.	Reflected radiation	Empirical correlations.	Several percent, the scale is less than for typical quasi-homogeneous regions.	Satellite data serve, largely, to identify the type of surface and observation conditions.	Multispectral images of the Landsat type.

Table 1.36. (continued)

3. OPTICALLY ACTIVE COMPONENTS

1	2	3	4	5	6	7	8
Radiation flux divergence in the atmosphere and latent heat flux	Effect on the thermal regime and dynamics.	Water vapour vertical profile.	Emission spectral in the IR and microwave regions.	Retrieval algorithms.	Troposphere: accuracy 0.25° per day of radiative cooling calculations in 3–5 km layers. Stratosphere: 0.3–0.5 ppm for 3–5-km layers; daily; 500 km horizontally.	Retrieving gives a low but, at present acceptable vertical resolution.	Multispectral, IR and microwave radiometers; microwave limb scanning over the nocturnal Pole.
UV heating and IR cooling of the stratosphere	To calculate energy balance of the atmosphere and to test stratospheric models.	Vertical ozone profile; CO_2 concentration in the stratosphere.	Emission spectra with synchronous ground balloon, and rocket observations.	Same	10% or 0.5 ppm for diurnal means; 2%—monthly means; 50 km horizontal 3–5 km vertical 1% global means; daily; 5% with 500 km averaging; daily; 1% with 500 km averaging over a month.	Ground-based network for ozone observations must be improved balloon and rocket observations must be developed Comparison of data from satellites and ground network is important.	UV radiometers and spectrometers; limb scanning in the IR and microwave intervals.

Absorption and scattering of radiation	Effect on atmospheric energy balance.	Aerosol properties (optical thickness, size distribution or average size, complex refraction index and lidar data).	Multispectral extinction and polarization, images and lidar data.	Same	0.3 μm (size) 0.1 (optical thickness); 0.02 (refraction index).	Revealing first-order effects and assessing atmospheric transfer function.	Photometers, polarimeters, lidars.
IR cooling of the atmosphere	Affects the atmospheric radiation.	Total content or mean concentrations of CO_2.	Concentration at selected ground stations.	Absorption in a gas cell.	Available accuracy is high enough to reveal the trends.	Observations from space are not needed.	IR radiometers.
			Emission spectra as a function of height in the stratosphere.	Spectroscopic calibration.	Accuracy to be determined; several times per year.		
Chemical interaction with ozone	Controls the ozone concentration stratosphere.	Nitrogen oxides, chlorofluoro-carbons	Outgoing radiation or absorbed radiation (occultation experiments).	Retrieval algorithms.	To be determined.	Observations are of a search	Various instruments to
Aerosol formation processes	Determine the distribution and properties of aerosols.	Sulphur compounds.	Same	Same	Same		

Table 1.36. (continued)

1	2	3	4	5	6	7	8
			4. OCEAN–ATMOSPHERE INTERACTION				
Ocean-atmosphere exchange.	Energy component of the climate system.	SST	IR and microwave outgoing emission.	Same	1% or better; 10 km resolution; daily.	Correct account of atmospheric transfer function is a principal problem.	IR and microwave observations.
Meridional heat transport in the ocean	Energy component can determine the short-term climate variability.	Heat content and velocity field in the upper layer of the ocean (above the seasonal thermocline).	Profiles of temperature and speed of currents	Direct measurements and tracing the buoys trajectories.	Tenths of degree 1 cm s^{-1}, 10-km resolution	Space-based monitoring technique is to be tested.	Small buoys.
Mass and momentum exchange between the ocean and the atmosphere	Connected with the ocean upper layer dynamics, affects the short-period climate variability.	Wind stress near the surface.	Near-surface wind at a height of 20 m and at a level of trade-wind cumulus cloudiness.	Empirical correlations	About 1 dyn cm^{-1} resolution up to 10 km.	Seasat scatterometer has been tested.	Direct ship measurements of wind and space-based monitoring of clouds.
			5. CRYOSPHERE AND HYDROSPHERE				
Process of cooling; formation of polar bottom	Ice-ocean interaction in polar regions, affecting the	Salinity profile in the upper layer.	Direct measurements of electrical conductivity	Dependence of electrical conductivity on salinity;	About 0.1%; 200–500-km resolution.	Actual local studies of the parameterization technique.	Salinometers on buoys; remote sensing techniques are

Parameter	Importance	Data	Processing	Resolution	Comments	Instruments
waters	energetics of the climate system.	and multispectral microwave reflectivity.	retrieval algorithms.			under development.
Snow cover extent.	Formation of snow cover albedo, and heat flux in the atmosphere.	Images in the IR and microwave regions	Direct processing of images.	50–100 km for 5–10 days	Mapping of minimum brightness is useful.	Scanning photometers and radiometers.
Sea ice: Extent	Formation of ocean surface albedo, energy fluxes and divergencies effect of atmospheric dynamics on sea ice	Images in the visible, IR and microwave regions.	Same	50–100 km; 5–10 days; high resolution for special studies	Maps of relative reflectivity and analogy to maps of minimum brightness useful.	Scanning photometers and radiometers.
Type		Multispectral microwave emission; radar data.	Retrieval algorithms.	100–200 km; 10–30 days.	Different age of ice.	Passive and active radar technique.
Concentration		Images in the visible, IR and microwave regions.	Direct processing.	100 km; 5–10 days.	Important for studies of the heat budget and albedo of vast regions.	Scanning photometers and radiometers.
Drift and deformation		Images in the visible, IR and microwave regions.	Direct processing.	Drift to 5 km day; 100–500 km.	Average drift and deformation based on analysis of images.	Scanning instruments; radars.

Table 1.36. (continued)

1	2	3	4	5	6	7	8
Large-scale and persistent heat sinks	Continental glaciers as a factor and indicator of climate change.	**Glaciers:** Extent	Images in the visible, IR and microwave regions.	Direct processing.	1–5 km; month-season.	Typical velocity.	Scanning instruments.
		Accumulation, thickness, topography	Multispectral microwave emission, radioaltimeter.	Retrieval algorithms.	Annual accumulation to 10 cm, 200 km	Indicator of climate and accumulation mechanism.	Passive and active radar technique.
		Deformation	Images, ice buoys, topography	Direct processing.	1–10 m; 200 km; annually.	Polar-orbit radioaltimeter is needed.	Passive and active radar technique, buoys.
Latent heat release, the hydrological cycle	Important factors of the climate system's energetics.	Precipitation, water and moisture content.	Images; attenuation of microwave emission, radar data.	Retrieval algorithms.	4 levels of intensity; 100 km; 1–5-day averages.	Data repeatability (several times per day) is very important.	Scanning instruments in different ranges.
Evapo-transpiration processes	Surface–atmosphere interaction component.	Moisture profile of a 1-m soil layer	Multispectral microwave emission, annual change of temperature, the state of vegetation.	Same	To be determined.	Search studies are needed. technique.	Passive and active radar
Hydrological processes	Snow water content factor.	Surface runoff connected with	Images in the visible,	Same	0.1–1 cm; 50–100 km;	Important in studies of	Scanning instruments in

hydrological cycle	microwave regions; radar data are possible.		5–10-day averages	water balance.	different ranges.
River runoff	Part of the hydrological cycle.	Data via satellite transmission of surface sensors readings.	Direct processing	To be determined.	Use of experience in automated sensors readings.	Instruments for sensors readings.

Theoretical studies aimed at a better understanding of the interaction of processes within the global-scale numerical models and sensitivity studies needed for an objective planning of the observational system must be extremely important components of the programme. Retrieval algorithms must be developed further. From the viewpoint of developing the instruments and techniques for retrievals, of particular importance are efforts to raise the reliability of various retrieved data, such as soil moisture, rain rate, land surface temperature and emissivity, and wind vector.

Experience in data interpretation has shown (Earth system..., 1988) that it is possible to distinguish between three levels of soil moisture with a spatial resolution of 100 km and repeatability once every two days, whereas five levels must be identified with this resolution. The 21-cm channel is optimal to solve this problem, but in this case measurements are impossible when vegetation cover is thick.

A substantial increase in the surface temperature retrieval accuracy and a resolution of about 1 km can be reached with the MODIS instruments with the following channels (the width of the channels is given in brackets): 3.750 (90); 3.989 (50); 4.05 (50); 8.55 (500); 10.45 (500); 11.03 (500), and 12.02 (500) μm, with the combined use of MODIS and other remote sensing data. Retrieving the phytomass and its global mapping as well as a search for techniques to retrieve the surface heat balance components are important problems. Lidars and a 6-channel radar for centimetre wavelengths are being developed to retrieve atmospheric pressure near the ocean surface, with an accuracy of about 1–2 hPa.

The on-board measuring complex prepared for two polar-orbit satellites (the 850-km Sun-synchronous orbit passed at 09:00 and 13:00 local time) and for an orbital station (this complex consists of, largely, tested instruments) includes a monitor of the space environment parameters, instruments to measure the ERB, a mid-resolution radiometer and a moderate-resolution spectrometer to obtain calibrated multi-spectral images, advanced instruments for the operational sounding of the atmosphere, IR high-resolution sounder, microwave remote sensing unit, ozone global-monitoring radiometer, a monitor of the physical and chemical parameters of the atmosphere, lidar sounder and altimeter, Doppler lidar wind-sensor, synthetic-aperture radar, scatterometer, advanced microwave high-resolution multi-channel radiometer, instruments to obtain radio-thermal images, radiometer scanning along the satellite's orbit, instruments for multi-spectral imagery to obtain data on the ocean colour, instruments for localization, reading and transmitting the information from ground- and sea-based automated platforms.

The AVHRR characteristics are being improved. Starting from NOAA-K, it will have the following channels: 0.63 (No. 1); 0.86 (No. 2); 1.61 (No. 3); 3.74 (No. B); 10.8 (No. 4), and 12.0 μm (No. 5), with a narrowed (to 0.01 μm) width of shortwave channels and substantially increased S/N ratio. Also, the problem of substantiation of specified requirements for retrievals of various parameters (retrieval accuracy, spatial and temporal resolution, the choice of spectral channels) is very urgent.

The WMO decision to develop the Global Climate Observing System (GCOS) has further stimulated the efforts to substantiate requirements for climate dynamics observations (Report of the Fourth Session..., 1994; Report of the GCOS

Atmospheric..., 1994; Report of the GCOS/GTOS..., 1994; Report of the GCOS Space-Based..., 1994).

From the viewpoint of solving problems of the well being and economic security of people the significance of the following problems of studying atmospheric processes has been emphasized (Report of the GCOS Atmospheric..., 1994):

(a) At the seasonal-to-interannual time scale, improved monitoring and prediction will provide information that is potentially exceedingly valuable provided it is appropriately disseminated. Proposals are underway to develop an infrastructure that would provide such dissemination and increase the utility of such information.

(b) For the decadal-to-century time scale, the principal focus is on anthropogenically induced climate change. Key questions arise concerning the timing, the magnitude, and regional impact of the climate change. The observational data base and subsequent analyses should provide guidance to policymakers engaged in response and mitigation strategies. In this regard, the observations from GCOS will contribute to the Intergovernmental Panel on Climate Change (IPCC), and other political and economic fora in this arena.

The four specific scientific issues have been pointed out:

(a) Climate change detection—The issue is how to detect anthropogenic climate change in an unambiguous way in the presence of a very noisy background natural variability. Needed is a stable quality assured network of observations with homogeneous, long-term records;

(b) Seasonal to interannual prediction—The TOGA research programme has established the feasibility for skilful predictions up to several seasons in advance for certain regions. To support this activity, an ocean and surface climate observing network has been established and needs to continue. Some needs are common to those of Numerical Weather Prediction (NWP), namely timely observations over the Global Telecommunication System (GTS), 4-D Data Assimilation (4DDA) to produce global analyses and to initialize ocean models. Such data come in part from the Tropical Ocean–Global Atmosphere (TOGA) TAO Array. Detailed recommendations may be found in the GCOS document "Operational Ocean Observing System for Seasonal to Interannual Climate Prediction";

(c) Climate monitoring and regional climate anomalies—This activity monitors climate in near real-time and produces regional climate anomalies and diagnostics throughout the world. The analyses and statistics have many uses (e.g. research on empirical studies, model development and validation; climatology; hydrology; agriculture; impact assessment). In addition to observing conventional physical climate variables, this includes monitoring the chemical composition of the atmosphere (developing understanding of biogeochemical cycles, tracking emissions versus controls; international agreement requirements, etc.);

(d) Climate forcings—To determine the causes of climate change and further diagnose the feedback processes, several other forcing fields are needed. These include top-of-the-atmosphere radiation (solar, infrared, net), cloud cover, global precipitation, aerosol (loading and characteristics), and principal chemical species in the atmosphere. In addition, boundary forcing parameters including sea surface temperature, land surface characteristics (albedo, soil moisture, roughness, vegetation, etc.).

From the viewpoint of data requirement for the GCOS atmospheric component six specific categories have been idenfified (Report of the GCOS Atmospheic..., 1994):

(1) The 3-D state of the atmosphere including second-order moments, vertical fluxes of heat, moisture and momentum, as well as other similar physical and dynamical quantities.

   The data are presently produced by 4DDA systems using advanced high resolution general circulation models. The overall observational requirements for global NWP as formulated by the CBS Joint Working Group on Data Processing and Working Group on Observation Task Team on Data Requirements (see Tables 1.37–1.39). It has been noted that the observations being used by such data assimilation systems will also satisfy the requirements of the climate applications with the proviso that for such applications, the mean error must be a very small fraction of the root mean square error. In addition climate studies also need data throughout the whole middle atmosphere up to some 80 km; the observational requirements here are the same as in the lower stratosphere. Great importance has been stressed of accurate vertical profiles for wind and temperature which determine the quality of many other parameters.

(2) Data for the determination of the state of the surface of the Earth, SST, soil moisture, vegetation, albedo, roughness, snow, ice, etc.

   These requirements are more stringent than in numerical weather prediction (NWP) since small errors in these data may influence the large-scale circulation in a detrimental way, especially in long integrations. In addition, data must be available for the whole surface of the Earth. This is presently not the case since data for snow and soil moisture, for example, are not exchanged globally (see Table 1.38).

(3) Data for the determination of clouds, and of radiation fluxes at the surface and at the top of the atmosphere.

   Accurate knowledge of the large-scale radiation balance is important for reducing the overall systematic biases in climate models and to use data, for example, to better determine representative cloud properties for large-scale processes (see Table 1.39).

(4) Data on the composition of the atmosphere.

   The chemical composition of the atmosphere, in addition to the clouds, exerts a dominant influence on the radiation balance of the atmosphere. The atmosphere contains many gases, most in only trace quantities, which are critical in controlling climate. Observations of these gases are important elements of GCOS.

(5) Data for process studies.
Process studies in the form of specific field programmes play a central role in model development. GCOS presently has no specific requirements in addition to the programmes presently underway within WCRP, IGBP or other research programmes.

(6) Data for long-term monitoring.
The GCOS requirements include five datasets in this group:

(a) an upper-air baseline network consisting of selected upper-air stations;
(b) a surface baseline network of selected SYNOP stations;
(c) a surface baseline network for atmospheric composition;
(d) satellite systems for monitoring the temperature of the atmosphere;
(e) global observations of the hydrological cycle, precipitation, river runoff, lake water levels.

Table 1.37. Three-dimensional fields of meteorological parameters

	Horizontal resolution (km)	Vertical resolution (km)	Temporal resolution (hours)	Accuracy (RMS error)	Notes
Wind (horizontal)	100	0.1 up to 2 km 0.5 up to 16 km 2.0 up to 30 km	3	2 m s^{-1} in the troposphere 3 m s^{-1} in the stratosphere	(1) (2)
Temperature	100	0.1 up to 2 km 0.5 up to 16 km 2.0 up to 30 km	3	0.5 K in the troposphere 1.0 K in the stratosphere	(3)
Relative humidity (RH)	100	0.1 up to 2 km 0.5 up to the tropopause	3	5% (RH)	

Notes:
1. Accuracy specified as RMS vector error.
2. Hourly, wind data from geostationary satellites and from profilers are also required.
3. Geopotential height can be retrieved from specified T and RH with sufficient accuracy.

Table 1.38. Surface characteristics

1	Horizontal resolution (km)	Temporal resolution (hours)	Accuracy (RMS error)	Notes
	2	3	4	5
Pressure	100	1 h	0.5 hPa	
Wind	100	1 h	2 m s^{-1}	(1)
Temperature	100	1 h	1 K	
Relative humidity	100	1 h	5%	
Accumulated precipitation	100	3 h	0.1 mm	(2)
Sea-surface temperature	100	1 day	0.5 K	
Soil temperature	100	3 h	0.5 K	
Sea-ice cover	100	1 day	10%	
Snow cover	100	1 day	10%	
Snow equivalent-water depth	100	1 day	5 mm	
Soil moisture, 0–10 cm	100	1 day	0.02 m^3 m^3	
Soil moisture, 10–100 cm	100	1 week	0.02 m^3 m^3	
Percentage of vegetation	100	1 week	10% (relative)	
Soil temperature, 20 cm	100	6 h	0.5 K	
Deep soil temperature, 100 cm	100	1 day	0.5 K	
Albedo, visible	100	1 day	1%	
Albedo, near infrared	100	1 day	1%	
Longwave emissivity	100	1 day	1%	
Ocean wave height	100	1 h	0.5 m	

Notes:
1. Wind at 10 m over land;
Over sea, height in the range 1 to 40 m (to be transmitted with the observation).
2. Required principally for model validation, not time critical.

Table 1.39. Other two-dimensional fields

	Horizontal resolution (km)	Temporal resolution (hours)	Accuracy (RMS error)	Notes
Cloud fractional cover	100	3 h	10%	
Cloud top height	100	3 h	0.5 km	(1)
Cloud base height	100	3 h	0.5 km	(1)
Total liquid content	100	3 h	20%	
TOA net shortwave radiation	100	3 h	5 W m^{-2}	(2)
TOA net longwave radiation	100	3 h	5 W m^{-2}	(2)
Multipurpose IR/VIS imagery	5	30 min	—	(3)

Notes:
1. Accuracy higher in planetary boundary layer.
2. Required principally for model validation; not time critical.
3. Required to assist real-time observation monitoring and analysis/forecast validation.

As far as the Global Terrestrial Observing System (GTOS) is concerned the importance of the four classes of processes has been emphasized (Report of the GCOS/GTOS..., 1994):

(1) **Biogeochemistry**: The broad goal is to quantify changes in the major pools and fluxes. The primary focus should be on carbon, including measurements of carbon storage in soils and plants as well as carbon exchanges between ecosystems and the atmosphere and between terrestrial and aquatic ecosystems. Given the critical role of nitrogen and phosphorus as controllers of carbon pools over different time intervals, these elements should be a major focus of observations.

(2) **Land use**: Because changes in land use are likely to dominate near to medium term changes in both biogeochemistry and in the quality and quantity of goods and services provided by ecosystems to humans, it is critical to quantify changes in patterns of land use and intensity of land management. This should include assessments of land added to or abandoned from agricultural production as well as changes in cropping system, fertilizer and irrigation use, timber harvest practices, and low-intensity management (e.g. rubber harvesting).

(3) **Biodiversity**: The local and regional diversity of genotypes, species, plant and animal functional types, and landscape units have an important place in the global change research and monitoring agenda both in themselves, and through interacting effects on biogeochemistry and land use. The monitoring programme must acknowledge the importance of biodiversity at levels ranging from the genetic to the landscape level. The dramatic spread and often profound ecological consequences of plants and animals introduced over the last few centuries places a high priority on monitoring the status of non-native and especially invasive species.

(4) **Climate**: The interface between climate and terrestrial systems has two major components. One is the terrestrial characteristics that can be used as indicators of climate change. The second is the aspects of climate that are necessary for interpreting or establishing a context for ecological information. Several of the terrestrial characteristics that are useful as indicators of climate change are only indirectly linked to ecosystem structure and function. This class includes parameters like extent and mass of alpine glaciers and size and temperature of shallow lakes. In general, the aspects of ecosystem structure or function that are potentially useful as indicators of climate change, including presence or absence of indicator species, are regulated more by extreme events than long-term mean conditions.

The data in Table 1.40 characterize the proposed 4-level hierarchical scheme for a global surface observation system, while Table 1.41 contains information on the priority observations needed global and regional scales in continuous fields.

Table 1.40. Proposed 4-level hierarchical site scheme for a global surface observation system

Level	Emphasis		Examples of variables
I	(A) Spatial integration	(i)	dynamics of landscape units
		(ii)	transport of soils and nutrients
		(iii)	airborne flux measurements
		(iv)	planetary boundary layer flux methods
	(B) Point measurements	(i)	trace gases
II	(A) Spatial integration	(i)	population structure
		(ii)	continuous tower flux of CO_2, H_2O energy
		(iii)	soil moisture
	(B) Point measurements	(i)	diurnally resolved weather
		(ii)	complete radiometry
		(iii)	isotopic soil and plant studies
III	(A) Stocks and fluxes	(i)	NPP
		(ii)	biomass
		(iii)	soil C and N by depth
		(iv)	atmospheric deposition
	(B) Land use	(i)	management system (cropping, tillage)
		(ii)	fertilizer and irrigation
	(C) Spatial integration	(i)	bio- and geo-diversity
		(ii)	phenology
	(D) Point measurements	(i)	leaf chemistry
		(ii)	phenology
	(E) Daily weather	(i)	precipitation
		(ii)	temperature
		(iii)	wind
		(iv)	shortwave radiation and PAR

Table 1.40. (continued)

Level	Emphasis		Examples of variables
IV	(A) Point measurements	(i)	decadal soil C, N, depth, bulk density
	(B) Land use	(i)	land cover and land use type
		(ii)	disturbance
	(C) Biodiversity	(i)	decadal enumeration of vertebrates, invertebrate groups, plants, & microbes
		(ii)	decadal status of invading species
	(D) Weather	(i)	interpolated monthly climate from nearest stations

Table 1.41. Tabulation of the priority observations needed at global and regional scales in continuous fields

1: LAND COVER

Users:
GCM modellers, biogeochemical cycle (BGC) modellers (global, regional), ecosystem modellers, climate impact modellers; also regional analysts/planners.

Rationale:
Several land cover maps are available. However, there are large disagreements due to different methodologies used to prepare them. What is needed is an adequate characterization of the spatial distribution of actual vegetation cover. For historical periods, current methods probably cannot be improved. For the recent past, present, and future, land cover will optimally be provided by remote sensing. For spatial extrapolation purposes the spatial resolution in general does not have to be great. 1–5 km is finer than most investigators are currently using, but not finer than the scale over which significant variations in vegetation processes occur. It is important to distinguish land cover categories using criteria related to carbon storage and turnover. Olsen et al. (1984) suggested a scheme that resulted in about 30 categories that included possibilities for missed pixels at 0.5pi1 > 8 resolution. At a finer spatial scale and using different methods or tools, other classification schemes will undoubtedly be necessary. However, it is thought that 20–40 categories of land cover would be adequate. For wetland categories that have special carbon dynamics, higher spatial resolution may be required. A rationale for change detection and parameters is required.

Frequency of measurement:
Full mapping: Once every 5 years; Change detection: Annual
(Note: A really good change detection programme should remove the need for remapping until a better data source becomes available; this would mean the change detection procedure can identify the new land cover type.)

Spatial resolution of measurement:
Initial Observing System (IOS): 1 km for global coverage, 30 m for regional to local coverage; Post-IOS: 0.25–0.5 km for global coverage, 30 m for regional to global coverage.

Table 1.41. (continued)

Accuracy/precision required:

Highly dependent on application. For example 80% global accuracy may be sufficient for operation of GCMs, but for accurate estimation of changes in carbon stocks for carbon modelling, accuracies of better than 95% are required.

R & D needed:

Validation of classification methodology.

Present status:

Global coverage can be obtained from the Global 1 km AVHRR data set (10-day composite images over 18 months) which will be completed in 1995. A methodology for regional land cover mapping was demonstrated in North America. Methodologies for change detection using 1 km-type data are under development; this work needs to be strengthened and expanded to various parts of the glob. Special techniques need to be used for fire detection and mapping. The further development, validation and implementation of these should be encouraged.

High resolution coverage is provided by high resolution satellite data (Landsat, SPOT, etc.). The methodologies for mapping have been well demonstrated. Methodologies for change detection continue to be developed, with operational techniques expected in 2–3 years. Significant regional coverage is feasible with newly obtained and archived data.

A good representation of wetlands distribution is especially important for BGC studies. At the global level, it will be more reliably derived by combining satellite data outputs with soil (possibly also vegetation and topographic) data.

Action required:

Near term

—Endorse completion of the initial global 1 km AVHRR data set;

—Promote continuation of the Global 1 km AVHRR project to provide a continuing series of global observations;

—Promote validation of cover mapping methodology for 1 km data in various regions;

—Encourage development of robust change detection algorithms.

Mid-term

—Promote expanded use of high resolution data for land cover mapping for large areas (national to regional levels);

—Promote generation of global data sets with higher spatial resolution from existing or new sensors.

2: LAND USE

Users:

BGC modellers, ecosystem modellers.

Rationale:

One of the most controversial components relating to the global carbon cycle concerns the magnitude of release and uptake of CO_2 resulting from human activities. Currently, the most authoritative accounting of these fluxes is based on interpretations of land use statistics compiled by Food and Agriculture Organization (FAO). A more objective system that can be updated annually, rather than every five years, may be possible using remote sensing of land cover change (possibly combined with agriculture and forestry production statistics, and socio-economic spatial data such as population and transportation). Landsat is perhaps one of the most appropriate data streams for land use monitoring. While the methodology for using these data to produce a land-use product is still a research issue, it is important that this data stream continues to be archived and made accessible.

Frequency:
Annual, observations during growing season.

Spatial:
5 m–1 km depending on the spatial heterogeneity of land use; at least 30 m for many regions.

Frequency of measurement:
Once every 5 years.

Accuracy/precision required:
To be determined.

R & D needed:
Development of regionally specific relationships between land cover and land use. Definition of the lowest acceptable spatial resolution (also regionally specific, depending on land use heterogeneity).

Present status:
Land use maps have been completed for many specific areas of the world. These efforts were based on various data sources and are not generally compatible with each other. A consistent, hierarchical classification system is presently under development; this is to be encouraged.

Action required:
Near-term
—Complete the development of land use classification scheme;
—Identify areas of the world for which acceptable and accessible products exist; compile these into a consistent data base;
—Carry out pilot studies for filling the critical gaps in coverage using land cover mapping procedure and the relationships between land cover and land use; validate preliminary products.
Mid-term
To be determined.

3. SEASONAL VEGETATION INDEX PROFILE (SVIP)

Users:
Climate, ecosystem, BGC modellers.

Rationale:
SVIP provides information on the intensity of ecosystem activity during the growing season, thus permitting estimation of energy and mass exchange with the atmosphere.

Frequency of measurement:
Daily.

Table 1.41. (continued)

Spatial resolution:
IOS: 1–8 km;
Post-IOS: 0.25–1.0 km.

Accuracy/precision required:
Within 10% of true value.

R & D needed:
The main challenge is to obtain precise corrections for artifacts in raw data (e.g. from sensor calibration, atmospheric effects, bidirectional effects).

Present status:
SVIP based on NDVI or SR has been used extensively in recent years. Two projects (Pathfinder and the global AVHRR 1 km project) produce the initial data set from which SVIP can be produced. These data sets require further refinements for use by the modellers. Such methodologies are becoming available but their further development and validation are to be encouraged.

Action required:
Near-term
—Encourage continuation of the global AVHRR 1 km and Pathfinder projects;
—Stimulate production of SVIP data sets.
Mid-term
—Replace SVIP by derived variables such as FPAR and LAI.

---

4. FPAR

Users:
Climate, ecosystem, BGC modellers.

Rationale:
Essential quantity for understanding relationship between incoming solar radiation, its absorption for photosynthesis and the impact of the latter on evapotranspiration local terrestrial energy balance, carbon sequestration and other biogeochemical cycling.

Frequency of measurement:
Daily, to derive a product every 10–30 days.

Spatial resolution:
IOS: 1–8 km;
Post-IOS: 0.25–1.0 km.

Accuracy/precision required:
IOS: 10–20% of the true value;
Post-IOS: 5–10% of true value.

R & D needed:
Methods for deriving FPAR need to be developed and validated for different biomes and different satellite data sources (resolution, spectral bands).

Present status:
Definitive algorithms are not yet available. Methodology development is being undertaken in various projects (e.g. FIFE, BOREAS). The capability to produce experimental data sets has been demonstrated through ISLSCP. However, these data have not been validated in sufficient detail.

Action required:
Near-term
—Stimulate production of FPAR data sets using ISLSCP or similar approaches, to provide initial data sets for the user community. These products should use the best available knowledge at the time, the method should be explained in detail, and its limitations (in so far as known) should be outlined.
Mid-term:
—Endorse and encourage the development and validation of FPAR algorithms for various biomes.

5. LEAF AREA INDEX (LAI)

Users:
Climate, ecosystem, BGC modellers.

Rationale:
See SVIP.

Frequency of measurement:
IOS: Once per growing season in N & S hemisphere (peak green period);
Post-IOS: Daily, to derive a product every 10–30 days.

Spatial resolution:
IOS: 1–8 km;
Post-IOS: 0.25–1.0 km

Accuracy/precision required:
IOS: 15–25% of true value;
Post-IOS: 5–15% of true value.

R & D needed:
Methods for deriving LAI need to be developed and validated for different biomes and different satellite data sources (resolution, spectral bands).

Present status:
Definitive algorithms are not yet available. Methodology development is being undertaken in various projects (e.g. BOREAS). The capability to produce an experimental data set has been demonstrated through ISLSCP. However, these data have not been adequately validated.

Action required:
Near-term
—Stimulate production of LAI data sets using ISLSCP or similar approaches, to provide initial data sets to the user community. These products should use the best available algorithm, the method used should be explained in detail, and its limitations (in so far as known) should be outlined.

Table 1.41. (continued)

Mid-term:

—Endorse and encourage the development and validation of LAI algorithms for various biomes.

---

6. INCOMING PHOTOSYNTHETICALLY ACTIVE RADIATION (IPAR)

Users:

Climate, BGC and ecosystem modellers.

Rationale:

The PAR is the energy source for the growth and development of vegetation. Through photosynthesis, radiant energy in the 0.4 to 0.7 mm band is converted to chemical energy that is the source of vegetation activity.

Frequency of measurement:

Daily.

Resolution:

5 by 5 km.

Accuracy/precision required:

10 W m^{-2}.

R & D needed:

To be determined.

Present status:

To be determined.

Action required:

To be determined.

---

7. BIOMASS

Users:

Ecosystem and carbon modellers.

Rationale:

Biomass is a key variable in modelling carbon uptake and redistribution within the ecosystem. Woody biomass is of most interest.

Frequency of measurement:

Once every 5 years.

Spatial resolution:

To be determined.

Accuracy/precision required:

To be determined.

R & D needed:
Research is required to determine the feasibility of estimating live biomass from satellite data; radar measurements presently offer the best prospect. Imaging laser sensor technology is also promising but no space-borne missions are planned.

Present status:
Highly experimental.

Action required:
Near-term
—Currently it is uncertain how to obtain biomass data to meet modelling needs within the next 5 years.
Mid-term
—Encourage R & D on biomass estimation.

8. SNOW COVER AREA AND SNOW WATER EQUIVALENT

Users:
Climate, BGC modellers.

Rationale:
The presence or absence of snow cover is very important in determining the nature of the atmosphere–surface interaction. Snow cover changes surface albedo and surface energy balance. Snowpack liquid water content in some regions is a major input to soil moisture for seasonal vegetation growth. Mapping of permafrost has many similar ecological uses.
Snow cover dramatically changes surface albedo; thus global snow cover mapping is clearly important for climate modelling. In addition, snow melt, or the time derivative of change in snow/water equivalence, is important in recharging soil moisture where it influences evapotranspiration, nutrient cycling, seed germination and vegetation phenology, among many other biotic processes. Consequently, the global mapping of snow melt rates at 5–10 day intervals would be preferred for ecological purposes. However, global organization of such data may be questionable owing to the limited spatial representation of ground snow surveys. A comprehensive statement of cryospheric needs is still required.

Frequency of measurement:
Daily.

Spatial resolution:
50 by 50 km, or finer, if available.

Accuracy/precision required:
Area—nearest 25 by 25 km desirable
Snow water equivalent—5 mm of water.

R & D needed:
Present passive microwave algorithms work fairly well in areas with limited topography and with short or little vegetation cover. Significant problems exist in forested and mountainous areas. Research should be encouraged on the development of algorithms for these conditions.

Present status:
Ground networks of periodic snow depth/snow water field measurements already exist in the

US, Canada, Scandinavia, Russian Federation and some former Russian states. Organizing a data archive of this database would be desirable as a GTOS activity. Satellite and aerial photo-based mapping of snow cover is already done by NOSS in the US at the National Snow Center in Minnesota.

Action required:
To be determined.

9. TOPOGRAPHY

Users:
Ecosystem modellers concerned with land cover change and deforestation as it affects carbon cycle. Hydrological cycle modellers, including GEWEX and BAHC projects. Remote sensing specialists carrying out high quality image rectification for change detection purposes.

Rationale:
Topographic data are necessary to properly quantify the interactions between the solar radiation, water, and the heterogeneous land surface, including the measurements of these interactions from remote platforms.

Frequency of measurement:
1 km for use with AVHRR data (and for regional applications);
10 –30 m for high resolution data and for hydrological modelling.

Accuracy/precision required:
Vertical: 100 m with AVHRR data, 5–20 m for higher resolution requirements and for hydrological modelling.

R & D needed:
To be determined.

Present status:
In the near-term, only topographic data presently available can be realistically expected to form the basis for global and regional data sets. The best quality global topographic data sets are presently classified, and although discussions have been held to have them declassified, they are not available. The presently available digital chart of the world contains elevation information from 1:1,000,000 ONC maps, with coarse vertical resolution. Most of the world land mass has been mapped at 1:250,000, thus providing a good basis for digital elevation data with a grid spacing of 100 m. It should be noted that the vertical accuracy of the above data sets is likely to be marginal at best. For many local or regional applications higher resolution topographic data will be required (1:50,000 or higher).

Action required:
Near-term
—Work toward the release of the highest resolution global data set presently available;
—In parallel, evaluate the utility of DCW topographic data.
Mid-term
—Pursue the availability of higher resolution topographic data (1:20,000 to 1:50,000) for
    regional to continental applications.

In the context of global change priorities NASA scientists have identified the following problems (Asrar and Dozier, 1994):

(1) Ozone depletion in the stratosphere, resulting in a significant increase in the ultraviolet radiation reaching the Earth's surface, which could cause considerable health hazards.
(2) Climate variability caused by natural and human-induced activities that could affect patterns of precipitation and temperature, thus agricultural and industrial production and distribution.
(3) Global warming and long-term climate change, which could contribute to diminished water supplies of suitable quality for agricultural and industrial use, and can be traced to deforestation, other anthropogenic changes to the Earth's surface, and human-induced introduction of trace gases to the atmosphere.
(4) Decline in the health and diversity of animals and vegetation because of long-term changes in atmospheric chemistry, precipitation, runoff, and groundwater.
(5) Social and economic consequences of climate changes and their effects on health, standard of living, and quality of life.

The data in Table 1.42 illustrate the EOS potential concerning social and economic implications of global climate change. The EOS data will open broad new horizons for solving many urgent environmental problems.

Table 1.42. Social and economic implications of global climate change

Global change	Priority research questions	Relevant EOS instruments	Key contributions
	What are the interactions with land cover?		Observed changes in land cover, surface albedo, etc., as basis to assess human activity and to define climate-agriculture interactions
	Freshwater resources?		Emphasis on water balance at all scales to assess water resource availability/vulnerability
	Coastal zones, including fisheries?		High-resolution coastal circulation studies (including biology) to provide important data on primary productivity, a key element in fisheries
Social and economic implications	Human health, including disease vectors, air quality, and UV-B radiation?	All EOS instruments	Advances in understanding of tropospheric pollution and stratospheric ozone depletion (thereby anticipating UV-B increases) Identification of volcanic gas

	hazards
	Early-warning capability for natural disasters
	Ability to isolate as-yet-undiscovered risks to human health and safety
Land use, including soils and erosion?	Unprecedented measurement of the scale and magnitude of land cover associated with land-use management practices
Business and commerce?	Identification of agricultural implications such as water resource availability
	Identification of volcanic hazards (e.g. disruption of commercial air traffic)
	Effect on regional commerce
	Management of renewable and non-renewable natural resources

2

Satellite and aircraft instrumentation for remote sensing: Russian experience

2.1 PRINCIPAL TYPES OF SATELLITE SYSTEMS FOR ENVIRONMENTAL AND NATURAL RESOURCES MONITORING INVESTIGATIONS

The increasing scope of man's activity, the growing anthropogenic impact on the environment and the resulting deterioration of the ecological situation, as well as the need for rational development and use of natural resources, the problems of long-range weather and climate forecast require the development of techniques and instruments for global control of the natural environment and Earth's resources (Kondratyev, 1987a, 1990c; Kondratyev and Pokrovski, 1989a; Programme..., 1988; Holender and Wulf, 1983).

The aerospace observation means open up wide possibilities in this direction: they are based on the use of techniques and instruments for remote sensing from aircraft laboratories, automatic satellites and manned orbital stations (MOS) (Avanesov et al., 1981a; American satellite..., 1974; Andronikov, 1979; Armand, 1960; Beregovoi, et al., 1972a; Information capabilities..., 1988; Kondratyev, 1980a; Kondratyev and Buznikov, 1981)

The remote sensing of the environment is a study of natural objects at a distance, without any contact between the sensors and the surface of these objects. Practically, studies of the Earth's resources and ecology are based on remote sounding techniques; that is, various kinds of photographic (Bolshakov and Lavrova, 1982; Final report..., 1987; Kienko, 1987; Kronberg, 1983; Lavrova, 1983; Lavrova and Stetsenko, 1981; Soyuz-22..., 1980), TV (Kronberg, 1983; Selivanov, 1981; Selivanov et al., 1977, 1981), spectral (Beregovoi et. al., 1972a; Buznikov, 1980a, b, 1981, 1982, 1983a, b, c, 1984, 1986; Kondratyev and Buznikov, 1981), lidar (Kanevski et al., 1985; Kondratyev and Pozdnyakov, 1988), thermal (Kronberg, 1983; Shilin, 1982), radar (Beliavski and Pokrovski, 1984; Kondratyev et. al., 1990; Mel'nik et al., 1980; Salganik et al., 1990) and other kinds of survey of the atmosphere, Earth's surface and the World Ocean from the ground, ship, aerospace and other platforms to study their state or for thematic mapping.

Mankind has achieved some progress in solving the fundamental problems and practical use of the materials of space-based survey for studies of the Earth's resources and ecology. Experimental space means have been developed to solve the scientific and economic problems, as well as problems of meteorology, weather and climate forecast, oceanography, studies of Earth's resources and environmental control.

The space-derived data play an important role in the solution of various problems of agriculture, forestry and fishery. For example, it is now possible to use the remote sensing techniques in agricultural and ecological monitoring during the whole technological cycle of agrotechnical production, from assessments of the snow and moisture content of soil, conditions of the winter crops wintering, and the state of crops at different vegetation stages before harvesting, which is very important both for the yield forecast and for the effect of the agro-ecosystems on the ecological state of the region, on the whole (Kondratyev et al., 1986b; Kondratyev and Fedchenko, 1982). The multispectral survey serves the basis for an operational mapping of soils and assessing their fertility (Kondratyev et al., 1986b; Kronberg, 1983; Mishev, 1985; Yugas and Kudela, 1989). The aerospace techniques are also efficient in solving the problems of forestry (forest cadastre, damage by pests and diseases, risk of conflagration, fires, etc.) (Daniulis et. al., 1989) and water economy (water resources, hydrological resources, hydrological forecasts, reclamation regimes, etc.). The problems of atmospheric and oceanic pollution, changes in the Earth's surface (soil ploughing, forest clearing, reclamation and irrigation works, etc.) and the resulting consequences (climate change, soil erosion, etc.) make systematic global-scale monitoring of the environmental state a necessity.

Among the practically important problems of the environmental studies of primary importance are the use of space-derived information in studies of the Earth's climate change (Gorshkov and Kondratyev, 1988; Kondratyev, 1988c; Programme..., 1988). In this connection, of great importance is the study of anthropogenic impacts on the global cycles of carbon, sulphur, nitrogen, and monitoring the atmospheric pollution caused by fuel burning, ejections of freons and application of fertilizers.

At present all kinds of ecosystems (vegetation, soils, animals, seas, oceans, rivers, inland water basins) and their individual components are objects of monitoring—the aerospace one, in particular (Kondratyev, 1990d; Buznikov and Lakhtanov, 1991; Kronberg, 1983; Daniulis et al., 1989; Buznikov, 1992; Kondratyev et al., 1992b; Buznikov, 1990; Buznikov et al., 1994; Buznikov, 1994; Buznikov et al., 1995a,b, 1993, 1978, 1989a, 1977).

Considerable variability of the ecosystems due to anthropogenic impacts and irrational land use as well as the global scale of the phenomena observed require the use of aerospace remote sensing techniques, which enable one to solve numerous problems of ecological monitoring. Table 2.1 lists the respective problems of ecological monitoring, objects of monitoring, and the aerospace instruments used for this purpose.

Space means of observations should play the basic role in the information support to the problems enumerated above.

Table 2.1. The use of aerospace remote sensing instruments to solve the problems of ecological monitoring

Problems of ecological monitoring	Objects of studies	Parameters to be measured	Multi-zonal devices for aerophotometry	TV cameras	Multi-channel scanner devices in the visible and IR	Thermal-vision devices	1- and 2-channel radiometer, 3.5–4.0 and 8.0–14.0 μm	Multi-channel microwave scanning radiometer	SAR	Visible and IR spectrometers	Visible trace polarimeters	Lidars	Scatterometers	Actinometric complex	Correlation gas analysers
Control of atmospheric pollution	Change in atmospheric chemistry, atmosphere of cities and industrial centres, large-scale sources of industrial pollution, fire centres, precipitation, transcontinental transport of pollutants, state of ozonosphere.	Nitrogen oxides	–	–	–	–	–	–	–	+	–	+	–	–	+
		Aerosol	+	–	–	+	–	–	–	+	–	+	–	+	–
		Sulphur dioxide	–	–	+	–	–	–	–	+	–	+	–	–	+
		Ozone	–	–	–	–	–	–	–	+	–	+	–	–	+
		Carbon oxide	–	–	–	–	–	–	–	+	–	+	–	–	+
		Hydrocarbon	–	–	–	–	–	–	–	+	–	+	–	–	+
		Carbon dioxide	–	–	–	–	–	–	–	+	–	+	–	–	+
		Salt outbreaks	+	+	+	–	–	+	–	+	–	+	–	–	+
		Amount and quality of precipitation	+	+	+	+	–	+	+	–	–	+	–	–	–
Control of the state of land surface	Vegetation (oases, crops, pastures, tropical forests, mangrove thickets, boreal forests, marshes, vegetation in tundra)	Projected cover	+	+	+	+	–	+	+	+	+	+	–	–	–
		Leaf index	+	+	+	–	–	–	–	+	+	–	–	–	–
		Phytomass	+	+	+	–	–	–	–	+	–	–	–	–	–
		Chlorophyll content	+	–	+	–	–	–	–	+	–	–	–	+	–
		Soil feeding	–	+	+	–	–	–	–	+	–	–	–	–	–
		Moisture	+	–	+	+	–	+	+	+	+	–	–	+	–
		Radiation temperature	–	–	–	–	+	+	–	–	–	–	–	+	–

Soils	Erosion	+	+	+	+	+	−	+	+	−	−
	Mineral composition	−	+	+	−	+	−	+	+	−	−
	Types of soils	+	+	+	+	+	+	+	+	+	−
	Moisture	+	+	+	+	+	+	+	+	−	+
	Salinity	+	+	+	−	+	−	+	+	+	−
Underground waters	Areas of sources, sinks and discharge	−	−	+	+	+	+	+	+	−	−
Control of the state of water basins	Oil film (detection)	+	+	+	+	+	+	+	+	+	−
	Oil film (thickness)	−	−	−	−	+	−	−	+	−	−
	Area under microphytes	+	+	+	−	+	+	−	−	−	−
	Phytoplankton	+	+	+	+	−	+	+	+	−	−
	Inorganic suspensions	−	−	−	+	+	−	−	+	−	−
	Water colour	+	+	+	+	+	+	−	−	−	−
	Thermal pollutions	−	−	−	+	+	+	−	+	−	−
	Changes in river beds,	+	+	+	+	+	+	+	−	−	−
	Coastlines	+	+	+	+	+	+	+	+	−	−
	Erosion (motion of shallow)	+	+	+	+	+	+	+	+	−	−
	Temperature	−	−	+	+	+	−	+	−	−	−
	Wind direction	−	−	−	−	−	−	−	−	+	−
	Wave height	−	−	−	−	−	−	−	+	+	−
	Motion of water masses	+	+	+	+	+	+	+	−	−	−

The Earth's-resources and ecological studies with the use of space-borne means are connected with the solution of several complex problems:

1. Development of space-borne systems (American satellite..., 1974; Glushko, 1987; Grishin, 1987; Kondratyev et al., 1992b; Permanent..., 1990; Research..., 1993; Trifonov, 1981; Vetlov, 1980).

2. Development of measurement techniques and creation of the on-board equipment (Beliajev et al., 1978; Buznikov, 1980a, 1992; Buznikov and Lakhtanov, 1976, 1991; Buznikov and Orlov, 1989; Buznikov et al., 1980; Elizarenko et al., 1984; Information capabilities..., 1988; Kondratyev and Buznikov, 1981; Kronberg, 1988; Mirzojeva et al., 1992; Mishev, 1985; Salganik et al., 1990; Siachenov and Zimmermann, 1989; Ziumnikh, 1989).

3. Development and creation of the means of transmission and processing of space information (Belchanski et al., 1982; Buznikov, 1983b, 1986, 1987, 1994; Buznikov et al., 1994a; Deidvid, 1979; Ismailov et al., 1982; Vasilyev, 1982; Vasilyev and Vedeshin, 1989).

4. Development of techniques and means of metrological support of space systems, on the whole, including the validation of satellite data and accomplishment of synchronous sub-satellite observations over specially chosen test areas (Avanesov et al., 1981b; Buznikov and Karasev, 1989; Buznikov et al., 1993c, 1994b, 1995a,b; Grigoryev and Kondratyev, 1989; Ismailov, 1980; Kondratyev et al., 1971a, 1990; Mel'nik et al., 1980; Prather, 1988; Shilin, 1982; Turchin et al., 1970).

5. Creation of the services delivering the information to the users for its operational application (Bodechtel, 1981; Bogomolov, et al., 1981; Buznikov, 1994; Kondratyev and Pokrovski, 1989; Kronberg, 1988)

6. Development of methods for the practical use of the data obtained to solve the ecological and Earth's-resources problems (Application..., 1981; Buznikov et al., 1994b; Kondratyev and Fedchenko, 1982; Kondratyev et al., 1986a, b; Yugas and Kudela, 1989).

Automatic satellites carrying photographic, TV, and multispectral instruments are the basic means to monitor the environment and the dynamics of its state. These are continuously operating space systems "Meteor", "Meteor-Priroda", "Resurs-F", "Resurs-0", "Ocean-0", Landsat, SPOT, "Kosmos", etc.

The manned orbital stations, for example, "Salut", "Mir", Skylab, Shuttle, have become scientific orbital laboratories to realize a complex of experimental and modelling work, to work out the models of scientific instruments to the last detail, to accomplish visual and visual-instrumental scientific studies. The MOS and automatic satellites have opend up wide possibilities to study the Earth's surface, atmosphere, and the World Ocean by using the techniques of the remote sensing of the environment.

At present, studies from space are characterized by great concern for the use of satellites and other space platforms to study our planet (Kondratyev, 1990c; Programme..., 1988; Pszenny et al., 1989). The basic programme of international cooperation with the use of space-borne systems is the International Geosphere–

Biosphere Programme—IGBP (Kondratyev, 1987a, 1989a; Kondratyev and Pokrovski, 1989; Kotliakov, 1988), and that of the USA—"Mission to Planet Earth" (Raven, 1988). All this is explained by an objective necessity to use space-borne means, techniques and instruments for the remote sensing of the environment and natural resources for global-scale ecological studies, as well as for the economic advantages that can be derived from these studies.

In conditions of the development and existence of various space multi-purpose systems of great importance is the development of a single strategy for their functioning and further development in the interests of solving the Earth's-resources and ecological problems for a certain period, for example, to the year 2005.

Table 2.2 lists the basic space-borne systems developed in the former USSR, which can be used by Russia to study the Earth's-resources and ecology within a single strategy of the remote sensing of the Earth during the next 10–15 years.

Naturally, the use of all the systems enumerated above is irrational and economically inexpedient. In this connection, the most urgent objective of Russian scientists dealing with the Earth's-resources and ecological investigations from space is to determine the strategy of development and functioning of the space-borne systems which should include:

— analysis of home and foreign experience in the remote sensing of the Earth (RSE);
— strategy of the development of the measuring and scientific on-board RSE equipment with indicated priorities;
— strategy of the development of the ground-based complex to receive, process and deliver the space-derived information in the interests of science and economy.

2.2   SATELLITE SPECTROPHOTOMETRY OF THE ENVIRONMENT

2.2.1   Basic methods of satellite spectrophotometry

The largest volume of information from space on the state of the atmosphere and surface of the Earth is obtained now with the use of photographic (Avanesov, et al., 1981a; Lavrova 1983; Lavrova and Stetsenko, 1981; Soyuz-22..., 1980) and multi-spectral scanning instruments (American satellite..., 1974; Avanesov et al., 1981a; Kronberg, 1988; Research..., 1993; Selivanov et al., 1981, 1985; Space opportunities..., 1987). One advantage of photographic and multi-spectral images consists in the spatial and factor integration and the associated possibility of a complex analysis of the laws of spatial and temporal variability of various characteristics of natural formations. However, only the data on the spatial distribution of the brightness field in any spectral interval characterized by the image are insufficient for the reliable indication of the objects observed and determination of their properties. Quantitative measurement techniques are also needed. Among them, the technique of spectrophotometric measurements (Buznikov, 1983a, 1990; Kondratyev and Buznikov, 1981) of the optical characteristics of the environment is the most informative. Measurements of the reflection spectra of natural formations are an effective means of studying the environment and to control its state. They

Table 2.2. Space systems of Earth remote sensing to be used for solving natural resource and ecological problems (work carried out in the former Soviet Union)

N	Satellite type	Main characteristics of satellites and space-borne instruments	Main purposes	Desirable period of exploit-ation	Russian stations both receiving and processing data	Frequency of survey
1.	"Resurs-01"	H = 650–830 km; i = 98°. Period of active life—2 years. Satellite mass—2400 kg. 3-channel high-resolution optical instrument, resolution Δx = 30 m; 5-channel medium-resolution instrument, Δx = 160 m (visual range), Δx = 600 m (infrared range); multizonal high-resolution scanning device, Δx = 8–15 m (near the Earth's surface); synthetic aperture radar (SAR) of a high-resolution and microwave radiometer; radioline-32 Mbod	Natural resource survey, Solving of ecological problems.	1990–1998	Moscow, Novosibirsk, Khabarovsk, Pevek, Dixon.	Every 48–72 h.
2.	"Meteor-3M"	H = 850–950 km; i = 83°. Period of active life—2 years. Satellite mass—2400 kg. Survey multizonal optical device of low resolution; microwave complex of instruments; infrared spectrometer for vertical profiles of temperature and humidity data. Radio line—15 Mbod.	Hydrometeor-ology and ecology.	1993–2000	Moscow, Novosibirsk, Khabarovsk, Pevek, Dixon.	4 times in 24 h.
3.	"Ocean-01" (02)	H = 650–850 km; i = 83°. Period of active life—6 months (2 years since 1994). Satellite mass—up to 2.2 t.	World Ocean investigations.	1990–2000	"	Once in 24 h.

N	Satellite type	Main characteristics of satellites and space-borne instruments	Main purposes	Desirable period of exploit-ation	Russian stations both receiving and processing data	Frequency of survey
		Survey multizonal optical device of low resolution (visual and IR-ranges); microwave radiometric complex of instruments. Survey side-looking radar of low resolution. Radio-line—15 Mbod.				
4.	"Ocean-0"	$H = 650$ km; $i = 98°$. Period of active life—1 year. Satellite mass—6800 kg; Multizonal optical device of high resolution, $\Delta x = 30$ m; multizonal scanning device of a medium resolution, $\Delta x = 160$ m (visual range), $\Delta x = 600$ m (IR range); survey side-looking radar of low resolution; microwave radiometric complex of instruments; radio-line—32 Mbod.	Natural resource investigations of Earth and World Ocean.	1993–1996	Moscow, Novosibirsk, Khabarovsk, Pevek, Dixon.	Every 48–72 h. for high-resolution data, once in 24 h. for survey devices of low resolution.
5.	"Electro"	$H = 36000$ km. 2-channel survey instrument (visual and IR ranges) with resolution 1 km (visual) and 8 km (IR) Radio-line—2.56 Mbod; retransmitting complex—5.12 Mbod.	Meteorology and World Ocean investigations.	1991–1998	Moscow, Novosibirsk, Khabarovsk.	4 times in 24 h.
6.	"Resurs-F1"	$H = 250$–400 km; $i_1 = 62°$, $i_2 = 82°$; Period of active life—25 days. Satellite mass—6300 kg. Photocamera with resolution 6–8	Natural resource investigations of the Earth.	1990–1995	Moscow.	Every 5–6 days in a period of active life of the satellite.

N	Satellite type	Main characteristics of satellites and space-borne instruments	Main purposes	Desirable period of exploit-ation	Russian stations both receiving and processing data	Frequency of survey
		m (1 channel) and 20–30 m (3 channels).				
7.	"Resurs-F2"	$H = 170$–450 km; $i_1 = 62°$, $i_2 = 82°$ Period of active life—30 days. Satellite mass— 6300–6450 kg. Photocamera with resolution 9–18 m (4 channels).	Natural resource investigations of the Earth	1990–1995	Moscow.	Every 5–6 days in a period of active life of the satellite.
8.	"Kuban"	$H = 250$–410 km; $i = 56.65°$. Period of active life— 60 days. Satellite mass—up to 7000 kg. Photocamera with resolution 3–4.5 m (1 channel), 8–10 m (4 channels).	Natural resource investigations of the Earth.	1995–2000	Moscow, Novosibirsk, Khabarovsk.	Every 5–6 days in a period of active life on the satellite.
9.	EKOS	$H = 650$–830 km; $i = 83°$. Period of active life—3–5 years. Instrument with 8-change spectral filters. Resolution $\Delta x = 5$–7 m. Radio-line 32 Mbod.	Natural resource investigations of the Earth and ecology.	1993–1998	Moscow, Novosibirsk, Khabarovsk.	Daily monitoring.
10.	ALMAZ	$H = 350$ km (600 km since 1996), $i = 73°$. Period of active life—2 years. Satellite mass—18000 kg. Synthetic aperture radar with resolution 15 m and swath width 40 km × 2; Multizonal scanning device of a high resolution. Radio-line-64—128 Mbod.	Natural resource and ecological investigations of the Earth.	1996–2000	Moscow, Novosibirsk, Khabarovsk.	Every 48–72 h.
11.	"Jantar-NH"	$H = 650$–830 km; $i = 83°$. Period of active life—1 year. Satellite mass—6600 kg.	Natural resource investigation of the Earth and ecology.	1993–1996	Moscow	Every 2–3 days.

N	Satellite type	Main characteristics of satellites and space-borne instruments	Main purposes	Desirable period of exploit-ation	Russian stations both receiving and processing data	Frequency of survey
12.	"Planeta-L"	Multizonal scanning device (6 channels) with resolution 30–40 m. H = 650 km; i = 83°. Period of active life—2–3 years. Satellite mass—320 kg. Multizonal optical device. Radio-line—32–64 Mbod.	"	1994–1998	Moscow, Novosibirsk, Khabarovsk, foreign stations.	Every 2–3 days.
13.	"Planeta-RE"	H = 850 km; i = 98°. Period of active life 3–5 years. Satellite mass—up to 3000 kg. Multizonal scanning device with resolution 500 m; synthetic aperture radar (SAR) with resolution—20–30 m and swath width—80–90 km. Radio-line—512 Mbod.	"	1997–2005	Moscow, Novosibirsk, Khabarovsk, Pevek, Dixon, foreign stations.	Every 2–3 days.
14.	Manned orbital station "Mir-2"	H = 350–450 km; i = 63°. Period of active life—5–7 years. Complex scientific instruments in visual and microwave ranges. Radio-line— 512 Mbod.	Check tests of experimental instruments. Solving of separate tasks. Solving in connection with environmental investigations hydrometeor-ology and ecology.	1996–2005	Moscow, Novosibirsk, Pevek, Dixon.	In 4–5 days.

substantially broaden the possibilities of solving the inverse problems from the results of aerospace surveys. Besides, they are needed to optimize the parameters of multispectral space-borne systems and multizonal cameras and, first of all, to choose the most informative spectral intervals (Kondratyev et al., 1992b; Pokrovski, 1981, 1989b).

Thus, one of the most efficient techniques for the remote sensing of the environment from space is space-based spectrophotometry (Buznikov, 1980b, 1981, 1982, 1983c; Buznikov et al., 1991; Kondratyev and Buznikov, 1981; Mishev, 1980).

The spectrophotometry of the environment from space can be defined as a scientific direction that foresees the development of techniques and devices to measure from satellites the spectra of reflection, absorption and scattering of solar radiation by natural formations, and the optical characteristics of the environment (spectral coefficients of reflection, absorption, emission, polarization degree, spectral brightness and contrasts) to study the natural dependences of the characteristics of the electromagnetic emission field measured from space on the environmental parameters, such as the type and the state of natural objects, concentration of gas components and aerosols at different altitudes in the atmosphere, the state of the World Ocean surface, etc. The space-based spectrophotometry of the environment is based on the scientific principles of classic photometry with its strict system of theoretical rules, calculations and quantitative methods of radiance measurements. Spectral measurements from space platforms are made through atmospheric thickness, and therefore the problems of radiation transfer in a real spherical atmosphere are very important.

The spectrophotometry from space includes several techniques of measurements, among which most widely used are the method of spectral measurements of solar radiation reflected and scattered by the Earth–atmosphere system (Buznikov, 1983a; Buznikov et al., 1975a,d) and the method to measure atmospheric transparency by the Sun on optical traces (Buznikov, 1981; Buznikov et al., 1983, 1991; Kondratyev and Buznikov, 1981; Kondratyev et al., 1976a). The technique of measurements of reflected and scattered solar radiation can be used both in the visible and near-IR ranges (up to 3–4μ), where the upward radiation is formed owing to the transformation of solar radiation determined by several processes: reflection from the Earth's surface, molecular and aerosol scattering and absorption by the atmosphere. Its sensitivity to variations in the optical properties of natural formations, in atmospheric composition and atmospheric aerosol content makes it useful to study the atmosphere (Buznikov, 1982; Buznikov et al., 1972a; Heath and Krueger, 1975; Kondratyev et. al., 1977b, f) and the natural formations of the Earth's surface (Buznikov, 1983c, 1982; Buznikov et al., 1986, 1995; Kondratyev et al., 1972a, 1974b). Note, that studies of the spectra of natural formations on the Earth's surface from space are hindered by the necessity to consider the effect of atmospheric thickness on the results of the spectral survey (Kondratyev et al., 1971b, 1974a, 1975a, 1977a, 1985b).

The method of recording the solar radiation reflected and scattered from different atmospheric layers has been used in the American scanning system TOMS (Heath and Krueger, 1975) for the global monitoring of the state of the atmosphere and, first of all, the state of the ozonosphere, which protects all living beings on the Earth, including vegetation cover, from the disastrous effect of hard UV solar radiation.

The technique of measurements of atmospheric transparency by the Sun on the optical traces (occultation sounding of the atmosphere) (Buznikov, 1981; Kondratyev et al., 1976a, 1977a,d, 1978) considers, first of all, the process of radiation transformation—the true absorption of radiation by atmospheric gaseous components. In its practical realization, it is necessary to take into account a refraction of solar radiation in the terrestrial atmosphere. This technique is very sensitive to variations in the atmospheric composition and can be sufficiently precise. Solutions involve the technique of measuring the atmospheric transparency by the Sun on optical slanted paths using fast-operating spectrometers with a high angular and spectral resolution and high accuracy of measurements. The global scale of measurements requires special manoeuvres of a space platform and creation of monitoring systems that provide the aiming of the spectrometer's input slit at the geometric centre of the Sun's disc to an accuracy better than one angular minute (Buznikov, 1981; Kondratyev and Buznikov, 1976a, 1981).

The solution to Earth's numerous resource and ecological problems with the use of aerospace means is based on the remote sensing techniques, based, in turn, on an indication of the state of natural formations on the Earth's surface from their measured optico-physical characteristics (Beregovoi et al., 1972a; Buznikov, 1983c, 1986; Buznikov and Lakhtanov, 1991; Buznikov et al., 1977, 1989a; Kondratyev and Fedchenko, 1982; Kondratyev and Pozdiakov, 1988; Kondratyev et al., 1986b; Mishev, 1985). They are based on measurements of various quantitative characteristics of the field of electromagnetic emission. As a rule, measurements are made of the radiation of either the Sun or artificial sources transformed by the atmosphere and reflected and scattered by the surface.

In the IR and radio-ranges the thermal emission and radio emission of the "surface–atmosphere" and "ocean–atmosphere" systems are recorded. The characteristics of the measured electromagnetic radiation—intensity, polarization, spectral, spatial—frequency, and angular distributions (reflection indicatrix), etc.—contain information on the concrete types of natural formations and their physical state.

The possibilities of using the data of remote sensing to obtain information about the state of the atmosphere, World Ocean's surface and natural formations on the Earth's surface for the practical solution, on this basis, of numerous ecological problems are determined, first of all, by knowledge of the natural dependences of the characteristics of the electromagnetic emission field on the environmental parameters, such as the state of vegetation and the properties of soil, concentration of gas components and aerosol at different altitudes in the atmosphere, air temperature, SST, etc.

The accuracy of measurements of these characteristics depends on the choice of the recorded radiation spectral range (Pokrovski, 1988), instruments used, viewing direction, zenith and azimuthal solar angles, etc., that is, on the parameters characterizing the conditions of the experiment.

The urgency of using remote sensing techniques to study the Earth from space to solve global ecological problems (Kondratyev, 1987a, 1988c), as well as the special character of satellite measurements (Armand, 1960; Beregovoi et al., 1972a; Kondratyev and Buznikov, 1981; Saulski, 1989), bring forth an urgent problem of developing special measurement techniques to make it possible to accomplish a systematic remote sensing of the global-scale ecological changes. Particularly important here are the indirect optical and radiotechnical methods. They are called indirect because when the measurements are made from aerospace platforms, the parameters of interest for the use (e.g. the temperature of the Earth's surface and atmosphere, pressure, wind speed, distribution of ozone, water vapour, nitrogen oxides, sulphur anhydride, and other trace gases) are measured not directly but through the characteristics of the outgoing radiation which are complicated functionals of the environmental state.

When developing, improving and using the on-board aerospace instruments designed to study the environment, the processes in the World Ocean, as well as to investigate the Earth's resources, it is necessary to take into account the following principally important facts:

1. Most informative is the information in the form of the brightness fields for different wavelength ranges—from UV to microwave—which permits both the quantitative interpretation through the computer-processing of data (Avanesov, 1981a; Buznikov et al., 1990, 1994a, 1995a,b; Daniulis et al., 1989; Information capabilities ..., 1988; Price, 1987; Selivanov et al., 1981; Vasilyev and Mironova, 1974; Yugas and Kudela, 1989) and the qualitative analysis of the visual data in the form of images (Beregovoi et al., 1972a; Grigoryev, 1975; Grigoryev and Kondratyev, 1989).

2. Incorrect inverse problems of the remote sounding of the environment and the Earth's resources (Kondratyev, 1966, 1988a; Kondratyev et al., 1985b, 1989) determine the necessity to combine satellite and conventional observation techniques (the latter are the source of control and calibration data bases) (Beregovoi et al., 1972a; Buznikov et al., 1993a, 1995a; Curran, 1982; Ismailov, 1980; Ismailov et al., 1982; Kondratyev et al., 1970, 1971a,b, 1972d, 1974b, 1990).

3. The combination of various requirements of science and economic branches (Buznikov, 1986; Daniulis et al., 1989; Final report..., 1987; Kalinin et al., 1977; Kozlov et al., 1981; Kronberg, 1983; Salganik et al., 1990) for the spatial and temporal resolution of the instruments carried by space vehicles is only possible with the use of complexes of supplementing devices and systems of satellites put in various orbits: polar, Sun-synchronous, geostationary, intermediate (American satellite..., 1974; Grishin, 1987; Permanently ..., 1990; Saulski, 1989).

4. The problems of recognition of natural objects and phenomena are most successfully solved based on the use of spectral images in any spectral interval (Beliajev et al., 1978; Buznikov, 1983a; Kondratyev and Buznikov, 1981; Kondratyev and Fedchenko, 1982; Kondratyev et al., 1972a, 1986b; Krinov, 1974; Mishev, 1985). In particular, this has been confirmed by the results of remote sensing to assess the state of crops and to forecast the yield (Buznikov,

1986; Kondratyev et al., 1982, 1986b).

5. In none of the wavelength regions is it possible to make correct assessments of the characteristics of the land and ocean surface without accounting for the distorting effect of atmospheric thickness (Buznikov et al., 1989a; Kondratyev et al., 1970, 1974a, 1975a, 1977a, 1985b).

6. Though automated satellites should play the dominating role in the global system of observations (American satellite..., 1974; Bodechtel, 1981; Curran, 1985; IEEE..., 1986; Information capabilities..., 1988; Glushko, 1987; Grishin, 1987; Kozlov et al., 1981; Selivanov and Gektion, 1982; Space-based..., 1977; Space opportunities..., 1987), manned spacecraft are invaluable for observations of the dynamic phenomena in the atmosphere, on the land and ocean surface, as well as working out the measurement techniques and complicated instrumentation (Beregovoi et al., 1972a; Kondratyev, 1980a; Kondratyev and Buznikov, 1981; Permanently..., 1990).

2.2.2   Physical bases for the development of instruments for the remote sensing of natural formations from aerospace platforms

The solution of the problems of the remote sensing of the Earth's surface and its vegetation cover is based on measurements from aerospace platforms of the quantitative characteristics of the fields of electromagnetic radiation. These are the fields of solar radiation transformed by the atmosphere and reflected from the Earth's surface, and the thermal emission of the "surface–atmosphere" system. The Sun is the main source of electromagnetic radiation. With a surface temperature of about 6000 K it emits a continuous spectrum of energy from the UV to the IR. A maximum of solar radiation falls on 0.47 μm. In the UV it rapidly decreases, and in the IR it propagates in the form of a slant curve (Fig. 2.1). Solar radiation, penetrating the atmosphere and reaching the Earth's surface, is partially reflected and partially absorbed by the planetary surface and its natural objects.

The reflective, absorptive and emitting properties of natural surfaces, including the "soil–vegetation" system, depend on the type of natural formations and the wavelength emission.

Vegetation, bare soil, and water surfaces that are interesting for global ecological studies by remote sensing techniques, follow the laws of interaction between the electromagnetic radiation and the substance. The spectral width of their thermal emission depends on both the temperature and the substance and its state. Most of the surfaces and natural formations have the characteristic spectrum of reflected, absorbed or secondary thermal emission of their own in the visible, IR and microwave regions.

For the remote sensing of natural objects it is important to know the reflective and absorptive properties of their materials on the Earth's surface. To assess the state of objects, it is necessary to study how their spectra of absorption or emission change with the changing state of these objects. For example, vegetation reflects solar radiation differently, depending on the season and vegetation phase. The same natural objects, being wet or dry, reflect and absorb solar radiation in different ways

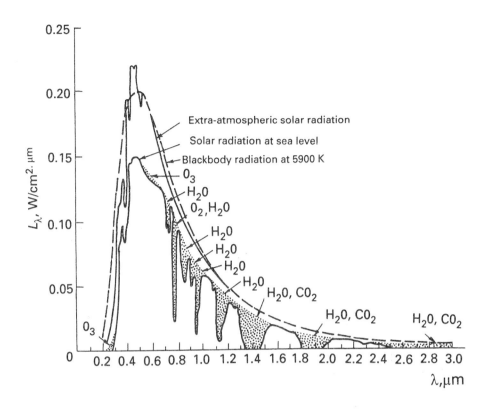

Fig. 2.1. Spectral distribution of solar radiation.

(Kondratyev et al., 1986b; Kronberg, 1988).

In the daytime the Earth's surface absorbs the Sun's energy and heats up. The soils, vegetation, and surface waters are heated and emit the heat in the form of IR emission. Both the energy and the spectrum of IR emission depend on the temperature of the object. Different objects get heated in different ways and differently emit their heat differently, that is, they have different emitting properties. The mean temperature of the Earth's surface is close to 290 K (17°C). The maximum of its secondary thermal emission falls on 9.7 μm. The thermal emission with an interval of 3.0–40 μm can be recorded by thermal receivers carried by aircraft or satellite. However, the atmosphere transmits radiation through its "transparency windows" only in two narrow spectral intervals: 3.5–5 and 8–12μm. Thus, studies from space of the Earth's surface objects can be realized in atmospheric transparency windows: in the visible and near-IR regions in several comparatively narrow intervals of the thermal IR region and microwave range from millimetre to decimetre wavelengths.

The atmosphere is a mixture of gases in which both solid and liquid particles from small-sized aerosol to thick clouds are suspended. Electromagnetic waves interact with the particles of dust, smoke, ice crystals and water droplets contained in the atmosphere. Processes of scattering and absorption of energy reduce the solar radiation intensity near the Earth's surface and change the range of radiation. Electromagnetic waves shorter than $0.27\mu m$ are completely absorbed by ozone, do not pass through the atmosphere and cannot be used for the remote sounding of the Earth's surface. The visible and near-IR regions are better known and make it possible to obtain most of the information about different types of natural formations. The main shortcomings of measurements in these regions are the strong dependence of the results on atmospheric haze and the possibility to measure only when the Earth's surface is irradiated. The latter fact can be excluded when the laser systems are used as light sources. With the measurements in the thermal IR range the results depend on changing temperatures of natural formations. These methods can also be used at night. However, they are less sensitive to changes in the physico-chemical characteristics of natural formations. The advantage of the remote sensing of the Earth in the microwave range consists in the possibility to control some thickness of the Earth's surface and ice, a strong sensitivity of measurement results to surface roughness and moisture content in soil. The disadvantages include potentially less information content of the method compared to the visible and IR regions, a lower resolution of the survey systems (except for the SAR systems) and somewhat lower sensitivity to chemical and temperature contrasts (Armand, 1960; Information capabilities..., 1988; Kondratyev et al., 1989, 1990; Salganik et al., 1990).

All this testifies to the fact that in the case of the remote sensing of the environment it is necessary to measure the reflected radiation or the emission of the Earth's surface and atmosphere simultaneously in several spectral intervals, that is, to use the multi-spectral technique. Bearing in mind that all natural formations reflect solar radiation or emit themselves in a certain way characteristic of only them and their state, the remote sensing techniques enable one to obtain various pieces of information about the observed objects and phenomena on the Earth's surface. The energy flux from natural objects is recorded on board the space platform. This information can be processed in either digital or analogue form, for example, in the form of a coded TV or photo image which can be used to identify various types of natural formations and to assess the state of vegetation cover.

The spectral signals from natural objects differ depending on their class, in intensity and in the width of the wavelength range of reflected and emitted fluxes. Therefore an energetic quantity of the signal from an object, that is, the intensity of energy flux, is assumed to be a characteristic of the object. It is recorded with special remote sensing systems and can be measured and systematized by the classes of natural objects (Krinov, 1947; Vasilyev and Mironova, 1974).

In other words, the spectral characteristics of natural objects are not only their identification signs but also the signs of their ecological state. Particularly important are the spectral characteristics of natural formations for the numerical processing of the remote sensing data and the automatization of the process of decoding the materials of the aerospace survey. At present they are studied using the techniques of recording and processing the spectral and multizonal images presenting differences

in the spectral characteristics of vegetation communities in the form of images with
the contrasts emphasized. First of all, of interest here are methods which make it
possible to determine a correlation of the properties or the state of vegetation with a
combination of spectral data for two or more channels.

With the introduction of multizonal survey techniques which foresee a
simultaneous survey of the same Earth's surface area in different spectral intervals,
it has become possible, from the wavelength-dependent reflective, absorptive and
thermal characteristics of plants and their communities, to identify grassland, bushes
or forest more accurately than from black and white or colour aerophotos.

In the aerospace survey of vegetation, soils and other natural formations one
should proceed from the fact that the spectral reflective properties of natural
formations are characterized by either the spectral albedo (SA) or the spectral
brightness coefficient (SBC).

The spectral albedo A_λ is the ratio of hemispherical radiation flux $F_\lambda^\uparrow$ reflected by
the surface to the flux $F_\lambda^\downarrow$ incident onto this surface in some wavelength interval $(\lambda, \lambda + \Delta\lambda)$

$$A_\lambda = \frac{F_\lambda^\uparrow}{F_\lambda^\downarrow} \qquad\qquad (2.1)$$

The total albedo A is determined from the relationship

$$A = \frac{\int_0^\infty F_\lambda^\uparrow d\lambda}{\int_0^\infty F_\lambda^\downarrow d\lambda} \cdot \qquad\qquad (2.2)$$

The SBC of the surface $r_\lambda(\vartheta,\varphi)$ in the wavelength interval $(\lambda, \lambda + \Delta\lambda)$, in a given
direction and under certain illumination conditions (illumination can be either
diffused or directed at a certain angle), is the ratio of the brightness of the surface
under study in a given direction $L_\lambda(\vartheta,\varphi)$ to the brightness of an orthotropic
(reflecting by the Lambertian law) completely reflecting surface in the same direction
$L^0_\lambda(\vartheta, \varphi)$, under the same illumination conditions

$$r_\lambda(\vartheta,\varphi) = \frac{L_\lambda(\vartheta,\varphi)}{L^0_\lambda(\vartheta, \varphi)} \qquad\qquad (2.3)$$

The total brightness coefficient or, simply, the brightness coefficient, is found by
analogy with (2.2):

$$r(\vartheta,\varphi) = \frac{\int\limits_0^\infty L_\lambda(\vartheta,\,\varphi)d\lambda}{\int\limits_0^\infty L^0{}_\lambda\,(\vartheta,\varphi)d\lambda}. \tag{2.4}$$

A surface representing a dependence of $r(\vartheta,\varphi)$ or $r_\lambda(\vartheta,\varphi)$ on the viewing direction (ϑ,φ) characterizes the spatial indicatrix of the brightness coefficient and is a vivid characteristic of the angular anisotropy of reflection.

There is a dependence between the spectral albedo and the SBC:

$$A_\lambda = \int\limits_0^{\pi/2}\int\limits_0^{2\pi} r_\lambda(\vartheta,\varphi)\cos\varphi\,\sin\varphi\,d\varphi d\vartheta. \tag{2.5}$$

In natural conditions the brightness of the surface under study illuminated by direct sun rays at zenith distance $Z_\odot$ and by diffused daytime sky radiation, is usually measured in the direction normal to the surface $\vartheta = 0°$. Omit the brackets (ϑ,φ) for r and r_λ. In this case the SBC $r_\lambda(Z_\odot)$ in the wavelength interval $(\lambda,\lambda+\Delta\lambda)$ is determined as the ratio of the brightness of the horizontal surface $L_\lambda(Z_\odot)$ in the direction normal to it, to that of the horizontal orthotropic completely reflecting surface $L^0{}_\lambda(Z_\odot)$ in the normal direction, with both surfaces illuminated by total solar radiation flux (direct solar radiation at a zenith solar distance $Z_\odot$ and diffuse sky radiation)

$$r_\lambda(Z_\odot) = \frac{L_\lambda(Z_\odot)}{L^0{}_\lambda(Z_\odot)} \tag{2.6}$$

For the total coefficient of reflection the following expression holds:

$$r(Z_\odot) = \frac{\int\limits_0^\infty L_\lambda(Z_\odot)\,d\lambda}{\int\limits_0^\infty L^0{}_\lambda(Z_\odot)\,d\lambda} \tag{2.7}$$

For the spectral and total albedo of natural surfaces the following expressions can be written:

$$A_\lambda(Z_\odot) = \frac{F_\lambda{}^\uparrow(Z_\odot)}{F_\lambda{}^\downarrow(Z_\odot)} \tag{2.8}$$

$$A(Z_\odot) = \frac{\int\limits_0^\infty A_\lambda(z_\odot)\,F_\lambda{}^\uparrow(Z_\odot)d\lambda}{\int\limits_0^\infty F_\lambda{}^\downarrow(Z_\odot)\,d\lambda} \tag{2.9}$$

The spectral and total albedo and the associated spectral and total coefficients of reflection of various surfaces, along with such parameters as sea surface temperature

(SST), total content and vertical distribution of water vapour, ozone, carbon dioxide, aerosol in the atmosphere, atmospheric transparency, refer to most substantial meteorological parameters, the measurements of which from space make it possible to create a global system to monitor the parameters of the atmosphere and the surface. Such a system enables one not only to perform a systematic study of various properties of the atmosphere, ocean, land and ice cover, but also to use these data in the long-range weather forecast and climate monitoring.

While studies of the spectra of natural formations from space are practically at their initial stage, measurements of the SBC and SA of natural formations in the field conditions and from aircraft have provided a rich experimental material, which, despite a difficult compatibility of measurements made with different types of instruments using different techniques, has been generalized repeatedly (Beregovoi et al., 1972a; Buznikov et al., 1995a,b; Kondratyev and Buznikov, 1981; Krinov, 1947; Mishev, 1985; Vasilyev and Mironova, 1974).

Various spectrophotometric methods and instruments are used to study the wavelength dependences of A_λ and r_λ. Their choice is determined by the problem posed and conditions of the experiment.

In laboratory conditions, most often used are standard serial spectrometers, monochromators and spectrographs, such as UM-2, MDR-2, MDR-4, IKS-12, IKS-21, IKS-29, etc. In some cases the laboratory studies are accomplished in a wide wavelength range with the use of specially made spectral instruments. Spectral studies in the field conditions and from aircraft are usually made with specially designed instruments (Buznikov et al., 1980, 1989a, b, 1991, 1992a, b, 1995c).

Studies of the spectra of the reflection of natural formations from space require the development of special spectral instruments, such as RSS-2, RSS-3, MSS-2, "Spektr-15", MKS-M, "Spektr-256", SKIF, etc. Note, that the space-borne spectrometers can successfully be used on aircraft. For example, the RSS-2 spectrographs have been used successfully on aircraft LI-2, AN-2 as well as on the ground to accumulate information about r_λ when accomplishing combined sub-satellite experiments (Beregovoi et al., 1972a; Buznikov, 1983b; Buznikov et al., 1995a,b; Kondratyev et al., 1971a,b, 1986a).

Regardless of which method (photographic or photoelectric) is used to study the spectral properties of natural formations, two types of measurements are mainly made to determine the spectral albedo or the SBC: (i) measurements of the brightness of the surface under study or solar radiation flux reflected from it; (ii) measurements of the brightness of the horizontal reference screen with r_λ known, or measurements of the solar radiation flux incident onto the surface under study.

When radiation fluxes are measured, they place an integrating nozzle in front of the input of the spectral: device either milk glass or globular photometers of different design, with a "cosine" dependence of sensitivity on the angle between the direction of the incoming radiation and the normal to the receiving surface.

When determining the brightness of various surfaces, the radiation flux is measured within some solid angle $\Delta\omega$, the same, when measuring radiation reflected from the surface under study and from the control surface. Either reflecting screens, whose optical properties do not practically change in time, or transparent screens—milk or frosted glass—can be used as a control surface.

The accuracy of spectrometric measurements depends much on the quality of the reference standard applied, to the quantitative estimation of the spectral reflective properties of natural formations. In this connection, the choice of the reference surface is very important. A sample chosen as a reference standard should scatter the incident radiation almost orthotropically and have the same brightness coefficient for all wavelengths at which A_λ and r_λ are measured. Thus, during the spectrophotometric measurements of the spectral characteristics of the reflection of natural formations, magnesium oxide, barium sulphate, gypsum, barite paper, fine sand, milk or frosted glass, etc. can serve as secondary reference standards. The secondary references must be tested against a special state reference standard.

By its optical properties, magnesium oxide, spread over a lightweight substratum in the process of burning of pure magnesium, is closest to an ideal scatterer. However, such a sample is not mechanically strong, and it is difficult to use it in the field conditions, on aircraft, to say nothing of space conditions. During the spectrophotometry of natural formations from manned orbital stations (MOSs) and manned spacecraft (MSC), the frosted light-transparent screens of the type MS-14, whose optical properties are well known, to calibrate the hand-operated spectrographs RSS.

Analysis of the published data shows that with the ground measurements of r_λ the relative error varies within 5 to 10% and is caused by an erroneous measurement technique, measurement conditions (e.g. Sun elevation, clouds, non-horizontal position of measuring platforms) or other reasons. The spectral albedo is determined from measured downward and upward fluxes with a relative error of 6 to 10%.

The Earth's natural formations are characterized by their strongly varying optical reflective properties. The causes of changing the spectral course of r_λ or A_λ of natural surfaces can be divided mainly into two groups. On the one hand, these are causes depending on external conditions of measurements and are independent of the properties of the object itself. The external conditions are determined by illumination of the surface under study and meteorological factors. A change in the zenith distance of the Sun leads to both changing the angle of the incidence of direct radiation and variations in the relationship between direct and diffuse radiation. The latter depends much on cloudiness. In this case the meteorological factors are as follows: the amount and type of clouds, atmospheric transparency, wind strength and direction. The wind should be taken into account when surveying the vegetation, since it changes the orientation of leaves.

On the other hand, the change in the spectral reflection of the surface under study is affected by the state of the surface itself. These are: the moisture content of the soil or plants' leaves, the state of the soil surface (harrowed surface, ploughed surface, the presence of lumps, clods, etc.), kind of vegetation (forest, bushes, agricultural crops, etc.), the state of the water surface (roughness, calm, contamination degree), projective coverage of one type of surface by another (combination of soils, ground covered with vegetation, etc.), the state of vegetation, its vegetation period, etc. The causes, depending on the properties of the objects themselves, affect their r_λ and A_λ in different ways.

A substantial variability of the optical reflecting properties of the Earth's natural formations requires a thorough fixation of the conditions of the remote sounding of natural formations and measurements of all the factors affecting the spectral change of r_λ and A_λ.

The incidence of electromagnetic radiation on a natural object is accompanied by the processes of reflection, scattering, diffraction, refraction, dual refraction of rays and absorption in the layer it penetrates. As a result, electromagnetic oscillations, initially oriented with equal probability in different planes in an incident ray of natural light, upon interacting with the object can obtain one dominating orientation. The reflected or scattered radiation becomes partially polarized. A classical description of the polarization of electromagnetic radiation can be found in publications (Sherclif, 1965). Along with the traditional mathematical description of the polarized light (Stocks vector) (Rozenberg, 1955), calculation matrices by Müller and Jones are also used (Buznikov and Lakhtanov, 1991; Sherclif, 1965).

Electromagnetic oscillations in the beam observed can be reduced to two constituents: L_1—normal to the plane of scattering; and L_2—parallel to this plane. In this case the radiation polarization can be characterized by the degree of polarization

$$P = \frac{L_1 - L_2}{L_1 + L_2} \qquad (2.10)$$

Besides, the state of polarization is described by the angle of roll of the maximum polarization direction with respect to the reference plane (the position of the polarization plane) and by ellipticity (Rozenberg, 1955). As shown by the studies undertaken, the values of degree of polarization and the angle of rotation of the polarization plane can be used (Chen and Rao 1968; Coulson, 1975, 1966; Fitch, 1981). As for ellipticity, the data obtained show that its value for different types of natural formations is practically at the level of the sensitivity threshold of measuring instruments (Chen and Rao, 1968; Sekera, 1967), and therefore is not used in the remote sounding, though there have been attempts to measure it.

The history of study of polarized light is contained in the monograph by U. Shercliff (1965). A review of the studies of polarization natural formations has been made elsewhere (Buznikov and Lakhtanov, 1991; Coulson, 1975). While polarization methods of measurements have been used in astronomy for more than 80 years, systematic studies of the polarization of sunlight reflected from the Earth's surface were started only 30 years ago (Buznikov and Lakhtanov, 1991; Buznikov et al., 1975c; Ksanfomaliti et al., 1975; Lakhtanov and Piotrovskaya, 1983).

As far back as 1917, when studying from aircraft the radiation reflected from the surface, G.A. Tikhov noted the possibility of using the radiation polarization to identify various natural objects. However, only from 1956 did K. Coulson (1975) start systematic measurements of the polarization of radiation reflected from different types of natural formations. In Russia, studies connected with measurements of polarization characteristics of upward radiation from aircraft (Buznikov and Lakhtanov, 1982, 1991; Buznikov et al., 1977, 1980) and from space (Ksanfomaliti et al., 1975) have been carried out during the last 20 years. The development of laser techniques (Kanevski et al., 1985; Vlasov et al., 1989; Zuev,

1981) has led to the practical use of geophysical studies of active polarization techniques. Radar techniques (Bogorodski et al., 1981; Salganik et al., 1990; Zagorodnikov et al., 1978) have added a new chapter to the use of polarization methods to study the state of natural formations.

The polarization method has been used to identify the oil slicks (Buznikov and Lakhtanov, 1982; Buznikov et al., 1975b), to make remote measurements of the concentration of suspensions in the water surface layer (Kondratyev et al., 1972b). There are also possibilities of the remote control of soil moisture (Buznikov et al., 1977, 1978) and the state of vegetation cover from the measured polarization of the upward radiation (Curran, 1982; Lakhtanov and Piotrovskaya, 1983).

An interesting example of the application of remote sensing techniques is an experiment on crop inventory over large territories (LACIE) started by the US Department of Agriculture together with NOAA and NASA in 1974. During this experiment, based on the analysis of the Landsat data, an attempt was made to recognize the crops, to assess their state and the future yield from the vegetation reflection spectra. However, as the processing of the multispectral scanner data has shown, some crops with practically the same spectra of reflection—for example, spring wheat and barley—could be misclassified. This has necessitated the need to search for other optical characteristics in addition to brightness, which would make it possible to raise the information content of the remote sensing data. In Purdue University (USA) a study has been carried out which, based on the consideration of a theoretical model describing the polarization of reflected light which can be used to control the growth of crops at different vegetation stages, to determine the moisture content in leaves, to measure the areas under hail-beaten or diseased crops (Vanderbilt, 1980). However, so far, few experiments have been undertaken to study the polarization of the light reflected from vegetation.

Laboratory studies (Lakhtanov and Piotrovskaya, 1983) have confirmed that the degree of polarization and its spectral change are determined by the composition of pigment systems and anatomic-morphological structures of the plants. W.J. Egan (1968) gives the results of polarization measurements from aircraft at altitudes from 300 to 2700 m over homogeneous plantings of red pines (*Pinos resinosa*) surrounded by broad-leaved trees. In has been shown (Curran, 1982) that the combined use of the brightness coefficient and the degree of reflected light polarization has made it possible to recognize many more types of plants at a height of 600 m over the test area in winter conditions. In summer, the use of these characteristics, both in combination and separately, has given similar results.

Spectrophotometers (Buznikov and Lakhtanov, 1991; Buznikov et al., 1980) are now used more and more for the remote sounding of water surfaces, coastal waters and inland water basins from aircraft and helicopters (Kondratyev et al., 1986a) as well as during the multilevel sub-satellite experiments (Ismailov et al., 1982; Kondratyev et al., 1986a). However, as shown by experimental data, the measurements made at the height of the flight of these aircrafts can be affected by the intermediate atmospheric layer. At the present time, the brightness characteristics of the upward radiation have been studied best. The contribution of the atmosphere to these characteristics has been estimated from results of measurements from aircraft and helicopters at different altitudes and from space, and the techniques of atmospheric correction have been presented (Kondratyev et al., 1975a, 1977a, 1985b). However, very few data have been published about the vertical profile of spectropolarization characteristics. Some results of measurements of the degree of polarization over the water surface are contained in some publications (Buznikov et al., 1989a; Egan, 1968). The data obtained refer to a very limited set of altitudes and azimuths with respect to the Sun's vertical plane, which does not permit one to obtain a complete idea of the effect of the atmosphere on the polarization of solar radiation reflected by the underlying surface.

A substantial contribution to measurements of the spectropolarization characteristics at different altitudes in the atmosphere has been made in Buznikov et al. (1989a), who published the results of experimental studies of the vertical profile of the upward radiation degree of polarization, its spectral change performed at much more atmospheric levels and azimuths with respect to the Sun vertical plane. A semiempirical method of the numerical account of the effect of the atmosphere for polarization measurements is also given, and a set of empirical coefficients is determined needed to take into account the atmospheric effect as well as conditions for obtaining them.

The polarization characteristics of radiation are most easily determined from four parameters called the Stocks parameters (Rozenberg, 1955; Shercliff, 1965; Vasilyev, 1969) with the dimensionality of intensity (brightness) and can be measured. If we denote the Stocks parameters I, Q, U, V, then for a quasi-monochromatic beam they can be expressed as follows:

$$I = \langle E^2_x + E^2_y \rangle$$

$$Q = \langle E^2_x - E^2_y \rangle$$

$$U = \langle 2E_x E_y \cos \delta \rangle$$

$$V = \langle 2E_x E_y \sin \delta \rangle$$

where E_x and E_y are the amplitudes of the electric vector constituents along the axes O_x and O_y of the rectangular coordinate system, normal to the direction of radiation propagation; δ is the phase difference between the constituents along the axes. The angular brackets denote the time averaging of the parameters.

In a general case of elliptically polarized radiation the degree of polarization is equal to

$$P = \frac{(Q^2 + U^2 + V^2)^{1/2}}{I} \tag{2.11}$$

The position of the polarization plane (for the elliptically polarized radiation—the position of the plane containing the long axis of the ellipse with respect to the axis O_x) is determined by the angle χ, which is

$$\tan 2\chi = U/Q \tag{2.12}$$

The degree of ellipticity $\beta = \arctan b/a$, where a and b are the short and long semi-axes of the ellipse, is determined by

$$\sin 2\beta = \frac{V}{(Q^2 + U^2 + V^2)^{1/2}} \tag{2.13}$$

In the case of linear polarization $V = 0$, and then the degree of polarization is

$$P = \frac{(Q^2 + U^2)^{1/2}}{I} \tag{2.14}$$

Since the polarization characteristics are determined through the parameters having the dimensionality of brightness, the polarimeters consist of the same units, like the radiometers used to measure the brightness characteristics (Elizarenko et al., 1984). However, in contrast to the latter, the optical schemes of polarimeters contain the components which make it possible to analyse the polarized light. These components are: linear polarizers (analysers) operating based on the phenomena of dual refraction of the beam and dichroism, as well as phase plates (Shercliff, 1965; Volkova, 1974).

The operation of each optical component used to analyse the polarized light can be described with the Müller 16-element matrix. With several components in the scheme, each is described by a matrix of its own, and the expressions for the Stocks parameters of radiation that passes through the analysing components can be obtained via some matrix algebraic transformations (Shercliff, 1965; Vasilyev, 1969).

We know the schemes of polarimeters with rotating phase plates and fixed linear analysers, as well as with, or without, rotating linear analysers and fixed phase plates. Depending on the presence and mutual orientation of the analysing components, several expressions have been obtained, relating the intensity of radiation that passes through these components, with the Stocks parameters, and, hence, with the polarization characteristics of radiation.

Using the scheme with the rotating phase plate and fixed linear analyser the post-analyser radiation intensity I_a is expressed as (Coulson, 1975):

$$I_a = I\{1 + P[\cos^2(\delta/2) \cos 2 (\chi - \psi) +$$
$$+ \sin^2 (\delta/2) \cos (4\omega t - 2\psi - 2\chi)] +$$
$$+ V \sin \delta \sin (2\omega t - 2\psi)\}, \tag{2.15}$$

where I and P are the intensity and the degree of linear polarization at the input; δ is the phase shift; ψ is the angle between the reference plane and the transmission plane of the analyser; ω is the frequency of the phase plate rotation; t is the time.

The resulting photocurrent will contain the constant constituents v_0 and the variable, in which the second v_2 and the fourth v_4 harmonics of the frequency of the phase plate rotation are present. These components are described with the following expressions:

$$v_0 = kI[1 + P \cos^2 (\delta/2) \cos 2 (\chi - \psi)],$$

$$v_2 = kIV \sin \delta \sin(2\omega t - 2\psi),$$

$$v_4 = kIP \sin^2(\delta/2) \cos(4\omega t - 2\psi - 2\chi),$$

where k is the calibration coefficient of the instrument, considering any neutral filters or regulating tension chain to regulate the sensitivity of the instrument.

Both I and P can be determined from v_0 and the amplitude v_4, χ from the phase v_4. If necessary, the Stocks parameters Q and U can be found from the combined Eqs. (2.12) and (2.14), and V from the amplitude v_2. This makes it possible to determine the degree of ellipticity β from (2.13).

In the scheme with the fixed phase plate and rotating linear analyser the intensity of the passing radiation can be presented as (Born and Wolf, 1970):

$$I(\psi,\delta) = \frac{1}{2} [I + Q \cos 2\psi + (U \cos \delta - V \sin \delta) \sin 2\psi]$$

Without the phase plate ($\delta = 0$)

$$I(\psi,0) = \frac{1}{2} [I + Q \cos 2\psi + U \sin 2\psi] \tag{2.16}$$

When a quarter-wave plate ($\delta = \pi/2$) is placed in the optical path

$$I(\psi, \pi/2) = \frac{1}{2} [I + Q \cos 2\psi - V \sin 2\psi] \tag{2.17}$$

With the analysed radiation assumed to be linearly polarized, in order to determine the first three Stocks parameters from (2.16), it is necessary to measure $I(\psi,0)$, as a minimum, for three values of the angle ψ. To determine all four Stocks parameters of the partially elliptically polarized radiation, it is necessary to perform additional measurements with a quarter-wave plate introduced to the optical scheme.

2.2.3 Instrumentation for spectral investigation of the environment from satellites

2.2.3.1 Hand-operated satellite spectrograph of the RSS type
The successful accomplishment of the programme of studies of natural resources from space depends much on studies of the spectral characteristics of natural formations. First spectra of the atmosphere and natural formations on the Earth's surface were obtained from manned space vehicles (Beregovoi et al., 1972a; Kondratyev and Buznikov, 1981). The choice of manned space vehicles and orbital stations for the first complex programme of spectral studies of the Earth's atmosphere and underlying surfaces was not accidental. In the orbit, the optical phenomena connected with scattering and absorption of solar radiation by terrestrial atmosphere and changing illumination of natural formations change rapidly. A cosmonaut-operator with a small portable spectral instrument could analyse the situation, choose objects for studies, and perform a spectrophotometry of the optical phenomena changing rapidly. For this purpose a series of small hand-operated

spectrographs of the RSS type has been developed (Buznikov, 1983a; Kondratyev et al., 1970, 1972a). For the first time the spectral studies of the atmosphere and natural formations on the Earth's surface have been accomplished on spacecraft "Soyuz-5", "Soyuz-7", "Soyuz-9", "Soyuz-13", and the orbital station "Salut-5" using the spectrograph RSS-2 (Buznikov et al., 1975d; Kondratyev et al., 1970, 1972a). The manned orbital stations (MOS) "Salut-3" and "Salut-5" were equipped with the spectrograph RSS-3 (Buznikov and Orlov, 1989; Buznikov and Kondratyev, 1981), being part of the measuring complex of the orbital station "Mir".

The RSS-3 is a spectrograph combined with a camera. Figure 2.2 shows a general view of RSS-3, and Fig. 2.3 gives its optical scheme. Changeable objectives 1 (with focal distances 135 and 300 mm) form an image of an object on the film 16 in the channel of fixed photography and on the plane of input slit 6. The light-dividing cube (prism) 3 divides the light flux into two parts, one (95%) being directed to the channel of the spectrograph (7, 8), the other (5%) to the film through the fixed photography window in the frame diaphragm. Spectrograms and photographs of the objects are taken on the same film, 16. The spectrograph is designed by the same autocollimation scheme. The diffraction grating 8 has 600 lines per mm, the working order, the first, gives the prevailing concentration of light in the spectral range 300–1100 nm. The spectral resolution is 5 nm.

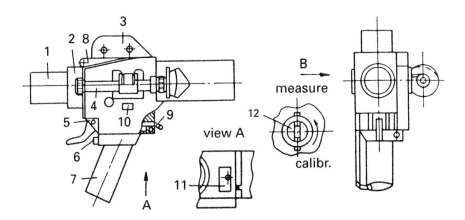

Fig. 2.2. The RSS-3 spectrograph, general view: 1—input objective; 2—shutter; 3—film cassette; 4—optical sight; 5—hammer; 6—trigger; 7—power supply; 8—cassette fastener; 9—tumbler; 10—frame counter; 11—clock cover; 12—"calibration-measurement" switch.

The polarimetric measurements are made with the polarization nozzle 1b (Fig. 2.3). It is based on the polaroid filter $1b_1$ which acts as an analyser. During the measurements the analyser is placed in front of the objective $1b_2$ at $f = 135$ mm, and in the process of the survey, with the help of the kinematic scheme, it turns at 60° from frame to frame. Information about the degree of polarization is obtained after processing three spectrograms taken with three positions of the analyser making use of the Fesenkov formula.

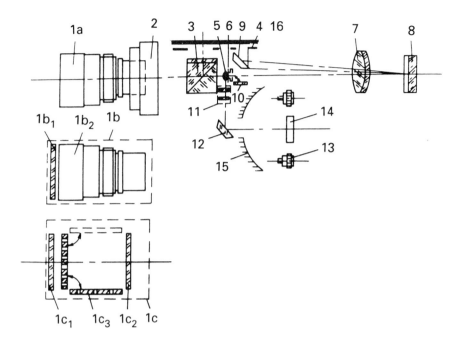

Fig. 2.3. The RSS-3 spectrograph, optical scheme: 1a—objective; 1b—objective with polaroid; 1c—calibration unit; 2—shutter; 3—light-splitting prism; 4—film diaphragm; 5—collective lens; 6—input slit; 7—collimator; 8—diffraction grating; 9—deviating mirror; 10—photometric wedge; 11—micro-objective; 12—deviating mirror; 13—illumination lamps; 14—clock; 15—reflector; 16—film.

The absolute calibration of the instrument in the orbit is made against the Sun with the use of the calibration unit 1c; the photometric wedge is placed behind the slit. The on-board timing is made by printing in the frame the 3-hand clock face 14 illuminated with the reflector 15, lamps 13, projected onto the film with the micro-objective 11 and the mirror 12.

The kinematic scheme of the spectrograph (Fig. 2.4) illustrates all operations in the instrument: the cocking of the shutter, film traction, printing the needed reference marks and clock-face in the film. The trigger cramp 1 connected to the driving cylindrical wheel 2, crown mechanism 3, and restoring spring 4, passes the effort of the operator's hand to the shaft I of the reductor. The cylindrical wheel 7 starts moving via the conical transmission 5 and the cylindrical wheel 6, which has the butt spline connected to the camshaft used for the cocking of shutter 9. The rotation from shaft I goes to shaft II. Spur gears 10, 11 switch on frame counter 12. The rotation from shaft II goes to shaft III, which is connected to shaft IV, the latter rotating drum 14 of the cassette mechanism through butt spline 13. By pressing button 17 the shutter is opened. The spectrograph has changeable cassettes, with about 100 frames in each.

The electrical scheme of the instrument switches on the illuminated indicator panel, which informs the operator that the spectrograph is ready to work, illuminates

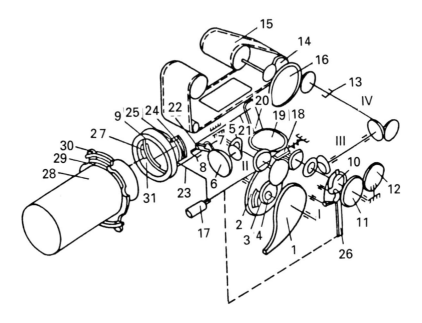

Fig. 2.4. The RSS-3 spectrograph, kinematic scheme: 1—hammer cramp; 2—driving cylindrical wheel; 3—crown mechanism; 4—restoring spring; 5—conical transmission; 6, 7—cylindrical wheels; 8—camshaft; 9—shutter; 10, 11—spur gears; 12—frame counter; 13—butt spline; 14—pulling drum; 15—film; 16—cylindrical wheels of the film-pulling mechanism; 17—trigger; 18–22—shutter-cocking system; 23—trigger driver; 24, 25—microswitches; 28—changeable objective; 27, 29, 30, 31—objective–spectrograph connection system.

the clock face briefly, and operates the matrix of light diodes which expose the film at the moment of snapping the shutter into action, and the work of the built-in exponometer. The power supply of the electric scheme is obtained from an autonomous power source.

The use of hand-operated spectrographs on MSC and MOS has made it possible to obtain from space the reflection spectra of practically all types of surface (Beregovoi et al., 1972a; Buznikov et al., 1975e,f; Kondratyev and Buznikov, 1981; Kondratyev et al., 1971e, 1972a,e, 1974b). From these spectra the SBC of various natural formations was determined. When determining the SBC, a record was taken of the Sun's height over the horizon in the sub-satellite point found by the moment of survey, and the coordinates of this point were determined from the orbital parameters. The scheme of an RSS-3 frame is shown in Fig. 2.5. The projection of the input slit of the spectrograph onto the image of the surface under study is marked by the dashed line. The fixed photography enables one to determine the geographical coordinates of the spectrophotometered site and to reference the spectrum obtained to an element of the surface image.

Owing to the printed-in clock face, the time reference of spectrograms was made with an accuracy of ±1s, which made it possible, together with the ballistic data of

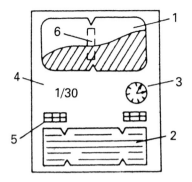

Fig. 2.5. Scheme of an RSS-3 frame: 1—photographic reference; 2—spectrogram; 3—clock dial; 4—exposition time; 5—reference wavelengths; 6—projection of the spectrograph's input slit onto the surface image.

the MOS flight, to determine the geography of the experiment and to make the geographical referencing of the objects under study.

Figure 2.6 shows an RSS-3 frame obtained during the flight of the MOS "Salut-5". Figure 2.7 gives the SBC of the vegetation-covered surfaces: (a) on bare ground and soil; (b) on water surfaces and cloudiness; (c) obtained from "Soyuz-9":

(a)

2.97–10—the thin mesophyll grassland of South Azerbaijan.

2.93–0.4—the xeromesophyll steppe vegetation on the flat outskirts of the Mesopotamian lowland.

2.50–10—the xerophyll thinned semi-desert vegetation in South-West Afghanistan.

2.92–10—the thick hydrophyll vegetation of marshes and lake coastlines of the Mesopotamian lowland.

(b)

2.50–0.2, 2.50–0.4—sand and loam deposits and soils on the plains of South-West Afghanistan.

2.51–10, 2.87–10, 2.88–10—stone and stone–detritus deposits and soils on the plains of South Syria.

(c)

2.82–10—cloudiness.

2.50–15—lake surface in South-West Afghanistan.

2.93–14, 2.92–0.3—lake surface in the Mesopotamian lowland

Several publications from results of measurements (Beregovoi et al., 1972a; Kondratyev and Buznikov, 1981; Kondratyev et al., 1972a) contain an analysis of the spectra of natural formations obtained from space (spectral brightness, SBC, and spectral contrasts). To identify the natural formations from their reflection spectra, a 1-D coding system has been developed (determinated model of recognition) based on the use of SBC at certain wavelengths (Beregovoi et al., 1972a; Vasilyev and Mironova, 1974). These publications show the main possibilities to use the reflection

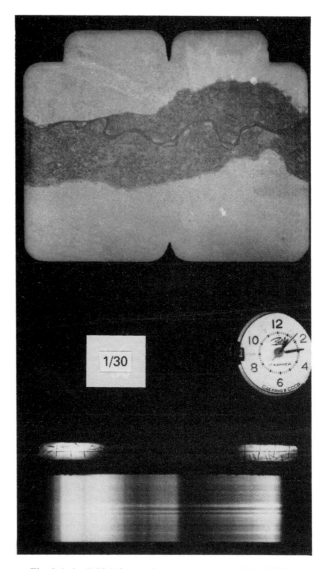

Fig. 2.6. An RSS-3 frame obtained during the Salut-5 flight.

spectra recorded from space to identify and assess the state of natural formations.

A comparison of the data obtained from MSC and MOS with the results of ground and aircraft measurements was made using the classification of surface objects by the optical properties developed by E. Krinov (1947). Figure 2.8 shows the results of a data comparison after reducing the space-derived spectra to the surface level with the use of atmospheric transfer function parameters obtained from synchronous sub-satellite experiments.

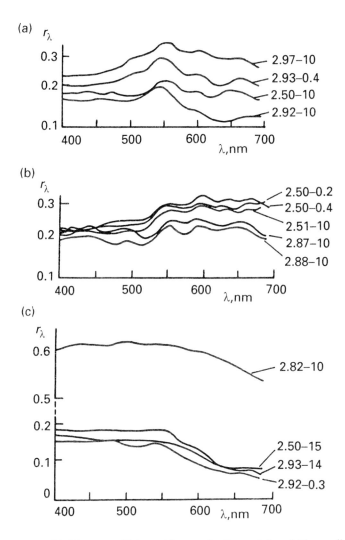

Fig. 2.7. Surface spectral brightness coefficients: (a) covered with vegetation; (b) bare soils; (c) water surfaces and cloudiness; from Soyuz-9 data.

The comparison of the surface reflection spectra obtained from MSC with the spectra drawn according to the classification by E. Krinov is illustrated in Fig. 2.9. The results of comparison show the possibility of using Krinov's classification both for air- and space-derived reflection spectra (Beregovoi et al., 1972a; Kondratyev et al., 1971a,b).

The in-flight tests of the satellite spectrographs RSS made it possible to assess the merits and the shortcomings of small-sized spectral instruments. Simplicity, autonomous operation, reliability, small size and light weight, capability of

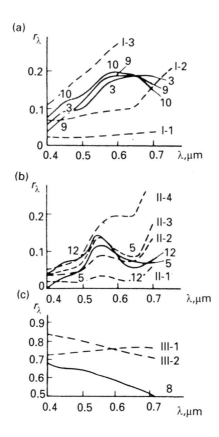

Fig. 2.8. Comparison of spectral data reduced to the surface level.

recording a large amount of information during a short time period are important qualities of hand-operated space-borne spectrographs and enable them to compete successfully with photoelectric on-board spectrometers.

Spectrographs RSS-2, RSS-3 have been used successfully for aircraft and helicopter spectral measurements during synchronous and quasi-synchronous combined sub-satellite experiments (Kondratyev et al., 1970, 1977a, 1986a), in spectral studies of forests and agro-ecosystems, and to obtain from aircraft the spectral characteristics of various types of natural formations. As an example, Fig. 2.10 shows the spectral characteristics of crops in different vegetation phases obtained during an accomplishment of the complex interdisciplinary programme "Kuban". Figure 2.11 shows the seasonal variations of the spectral characteristics of young coniferous forests, and Fig. 2.12 shows those of mixed forests in the Krasnoyarsk Krai. The data obtained testify to the possibility of using the RSS-3 for ecological studies and assessments of the state of vegetation cover.

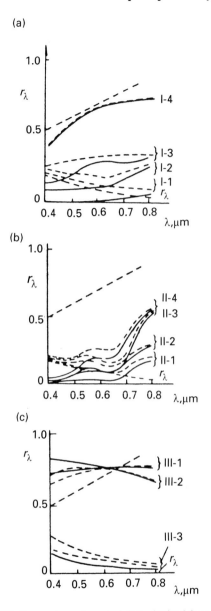

Fig. 2.9. Comparison of spectral data obtained from space.

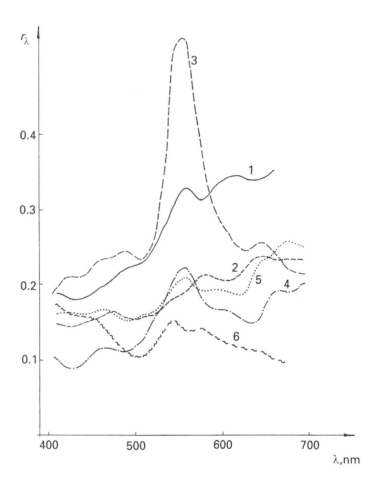

Fig. 2.10. Spectra of crops in various vegetation phases: 1—winter wheat in good state; 2—winter wheat, 30% lying; 3—maize at the 8th leaf stage (23 June 1988); 4—the same field, ripened maize (14 August 1988); 5—winter barley, 90% lying.

The RSS-3 has been designed for spectral and spectropolarization photometry of spatially inhomogeneous and changing objects illuminated by the Sun. The optical scheme of the instrument makes it possible to obtain the homogeneous spatial characteristic of the objects' field of brightness (along the height of the input slit of the spectrograph). Therefore the device has been very useful for measuring the brightness profiles of the twilight or daytime horizon (Beregovoi et al., 1971d, 1976b, 1977f) and to measure the reflectivity of the Earth's surface near the interface between two or more areas (Buznikov, 1975f). The RSS-3 measures: the absolute spectral brightness and the SBC of the objects; the spatial distribution of spectral brightness along the chosen route; the degree of polarization of reflected or scattered sunlight; and the colour characteristics of the observed objects (Buznikov et al., 1976b).

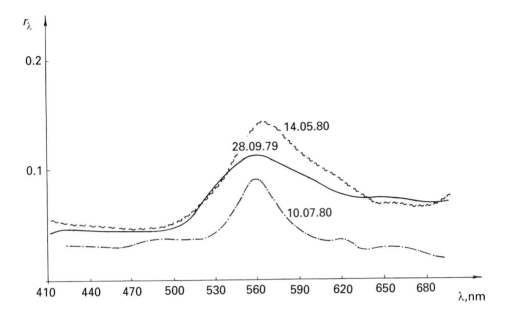

Fig. 2.11. Seasonal variations in spectral characteristics of young coniferous forests.

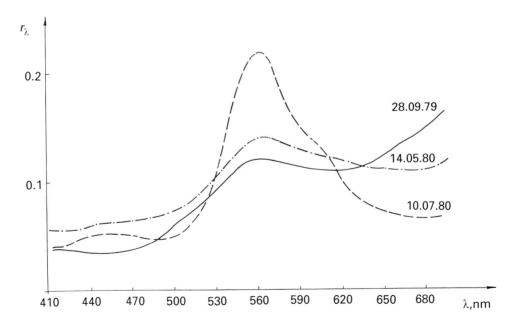

Fig. 2.12. Seasonal variations in spectral characteristics of mixed forests in the Krasnoyarsk Krai.

2.2.3.2 Spectra of twilight and daytime horizons as observed from the MSCs

The angular and spectral dependencies of the brightness of the terrestrial atmosphere in the zone of the horizon can be obtained through analytical (Sobolev, 1972) or numerical (Smoktiy, 1969; Marchuk et al., 1968) solution of the radiation transfer equation. However, theoretical calculations are fraught with difficulty, since it is necessary to use a model of the atmosphere close to its real state, to take into account the sphericity of the Earth's atmosphere, and, with a more detailed study, the effects of polarization and refraction of scattered solar radiation. This emphasizes the importance of an experiment in space to study the real field of brightness of the Earth as a planet. The most complete review of experimental studies of the terrestrial atmospheric brightness in the zone of horizon is contained elsewhere (Studies..., 1972). Most of the respective studies have been dedicated to the photographing of the twilight or daytime atmosphere near the horizon in the total flux or with the use of two or three light filters.

For the first time the spectra of the twilight atmosphere have been obtained from "Soyuz-5" (Buznikov, 1972). Then, with improved techniques and instruments the spectral studies of the atmosphere and surfaces were made from spacecraft and stations "Soyuz-7", "Soyuz-9", "Salut-1" (Kondratyev et al., 1977b), "Soyuz-13" (Buznikov et al., 1975e), "Salut-3" and "Salut-4". The first spectra of the daytime horizon were obtained from "Salut-1" and "Salut-5". However, these are the only platforms from which the spectral studies of the twilight and daytime atmosphere in the visible have been made from space.

The use of techniques for processing the spectrograms and absolute calibration of instruments (Kondratyev et al., 1971c; Studies..., 1972) enabled the characteristics of the spectral brightness of the twilight atmosphere to be obtained. Figure 2.13 shows the curves of the spectral brightness of the twilight horizon from the data in frame No.9, corresponding to various heights h_p of the perigee of the viewing line (Kondratyev et al., 1976b).

It is shown in Fig. 2.13 that most of the energy of the twilight glow in the visible falls on 430–530 and 640–700 nm. The maxima of spectral brightness observed at these wavelengths are formed owing to the distribution of energy over the solar radiation spectrum, its scattering in the atmosphere and absorption by ozone in the Shappui band. The location of maximum spectral brightness in the blue spectral interval changes with the changing height of the viewing line perigee h_p. With increasing h_p the maximum shifts towards shorter wavelengths. For example, in the case $h_p = 10$ km the maximum falls on $\lambda = 520$ nm, and at $h_p = 28$ km, on $\lambda = 470$ nm. The second maximum does not shift with the changing height of the viewing line perigee; the second maximum of radiation is always near $\lambda = 660$ nm.

The spectra clearly demonstrate the "two-headed" peak of the Shappui absorption band. The strong absorption of scattered solar radiation by ozone is explained by the great length of the optical path. The absorption band is well manifested at all heights, at which the spectrograph recorded the atmospheric radiance, including the heights which much exceeded the level of maximum concentration of ozone (25–27 km) (Kondratyev et al., 1977b). The Shappui band is comparatively weak for ozone absorption. Its substantial manifestation in the

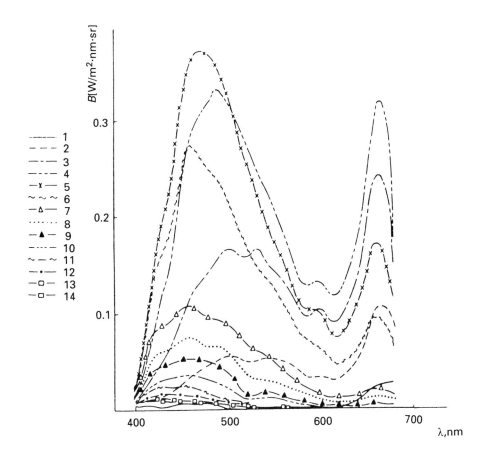

Fig. 2.13. Spectral brightness of the atmosphere near the Earth's twilight horizon from the data of Soyuz-5 (frame No. 9; cloudless atmosphere; $\delta_0 = 12'$; $\varphi = 8°$; $H_{or\,b} = 250$ km) for different heights of the viewing line perigee, h_p (km): 1–1; 2–5; 3–10; 4–15; 5–21; 6–24; 7–28; 8–34; 9–38; 10–43; 11–48; 12–53; 13–57; 14–62.

spectra of the twilight aureole corresponding to high altitudes of the viewing line perigee $h_p > 30$ km is also connected with the fact that the sun ray, before being scattered by the atmospheric volume considered, covers a long way in the lower atmosphere, where the concentration of ozone is rather high (Fig. 2.14).

Thus, the date of measurements of the twilight aureole brightness contain rich information about complicated processes of solar radiation propagation in atmospheric areas adjacent to both sides of the terminator line. The optical inhomogeneities in the atmosphere affect the spectral characteristics of the considered volume BCD (Fig. 2.14), both along the viewing line (MS and MB) and along the illumination line (AB and ED). In each case the viewing line and the illumination line can pass at different altitudes. This hinders an account of the effect of the optically active components of the atmosphere (first of all, global aerosol

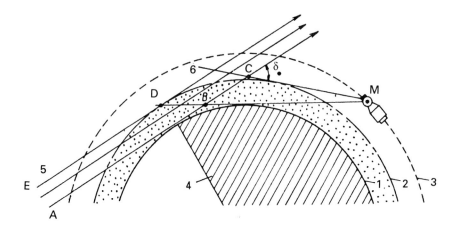

Fig. 2.14. Scheme of observation of the atmosphere near the Earth's twilight horizon from spacecraft: 1—the Earth's surface; 2—conditional upper boundary of the atmosphere; 3—spacecraft's orbit; 4—terminator line; 5—direction of the Sun's rays; 6—BCD—a luminous part of the atmosphere observed as a twilight aureole.

layers) on the spectra of brightness of the Earth's twilight horizon. As a result, the depressions connected with the effect of global aerosol layers manifest themselves much weaker in the vertical profiles of the twilight aureole brightness than in Rozenberg and Nikolajeva-Tereshkova (1965).

A comparison of the spectral characteristics of the twilight horizon for successive series of frames suggests some conclusions about the dynamics of the development of the twilight aureole as the sun is rising above the horizon. Analysis of the date on the spectral distribution of the twilight aureole brightness enables one to determine the most informative spectral zones to solve the inverse problems of atmospheric optics. A totality of vertical profiles of the twilight horizon brightness in three spectral regions: 450, 580, and 680 nm, is apparently optimal to solve the inverse problems. In these spectral regions the combined effect of the basic optically active components of the atmosphere (aerosol and ozone) as well as vertical variations of air density take place in different ways.

Using a simplified model of radiation transfer in a spherical atmosphere, the vertical profile of atmospheric brightness near the horizon can be determined from the following equation:

$$I(\lambda,\psi,h) = \int_{L(h)} B(\lambda, \psi, h, x) \exp\{-r_\lambda(x_s, x)\}dx \qquad (2.18)$$

where $L(h)$ is the length of the viewing line in the atmosphere at the tangential height of the viewing beam h for the boundary point from the observer's side x_s; ψ is the solar zenith angle; x is the current coordinate; r_λ is the total optical thickness corresponding to three optically active atmospheric components (ozone, aerosol, molecular component); $B(\lambda, \psi, h, x)$ is the value of the source function determined by intensity of radiation passing the point and scattered along the viewing line. $B(\lambda, \psi, h, x)$ can be presented as

$$B = B_s + B_A + B_M \tag{2.19}$$

where B_s is determined by the contribution of direct solar radiation, B_A by radiation reflected from the surface, B_M and by repeatedly scattered radiation.

For the twilight aureole $\psi > 90°$, $B_A = 0$, and B_M is neglected, therefore $B \cong B_s$.

With available information about the vertical profiles of brightness $I(\lambda, \psi, h)$ it is possible to solve the inverse problem of determining the profiles of atmospheric components $\rho_k(h)$ (Kondratyev et al., 1977e). With the atmosphere divided into elementary layers, the continuous distributions of $\rho_k(h)$ and $I(\lambda, \psi, h)$ were replaced with discrete analogues $\rho_k = \{\rho_k(1), \ldots, \rho_k(h)\}$ and $I(\lambda, \psi) = (I_1, \ldots, I_n)$. Since $k = 1, 2, 3$ in accordance with the results from Kondratyev et al. (1977b), the optimal wavelengths $\lambda_1 = 450$ nm, $\lambda_2 = 580$ nm, $\lambda_3 = 680$ nm were chosen. In this case, with a fixed value of ψ, Eq. (2.18) is reduced to a system of $3 \times n$ non-linear equations with the same number of unknown parameters. To convert it, a technique was used based on the Marcuardt algorithm (Kondratyev et al., 1977e).

Figure 2.15 gives the retrieved vertical profiles of the aerosol extinction coefficient β (1/km) for four successive spectrograms of the twilight aureole obtained from "Soyuz-13". Because of inadequate respective data of direct measurements, as an initial approximation, the aerosol profile is taken as a function exponentially decreasing with height (i.e. linear on a logarithmic scale).

Analysis of the profiles obtained reveals some things in common. The vertical structure of the aerosol distribution is clearly manifested: the presence of tropospheric (18–20 km) and stratospheric (50 km) layers with aerosol particles with increased concentrations. In this problem, a layer of the atmosphere 80 km thick with the number of elementary layers $n = 32$ for $h = 2.5$ km was considered. The upper atmospheric layer (30–75 km), including the upper stratosphere and mesosphere, is characterized by substantially stable results of the solution of the inverse problem. In the lower layer (0–25 km) the configuration of retrieved profiles and aerosol concentrations varies. This is connected with the fact that in the lower layer the contribution of the multiple scattering of radiation can be rather variable, and its role can be essential in connection with the solution of the inverse problem. Nevertheless, the retrieved profiles clearly manifest the Yunge layer, which means that for the lower stratosphere, too, the solution of the inverse problem is qualitatively correct.

2.2.3.3 Photoelectric spectrometers

Table 2.3 lists the characteristics of the spectral instruments to study the environment from the MSC and MOS. To measure spectral brightness, photographic and photoelectric recording techniques have been used. The absolute brightness of natural formations is measured using photographic technique roughly: (c. 5–10%), but this technique makes it possible to obtain simultaneously the spectra of several surface areas of natural formations, localized along the chosen direction

"Soyuz-13"

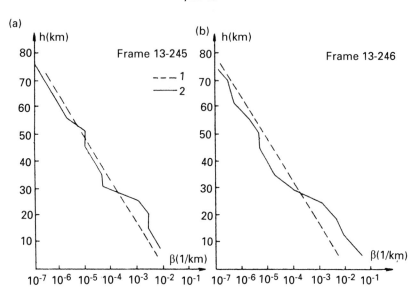

"Soyuz-13"

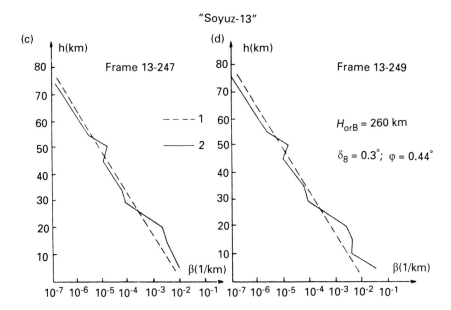

Fig. 2.15. Retrieved vertical profile of the aerosol attenuation coefficient from the vertical profiles of brightness obtained from Soyuz-13: (a) frame 13–245; (b) frame 13–246; (c) frame 13–247; (d) frame 13–249.

Table 2.3. Spectral instruments of the orbital station "Mir" (basic unit) for optical studies of the environment

Characteristic	RSS-3	MKS-M		Spectr-256	SKIF-M
		AS-spectrometer	BS-spectrometer		
Spectral range, nm	400–700	6 channels: 758.1; 760.6; 763.2; 766.7; 794.1; 823.	12 channels: 415; 450; 485; 520; 570; 620; 680; 713; 750; 790; 823; 880.	450–830; number of working channels— 256.	1. 400–1100 2. 400–510 3. 560–730 4. 720–880 5. 840–1010
Spectral resolution, nm	5	1.5	10	1.5 (by level 0.5)	In range 1–14; in range 2–5÷3
Objective, Focal length, mm	$f_1 = 300$; $f_2 = 135$	Kassegren 4/320	Sonnar 4/300	$f = 300$ Aperture ratio 1:2	
Viewing angles: —spectral channel —fixed photography —viewfinder	$50' \times 3'$	$1°$	$21°$	$8°$	$50' \times 10'$ $2\alpha = 28°$ $2\beta = 23°$
Spatial resolution of spectral channel	$f_1 = 300$ mm–1′ $f_2 = 135$ mm–2′				
FOV size of the Earth's surface, km	0.1×0.4 $H = 300$ km	0.5×6 $H = 300$ km	2.5×2.5 $H = 300$ km		
Dispersing element	Diffraction grating $N = 600$ lines/mm	Concave diffraction grating	Concave diffraction grating	Holographic grating	Diffraction grating $N = 1200$ lines/mm
Exposition (time for one spectrum record), s	1:4 1:30 1:500	1/16	1/16	20–30 μs	0.25
Radiation receiver	Film, type 15-800 isopanchrom	Silicon photodiodes P-103	Silicon photodiodes P-103	Linear discrete structure of semi-conductor detectors in the charge-accumulation regime	PEM-113*
Availability of fixed photography	Yes $f_1 = 300$ mm $f_2 = 135$ mm	Yes Camera "Praktika B-200"		Yes	Yes
Space object	"Salut-4" "Mir"	"Salut-7", "Mir"		"Salut-7" "Mir"	"Salut-7" "Mir"

*PEM stands for "photoelectric multiplier"

(the height of the input slit of the spectrograph). The instruments needed for this technique are simple, reliable, small in size, and fast in operation.

Photoelectric spectrophotometry is a more accurate technique (1–3%), but it enables one to obtain the spectrum of only that part of the surface which is projected onto the input slit of the optical system or whose image is projected onto the detector receiver placed behind the input slit of the optical system. Such photometric spectrometers include MSS-2 (Beliajev et al., 1978), MKS-M (Zümnich, 1989; Final report..., 1987), ISOH-010, ISOH-20, ISOH-111, "Spektr-215" and "Spektr-256" (Mishev, 1980, 1985), and "Field spectrometer" (Buznikov et al., 1995c). In MSS-2 and MKS-M the photoelectric multipliers (PEM) served as radiation receivers, and in "Spektr-15" and "Spektr-256", the lines of semiconductor detectors operating in the regime of change accumulation (CCD-structure).

The first soviet photoelectric spectrometer carried by "Salut" was MSS-2, developed in the Institute of Physics of the Byelorussian Academy of Sciences. The viewing angles of the spectrometer $\alpha = 7°$ by the height of the slit, $\beta = 1°30'$ by its width (if the slit is 1 mm wide). The spectral range of the instrument is 0.4–0.8 μm; the spectral resolution is 7 μm. The monochromator of the spectrometer MSS-2 is designed after the Ebert–Fastey scheme. The dispersing element is the plane diffraction grating (replica) with 1200 lines/mm, which operates in the first order.

The cycle of measurements with MSS-2 starts with recording the spectrum over 0.4 s, then, over 0.1 s, the zero level of the electronic path, and then, again, the spectrum over 0.4 s. The cycle is closed on recording the calibration signal over 0.1 s from the internal reference source of radiation—an incandescent bulb.

The commutation of light sources is performed with an obturator having a stepped attenuator. The spectrum is swept by swinging a diffraction grating with the help of a special kinematic scheme driven by the motor. The spectrum sweeping has a linear wavelength scale. With the 1-mm slit the resolved spectral interval is 7.10^{-3} μm; the reverse linear dispersion (average) is $5.4.10^{-3}$ μm/mm. The PEM-2 is used as a radiation receiver.

The shortcoming of the MSS-2 with the Earth-resources studies from space is a large FOV and the lack of fixed photography of its own. At an orbital height of 300 km with a FOV of $7° \pm 1°30'$ the spectrometer records the radiation reflected from the site of the surface, 45 ± 10 km^2. Taking account of the surface inhomogeneity, MSS-2 recorded from space the spectra of reflection not for individual types of natural formations but for the whole complexes. Only with over-large homogeneous surfaces (the World Ocean, large cloud fields) can the spectrometer obtain the spectra of concrete natural formations. The absence in MSS-2 of fixed photography capability required the use of the camera KATE-140 on "Salut-6". At present an improved spectrometer MSS-2M has been developed, which will include a camera in the device, and a visual display of the spectrum on the screen. The positive characteristic of MSS-2M is that the device can operate in the automatic regime.

Further modification of MSS-2M has led to the creation of the microprocessing spectrometric system SKIF-M (Kondratyev, 1990b) for operational measurements of the spectral composition of radiation reflected or scattered by various natural objects within the range 0.4–1.1 μm. The SKIF-M is part of the complex carried by the orbital station "Mir". The SKIF-M system consists of the on-board and ground complexes; the on-board complex includes two units: SKIF-OM, the optico-mechanical unit, and SKIF-HO, a combined a microcomputer, symbol-writing display, cassette-accumulator on magnetic tape, and the operator's panel. PEM-2 is a radiation receiver. A general view of the instruments is shown in Fig. 2.16, and its basic characteristics are listed in Table 2.3.

Fig. 2.16. The SKIF-M spectrometric system, general view.

Photoelectric spectrometers have certain advantages over spectrographs in accuracy and speed of spectral measurements. However, when accomplishing some studies of the environment from space, for example, studies of the vertical profiles of brightness of the twilight and daytime horizons of the Earth, studies of the spectra of reflection of various sites of inhomogeneous surfaces, which is very important for studies of the mechanisms for the formation of reflection spectra at the interface of inhomogeneous media (Buznikov et al., 1975a; Kondratyev and Buznikov, 1981) and the frequency-contrast characteristics (FCC), preference should be given to either RSS spectrographs (film is the radiation receiver) or spectral instruments of the type "Spektr-215" and "Spektr-256", with a line of CCD-structures placed behind the output slit, since they enable the distribution of spectral brightness along the prescribed direction, the height of the input slit, to be obtained. The instruments "Spektr-15" and "Spektr-256" have been developed in the Institute for Space Studies of the Bulgarian Academy of Sciences (Mishev, 1980, 1985).

The 15-channel system of the spectrometer "Spektr-15" makes it possible to record on the magnetic tape the signals corresponding to the spectra of radiation reflected from natural formations and emitted by them in the visible and near-IR ranges. The parameters of the channels of the system are listed in Table 2.4. The stuctural scheme of the optico-electronic unit of "Spektr-15" is shown in Fig. 2.17. The spectral characteristics of the sensitivity of the system "Spektr-15" (normalized

Table 2.4. Main parameters of the "Spectr-15" system

Channel number	$\Delta\lambda_{0.5}$, nm	λ_{max}, nm	W (W m^{-2} ster^{-1} μm^{-1}) for max output code 255
1	15.5	437	748.58
2	18.0	464	856.29
3	19.0	485	716.29
4	19.0	512	490.14
5	20.5	542	275.61
6	20.5	573	497.56
7	22.0	598	249.82
8	21.0	626	280.50
9	20.0	655	421.85
10	25.0	685	381.79
11	19.5	711	168.30
12	21.0	739	138.06
13	18.5	765	281.38
14	19.0	799	276.60
15	22.0	830	527.53

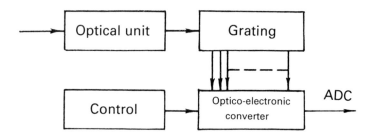

Fig. 2.17. Structural scheme of the optico-electronic unit "Spektr-15".

curves) are shown in Fig. 2.18. Table 2.5 gives the spectral characteristics of an improved version of the spectrometer "Spektr-15M".

The input optics of the spectrometer includes an objective with a focal distance 300 mm and aperture ratio 1 : 4. The dispersing arrangement is a diffraction grating with an objective and collimator. The photo-inverter is a linear discrete structure of 15 semiconductor detectors operating in the regime of charge accumulation. The scanning is electronic. The "Spektr-15" has 15 measuring channels in the range 450–850 nm. From an average height of the orbit of the "Soyuz-Salut" complex (about 300 km), the linear size of a pixel on the Earth's surface constitutes approximately 300 × 300 m². However, owing to the recording speed of 70 spectra/s, the secondary processing can give a resolution of about 70 m along the flight route. The digital data are made with an 8-bit analogue-to-analogue digital converter. Data are recorded on the magnetic cassette to an accuracy better than 0.5% and a speed of 80 Kbit/s. The duration of recording on one cassette (one path) constitutes about 7 minutes, which makes it possible to study from orbit a site on the Earth's surface 3000 km long.

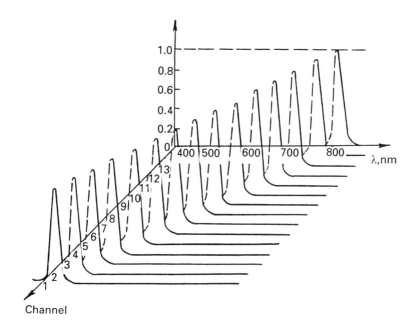

Fig. 2.18. Normalized spectral characteristics of the "Spektr-15" spectrometer.

Table 2.5. Main parameters of the "Spectr-15M" system

Channel number	$\Delta\lambda_{0.5}$, nm	λ_{max}, nm	W (W m^{-2} ster^{-1} μm^{-1}) for max output code 255
1	18.0	488	242.74
2	17.0	473	103.33
3	18.0	503	87.05
4	19.0	525	71.42
5	18.0	554	69.86
6	21.0	578	57.14
7	21.0	605	52.67
8	21.0	634	44.39
9	22.0	663	49.21
10	26.0	686	60.68
11	25.0	720	59.84
12	23.0	751	53.87
13	26.0	781	53.08
14	25.0	817	110.34
15	18.0	832	108.87

On the satellite "Interkosmos-21" is a multichannel spectroquantometer (MKS) developed by German scientists (Zümnich, 1989). The modernized version of this instrument, MKS-M, was installed on the orbital station "Salut-7" and now it is part of the MOS "Mir". The MKS-M is an optico-electronic-mechanical instrument ensuring measurements of reflected radiation in 18 spectral intervals in the range

415–880 nm. Since the spectrometer was designed to make measurements from the near-Earth orbit at comparatively small distances from the receiving stations on the Earth, the volume of information transmitted telemetrically can be rather large. Besides, there is a possibility of sending to the Earth the information recorded on the magnetic tape. The spectrometric complex, MKS-M consists of two spectrometers: biospectrometer (BS) and atmospheric spectrometer (AS). The BS is designed to determine the coefficients of surface brightness with a spectral resolution of 10 nm. The BS is a mid-resolution polychromator and makes it possible to make simultaneous measurements of the Earth's brightness in 12 spectral intervals in the range 415–880 nm, where the absorption bands of chlorophyll, ozone, and water "transparency windows" are located. The basic spectral characteristics of the BS measuring channels are given in Table 2.6.

Table 2.6. Main spectral characteristics of the spectroquantometer MKS-M spectral channels (BS spectrometer)

Channel	λ, nm	$\Delta\lambda_{0.5}$	$\Delta\lambda_{0.1}$	$\Delta\lambda_{0.01}$
1	415.8	9.2	15.2	19.0
2	449.6	9.0	15.0	18.5
3	485	8.7	14.4	17.6
4	519.3	9.0	13.8	16.8
5	570.4	7.8	14.1	16.6
6	620.6	8.8	14.1	16.3
7	680	8.8	14.1	16.3
8	712.5	8.7	14.1	16.0
9	749.4	9.0	14.8	16.3
10	787.9	8.8	14.1	16.6
11	820.7	9.0	14.1	16.6
12	879.5	9.0	14.7	17.9

The spectrometer AS is designed to measure the optical parameters of the atmosphere with a spectral resolution of 1.5 nm. The basic spectral characteristics of its measuring channels are given in Table 2.7.

Table 2.7. Main spectral characteristics of the AS spectrometer measuring channels

Channel	λ, nm	$\Delta\lambda_{0.5}$	$\Delta\lambda_{0.1}$	$\Delta\lambda_{0.01}$
1	758.2	1.55	2.58	3.76
2	760.6	1.33	2.48	3.76
3	763.0	1.52	2.54	3.61
4	766.3	1.44	2.48	3.70
5	793.9	1.42	2.54	3.10
6	823.0	1.65	2.96	4.04

Besides, the MKS-M complex has a specular scattering optical unit that turns through 180° to provide measurements of either direct solar radiation or scattered by the Earth, a viewfinder for visual observations of the regions under study, and a camera "Praktika-B200".

The MKS complex also includes an arrangement for the assembly and adjustment as well as the panel for the electric unit control.

The high-resolution spectrometer – polychromator SAS provides simultaneous measurements of the brightness of the "atmosphere–surface" system in three intervals of the absorption bands for molecular oxygen 760 nm (channels 2–4) and in two comparison intervals (1, 5), as well as in the water vapour absorption band.

The AS is designed after the Eagle scheme. The radiation receivers, matched with the input slits, are located on the Rowland circle. The dispersing element is the concave holographic grating.

The monochromator of the BS spectrometer, like that of AS, has the Eagle scheme. The silicon photodiodes R-103 with focusing lenses are used as radiation receivers. They are located at several points of the Rowland circle. The dispersing element is a diffraction grating. Linear dispersion constitutes 2 nm/mm. The fast-operating reaches 16 spectra/s. The light flux is not modulated. A direct current amplifier is used to amplify the signal. The measured spectral brightness is recorded with a digital telemetry system. Each optical channel has an amplifying tract of its own, ensuring measurements of the brightness of the atmosphere–surface system with the AS spectrometer within 0.3–40.0 μW cm^{-2} sr^{-1} nm^{-1} and with the BS – within 0.1–25.0 μW cm^{-2} sr^{-1} nm^{-1}.

A signal from the pre-amplifiers located close to the spectrometers' receivers is sent to two parallel inputs of basic amplifiers with sensitivities differing as $1:3:9$ (AS) and $1:4.5:20$ (BS). Every output signal of the measuring channels is normalized within 0–6 V, which is converted in ADC into 9 bit and goes in parallel to the auxiliary telemetric system to be recorded on magnetic tapes.

The digital information received in parallel is converted via the digital commutator with the help of a 9-bit parallel-series converter into the series data flux.

2.2.3.4. *Polarimeters for aerospace studies of the environment*

One of the first polarimeters for remote sensing was that developed in California University by Sekera and his group (Coulson, 1975). Their optical schemes consisted of a collimator, rotating phase plate, fixed analyser, filter, selecting a certain spectral range, and radiation receiver—a photomultiplier. The first polarimeter constructed by this scheme used a rotating quarter-wave plate in combination with a fixed analyser—a Glan–Thompson prism. The instrument had two channels, in each the spectral range needed was selected with two absorption filters, the effective wavelength of the quarter-wave plate being in the middle between the transmission peaks of the two filters of the channel. A wide dynamic range of the measured radiation was ensured with varying voltage of the photomultiplier, so that the anode current had a constant low value. The amplitudes of the second and fourth harmonics of the signal were recorded separately. The phase of the fourth harmonic was determined with the use of a phase detector.

Later on, Sekera and his group gave up measurements of elliptic polarization. This made it possible to use a new device (Sekera et al., 1963): instead of the quarter-wave plate, a half-wave plate was used to increase thereby the sensitivity to linearly polarized light. The new scheme used only one channel in which the spectral range needed was selected by four pairs of interference filters and half-wave plates. Instead of the Glan–Thompson prism with a sensitivity threshold near 350 nm, a Glan prism was used with a transmission limit near 300 nm, which raised the sensitivity of the instrument in the UV region. A large dynamic range was achieved by placing a quartz grey neutral filter in front of the photomultiplier, whose optical thickness (with a 345° turn) changed by four orders. The wedge was driven by the servomotor controlled by error signals from the photomultiplier's output. The angular shift of the wedge with respect to zero position, the constant constituent and the fourth harmonic were measured in the instrument, from which the parameters I and P could be obtained. The device was used in 1964 and 1965 on balloons to measure the polarization characteristic of the upward radiation.

One advantage of this scheme of polarimeters is the insensitivity of the photomultiplier's photocathode to the position of the plane of polarization of incident light due to the fixed position of the analyser. However, the use of such a scheme brings forth some difficulties. As seen from Eq. (2.15), the degree of linear polarization P is the coefficient in the second and third terms, which include a variable and generally unknown angle $\chi - \psi$ between the plane of the incident light polarization and that of the analyser. With the light strictly monochromatic (and the half-wave plate) the coefficient $\cos^2(\delta/2)$ will disappear, and P can be determined only from the amplitude of the fourth harmonic. However, the finite width of the optical filter eliminates such a possibility. The second term can be made to disappear, provided $|\chi - \psi| = 45°$. In the polarimeters the analyser was fixed at $\psi = 45°$, and the angle χ ought to have been either zero or 180°. Such values of χ are usually only to be found in the Sun's vertical plane. With measurements of P at other azimuths, difficulties appeared with the interpretation of the results. Later on, in California University, Hariharan (1966, 1967, 1969) developed modified polarimeters based on the schemes described with Eqs. (2.16–2.17).

From (2.16) and (2.17) one can obtain expressions for the four Stocks parameters, when the transmission plane of the analyser is placed at $\psi = 0$, 45, 90, and 135°, and the quarter-wave plate is placed in the optical path at $\psi = 45$ and 135°:

$$I = I(0°,0) + I(90°,0),$$

$$Q = I(0°,0) - I(90°,0),$$

$$U = I(45°,0) - I(135°,0),$$

$$V = I(45°,\pi/2) - I(135°,\pi/2). \tag{2.20}$$

Assuming that the polarization measured is linear, only the first three parameters are determined, and there is no need of the quarter-wave plate. Further simplification of measurements may demonstrate that it is not necessary to measure $I(135°,0)$ to calculate the third parameter, since the relationship holds:

$$I(135°,0) = I(0°,0) + I(90°,0) - I(45°,0)$$

and therefore

$$U = 2I(45°,0) - I(0°,0) - I(90°,0).$$

The position of the polarization plane and the degree of polarization are determined from (2.12) and (2.14).

The determination of the Stocks parameters making use of (2.20) can be realized both through simultaneous estimations by electronic techniques of the sums and differences needed in intensities measured in parallel-operating optical channels, and by calculating the sums and the differences with successive recording of intensities in one channel with respective positions of the analyser.

However, in the latter case, with the remote sounding, the results obtained can be rather erroneous due to inhomogeneities of the surface sounded, varying transmission of the atmosphere, and the zero drifting of the amplifier.

The construction of the first instrument developed by Hariharan and designed for ground measurements (Hariharan and Sekera, 1966) was based on four simultaneously operating channels. The optical system of each channel consisted of a collimator, analyser (Glan prism), interference filter, Liou depolarizer, and receiver (photomultiplier). The Glan prisms were oriented so that to transmit radiation with oscillation planes at 0, 45, 90, and 135° with respect to the reference plane. The PEM output signals were combined so that to obtain the sum and the difference of intensities according to (2.20) with the use of highly stabilized current amplifiers. Preliminary tests have shown that with a thorough choice of optical details the results can be obtained with an accuracy of 3%.

An attempt has been made to modify the polarimeter to remove the reasons for measurement uncertainty, and, first of all, such as the drift of some channels in detectors and multipliers, the complexity of optical details with similar characteristics. Modified polarimeters have been constructed for ground measurements of the characteristics of sunlight scattered in the atmosphere (Hariharan, 1967) as well as for aircraft measurements of radiation reflected from various types of terrestrial surfaces (Hariharan, 1969). The modification consisted in that after the analysers— four Glan–Thompson prisms, placed, as before, at the angles 0, 45, 90, and 135°— radiation was successfully transmitted with the help of an aperture disc onto a single receiver. The short-focus achromatic objective focused the beam that passed through each analyser onto the same point of the PEM photocathode. The dynamic range needed was ensured by means of neutral filters. Signals from PEM were separated and identified with the help of triggers controlled by the pulses from magnetic sensors placed near the prisms. The aircraft test measurements showed that the error in polarization measurements could reach 10%. This error was, apparently, caused by inhomogeneous surfaces and resulted from the fact that the Stocks parameters were determined from the sum and the difference of two values of intensities measured separately.

To increase the accuracy of aircraft measurements, the on-board polarimeter has been improved (Hariharan, 1969a): as before, there were one receiver and one amplifier, but the respective sums and differences were directly determined from the receiver's signals. Three Stocks parameters were determined by comparing the nonpolarized beam with the polarized one. There were three optical channels, two of which contained Glan–Thompson prisms placed at 90° and 135° with respect to the vertical; the third channel had a neutral filter with a 50% transmission. Radiation from three channels, successively, in needed combinations, controlled by the selective disc, went through the beam mixer of fibre optics to a single receiver.

With intensities from two channels with the prisms with the transmission planes placed at 90° and 135° to the vertical, denoted B and D, the Stocks parameters can be estimated from relationships (considering that the channel without the analyser transmits $I/2$ intensity)

$$I = 2(I/2),$$
$$Q = 2(I/2 - B),$$
$$U = 2(I/2 - D).$$

Laboratory tests of the improved polarimeter have shown that a 1% accuracy of the polarization measurements in the range from 5 to 75% can be reached, with the dynamic range of polarimeters Q and U changed by four orders. Apparently, the accuracy of measurements from aircraft or satellites will be worse, because the Stocks parameters are determined successively, and the inhomogeneity of the surface sounded can affect the results.

All the polarimeters considered above, constructed using relationship (2.20), are more or less connected with the necessity to choose the optical elements with similar characteristics. In this respect, construction with four simultaneously operating channels (Hariharan and Sekera, 1966), in which high requirements are made to the stability and identity of the receiving–amplifying electronic blocks, is very complicated. However, it can give the best results when measuring from space-borne platforms, since all three Stocks parameters of linearly polarized light are determined simultaneously. Besides, the absence in it of rotating parts promotes an increase in the instrument's operation in vacuum conditions (Buznikov and Lakhtanov, 1974).

The number of optical elements needed for the scheme with four simultaneously working channels can be reduced if, at the prisms, giving at the outputs two beams polarized in two mutually perpendicular planes and parted at some angular distance, are utilized. In this case the need for the optical elements to be in front of the prism halves, e.g. a polarimeter designed for astrophysical studies from space (Pellicori and Gray, 1967). The polarimeter consists of two optical channels with a telescope, Wollaston prism and two PEMs in each of them. The prisms are placed at 45° with respect two each other.

Thus, from the four receivers the signals are obtained that are needed to determine the Stocks parameters of the analysed emission. The accuracy of polarization measurements is 4%.

It should be noted that the use of prisms with two beams at the output causes some difficulties in arranging the instruments because of a comparatively small angular distance between the beams at the output. The Wollaston prisms have the maximum angle between the beams.

Several designs of polarimeters with the use of Eq. (2.20) have been developed to measure the polarization characteristics of the upward radiations from space-borne platforms.

A modified space-borne scanning radiometer for Nimbus-G (Stowe, 1977) has been developed, which measured the characteristics of linearly polarized reflected sunlight in broad intervals of the visible and near-IR ranges. Three Stocks parameters were determined from radiation intensities recorded with the analyses (Glan–Thompson prism) successively placed at 0, 90°, and 135° with respect to the reference plane. Having passed the prism, the beam halved and was directed by the rotating modulator to the spectral channels. The device was equipped with an arrangement which made it possible to scan from horizon to horizon in the Sun's vertical plane. However, Nimbus-G did not carry the device; it was mounted in 1976 on a high-altitude balloon.

For the space laboratory "Spacelab" a multi-spectral multichannel polarimeter was developed (Heinecke and Klosterman, 1978). It contains six measuring channels, in four of which the Glan–Thompson prisms are constantly oriented at certain angles in accordance with Eq. (2.20), and in the remaining two channels the prisms are combined with quarter-wave plates (also strictly oriented). Thus, the polarimeter enables one to measure all four Stocks parameters. In each measuring channel, having passed the analysers, radiation falls on five spectral beam-splitters, which reflect 95% of short-wave radiations and transmit 95% of long-wave radiations. The splitters have thresholds at $\lambda = 500, 600, 700, 800$, and 900 nm. After the splitters, radiation passes interference filters with halfwidths 20 nm and average wavelengths 450, 550, 650, 750, 850, and 950 nm, and falls on the receiver's photodiodes. Each measuring channel has six receivers and one integrating, operative, and regulating amplifier. On the whole, the information in the instruments is obtained from 36 radiation receivers. The mass of the instrument is 46 kg, and the average power is 160 W.

All four Stocks parameters can be determined also with the help of the polarization scanner developed in the Santa Barbara Research Center for the monitoring of atmospheric radiation from geosynchronous meteorological satellites (Chen, 1979). Like previous polarimeters, it has six channels with a constant orientation of the analysers and phase plates. The device should give a multispectral bright and polarized image of the Earth's surface in a sub-satellite point with a resolution of 5×5 km within a frame with the angular sizes $20 \times 20°$. West-to-east scanning is realized at the expense of the satellite's rotation; the north-to-south scanning is due to the device turning round its axis normal to that of the orbit.

The Stocks parameters can also be determined with the analyser's polarization plane placed at angles 0, 60° and 120°. In this case, from (2.16) the following expressions can be obtained for the first three parameters:

$$I = {}^2/_3(I_0 + I_{60} + I_{120}),$$

$$Q = {}^2/_3(2I_0 - I_{60} - I_{120}), \qquad\qquad (2.21)$$

$$U = -{}^2/_3(I_{120} - I_{60}),$$

where I_0, I_{60}, I_{120} are radiation intensities measured with the respective orientations of the analysers. The position of the polarization plane and the degree of polarization are determined, as before, from (2.12) and (2.14).

As for the instruments considered above, the polarization characteristics can be obtained with the analyser placed at angles differing by 60°, either using three parallel-operating channels (Prosch et al., 1983) or placing the analyser successively at respective angles in one channel (Beliajev et al., 1985).

A comparison of various versions of measurements of the polarization characteristics shows that when the analyser is oriented at the angles 0, 60, and 120°, the measurement errors are less, compared with an arrangement at 0, 40, and 90° (Snopko, 1983). However, in the latter case it is easier to determine the Stocks parameters from the sums and the differences of the measured intensities. It should be noted that techniques based on the arrangement of linear analysers at different angles are less erroneous than those based on the rotating phase plate. And of all the techniques considered, an arrangement of the analyser at 0, 45, 90, and 135° gives the least error.

The polarimeter developed in the Institute of Geophysics and Meteorology of Köln University, based on Eq. (2.21) (Prosch et al.,1983), realizes a new approach for obtaining information about the polarization characteristics consisting in the visual presentation of the measured characteristics. The instrument accomplishes an opto-electronic scanning of the objects with three TV tubes, in front of which the polaroids are placed with the transmission planes 60° apart. The video signals obtained from the display tubes are amplified, modulated and coded. The instrument foresees a correction of polarization change caused by different slopes of the beams falling onto the input surface of the polaroids. Information about the brightness, degree of polarization, position of the polarization plane is displayed as a false-colour image or in digital form. Such a system provides a prompt analysis, high spatial resolution with a wide FOV, study of the dynamics of the processes, motions, etc.

The polarimeters, in which the degree of the polarization of linearly polarized radiation is determined using the amplitude modulation technique with the rotating analyser, are widely used in remote sounding. On the basis of the Malus law, with the analyser rotating at an angular speed ω, the radiation passing through it can be expressed as

$$I = I_{max}\cos^2\omega t + I_{min}\sin^2\omega t = \frac{I_{max} + I_{min}}{2} + \frac{I_{max} - I_{min}}{2}\cos 2\omega t, \quad (2.22)$$

where I_{max} and I_{min} are intensities of the components polarized in two mutually perpendicular planes. Bearing in mind that the degree of polarization is expressed as

$$P = \frac{I_{max} - I_{min}}{I_{max} + I_{min}}$$

it can be stated that the value of 0 is equal to the ratio of the amplitudes of the variable and constant constituents.

The polarimeters based on the amplitude modulation technique have a comparatively simple construction. But their accuracy is lower than that of the polarimeters based on other measurement techniques (Snopko, 1983). The position on the polarization plane can be determined from the direction of I_{max}. The polarimeters described in the literature (Buznikov et al., 1980; Egan, 1968; Ksanfomaliti et al., 1975; Yakovlev et al., 1983) have been based on this technique.

The high accuracy of determination of the polarization characteristics has been obtained with the polarimeter based on the photon-counting technique (Coulson et al., 1974). The instrument has two channels, each consisting of a collimator input tube, rotating analyser, removable neutral and interference filters, and receiver-REMs. Besides, an opaque screen can be put into the optical path for the dark current photon counting, as well as a quarter-wave plate when it is necessary to measure the characteristics of the elliptically polarized light. The device management, including rotation of the analysers, choice of filters, orientation by azimuth and elevation, is realized with the help of a small-sized computer. The device has a digital output, which, also with the help of a computer, gives the values of the measured parameters within 1 s after measurements are made.

In the instrument using the photon-counting technique, the accuracy of measurements is proportional to the square root of the number of photons counted. Thus, there is a simple dependence between the date accuracy and speed at which they are obtained. For example, with photon counting in eight points during one rotation of the analyser with the integration time in each point 1 s, radiation intensity can be obtained with an accuracy of $\pm 0.15\%$, which corresponds to the error of radiation intensity measurements ± 0.002, and that of the angle of the polarization plane position $\pm 0.1°$. If the time of integration in each point is reduced to 0.1 s, possible errors will be $\pm 0.5\%$, ± 007, $\pm 0.3°$, respectively.

The basic characteristics of the polarimeters for the remote sounding of the environment are given in Table 2.8. The overview of the polarimeters developed shows that there are polarimeters which permit measurement of all polarization characteristics. However, available methodical instructions on the application of these devices do not allow one to use adequately all the possible information. As has been mentioned above, the ellipticity of reflected and scattered radiation is a very small value, and none of the publications states that this parameter could be used in the interests of remote sounding. The angle of rotation of the polarization plane has a limited application in studies of the sounded surfaces. This parameter, in particular, can be used to distinguish between positive and negative polarizations (Coulson, 1966).

With respect to other possibilities of its applications the data available are contradictory. It has been stated (Hallok and Halajian, 1983) that with reflection from different surfaces the polarization plane can have only two positions, corresponding to positive or negative polarizations; that is, the angle of rotation of the polarization plane is not a continuously varying parameter and cannot be used in mapping. At the same time, it has been shown (Lakhtanov and Churov, 1988) that when measurements are made over the water surface, the angle of rotation of the polarization plane can vary depending on the azimuth with respect to the Sun's vertical plane. However, the values are determined, apparently, by measurement

Table 2.8. Basic characteristics of polarimeters for the remote sensing of the environment

Instrument	Polarization parameters to be measured	Number of optical channels		Number of receiving-amplifying tracks	Dispersing element, spectral interval, spectral resolution	Analyser	Radiation receiver	Time of measurement	Measurement accuracy	Scanning	Fixed photography	Carrier
		Dependent	Independent									
Polarimeter to measure sky light (Coulson, 1975)	I,P,χ,β	—	2	2	Absorption filters: with λ_{max} = 365, 460, 513, 625 nm	Glan–Thompson prisms	Photo-multiplier					
Polarimeter to investigate the atmosphere and Earth's surface (Sekera et al., 1963)	I,P,χ	—	1	1	Interference filters: 332.5, 410, 510, 610 nm; $\Delta\lambda$ = 15nm	Glan prism	Photo-multiplier with antimony-calcium photocathode	One filter 1/12 s		Vertical		Balloon
Polarimeter to measure sky light (Hariharan and Sikera, 1966)	I,P,χ	4	—	4	Interference filters: 400–700 nm; $\Delta\lambda$ = 50–100 nm	Glan prism	Photo-multiplier		3%	Horizon-to-horizon, 5 min	Laboratory	model
Modified polarimeter to measure sky light (Hariharan, 1967)	I,P,χ	4	—	1		Glan–Thompson prisms	Photo-multiplier					Presumably high-altitude aircraft
Modified polarimeters to study the Earth's surface from aircraft (Hariharan, 1969)	I,P,χ	4	—	1	Interference filters 400, 460, 520, prisms	Glan–Thompson prisms	Photo-multiplier	One filter, $P\pm10\%$ 1/8–1/10 s		In flight plane; 0–105° from nadir for 15 s		Aircraft Convair-990

Description											
Advanced polarimeter to study the Earth's surface from aircraft (Hariharan, 1969a)	I,P,χ	3	—	1	Interference filters: 380, 500, 580 nm	Glan-Thompson prisms	Photo-multiplier	One filter, P within 5–75%; accuracy 1%	0.18 s		Presumably high-altitude aircraft and satellite
Polarimeter for space-based astrophysical studies (Pellicori and Gray, 1967)	I,P,χ	2	—	4		Vollaston prisms	Photo-multiplier	P up to 4%			Space vehicle
Polarimeter to study the atmosphere and the Earth's surface (Stowe, 1977)	I,P,χ	—	2	2	Wide-band filters: 350–700; 700–3000 nm	Glan-Thompson prisms	Silicon photodiode; cooled sulphur-lead photoresistor		3 s	Horizon-to-horizon, in the Sun's vertical plane; 96 s; 16-mm photo-camera	High-altitude balloon
Multispectral multichannel polarimeter to measure the content of aerosol in the atmosphere and investigate the Earth's surface (Heinecke and Klosterman, 1978)	I,P,χ,β	6	—	36**	Interference filters: 450, 550, 650, 750, 850, 950 nm; $\Delta\lambda = 20$ nm	Glan-Thompson prisms	Photodiodes			Synchronous fixed photography	Presumably Spacelab
Polarization scanner to monitor atmospheric radiation (Chen, 1979)	I,P,χ,β	6	Two sets	12	Wide-band filters: 0.40–0.48; 0.48–0.58; 0.63–0.69; 1.17–1.30; 1.55–1.75; 2.08–2.35 μm		Silicon photodiode; cooled indium-antimonide photoresistor		25.6 min for 6 bands	Over the frame 20 × 20°	Presumably geo-synchr. meteorol. satellite

Instrument	Measured parameters				Spectral range / filters	Analyzer	Detector	Measurement time	Accuracy	Scanning / imaging	Platform
Scanning polarimeter to study the Earth's surface (Bazilevski et al., 1974)	I,P	2	—	2	0.3–0.8 μm	Polaroid	Bolometers BKM-5			Normal to flight trajectory ±90°	IL-18 aircraft, "Meteor-8" satellite
Small-sized fast spectropolarimeter SFS-2P (Beliajev et al., 1985)	I,P,χ	—	1	—	Diffraction grid 1200 str/mm, 400–800 nm; Δλ = 7 nm	Polaroid	Photo-multiplier	1.4 s			Presumably flying vehicle of any type
Video-polarimeter for environmental studies (Prosch et al., 1983)	I,P,χ	3	—	3	Interference filter: 550 nm; Δλ = 50 nm	Polaroid	Plumbicon XQ1270 tubes		P ± 3% electronic	Opto-electronic	Aircraft
Polarimeter to study the Earth's surface (Egan, 1968)	I,P,χ	—	1	1	Interference filters or wide-band filters: 0.3–3 μm	Polaroid	Photo-multiplier or sulphur–lead photoresistor	0.08 s		Built-in 16-mm camera	Aircraft, car
Polarimeter to study the surface of Mars (Ksanfomaliti et al., 1976)	I,P,χ	—	1	1	Interference filters: 350, 400, 450, 500, 550, 600, 650, 700, 750 nm	Prism	Photo-multiplier	One filter, 1 s	P ± 0.32%		Inter-planetary station Mars-5
Polarimeter to indicate oil slicks on the sea surface (Buznikov et al., 1980)	I,P,χ	—	1	1	Interference filters: 448 (Δλ = 7.8), 525 (Δλ = 8), 642 (Δλ = 3), 770 (Δλ = 6) nm	Polaroid	Photo-multiplier PEM-51	6 s		Synchronous fixed photography	MI-8 helicopter, ship

Instrument	Measured		Dependent**	Independent	Spectral range	Polarizer	Detector	Time	Accuracy	Scan	Platform
Spectorometer–polarimeter for sub-satellite experiments (Yakovlev et al., 1983)	I, P, χ	—	1		Diffraction grid: 450–1150 nm, $\Delta\lambda = 10$ nm	Polaroid	Silicon photodiodes	1.5 s	$I \pm 10\%$; $P \pm 3\%$		Ka-26, MI-4 helicopters
Polarization radiometer with photon-counting to study the atmosphere and the Earth's surface (Coulson et al.,1974)	I, P, χ, β	—	2	2	Interference filters: 320, 365, 400, 500, 600, 700, 800, 900 nm	Glan–Thompson prisms	Photo-multipliers			Horizon-to-horizon 30 min.	

Note:
*Dependent channels are the optical channels that make it possible to assess the polarization characteristics only from a set of data obtained in each of these channels. Independent channels enable one to obtain polarization characteristics from the data of only one channel.
**In each dependent optical channel a light beam is subdivided into 6 spectral channels. Therefore the instrument has 36 radiation receivers but only 6 amplifiers (one for each dependent channel).

geometry. Though the position of the polarization plane in water depends on its optical properties, this dependence is rather weak; therefore the effect of the rotation of the polarization plane cannot be used, apparently, for the remote sounding of the primary hydro-optical characteristics. The polarization degree parameter has been used most in the remote sounding technique.

Further developments of polarimetric instrumentation should be supplied with methodical instructions on its use, so that the respective requirements be well substantiated.

2.3 AEROSPACE PHOTOGRAPHY INSTRUMENTATION

2.3.1 MKF-6 multizonal camera
The space vehicle "Soyuz-22" and orbital stations "Salut" were equipped with the MKF-6 camera made in Germany for the multizonal survey of vegetation and other natural formations (Kronberg, 1988; Soyuz-22..., 1980). It enables six synchronous images in different spectral zones to be obtained.

MKF-6 consists of a camera, six cassettes, an electronic unit, and a control panel. The camera has six objectives of the type Pishanar 4/125 with narrow-zonal light filters for the range 0.48–0.84 μm. The filters are chosen so that the ranges of the incoming light flux do not overlap. Six filters with different illumination power on the six objectives of the camera MKF-6 determine its different spectral resolution (or spectral sensitivity) in the chosen spectral zones, as shown in Fig. 2.19, which illustrates the spectral resolutions of negative on the colour one-type (channels 1–4) and colour IR (channels 5.6) film.

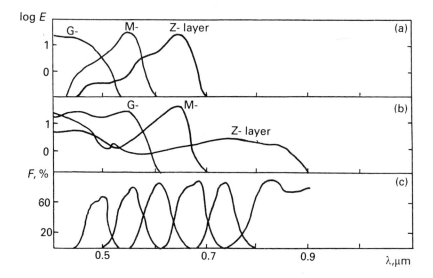

Fig. 2.19. Spectral sensitivity of the multizonal MKF-6 camera.

The negative 70×91 mm^2 contains the basic image 55×81 mm^2 and additional information printed on the margins of the image, outside the basic field of the image: sensitometric wedge, clock face, indicator panels, exposure code, frame number. The basic technical characteristics of MKF-6 are given in Table 2.9.

Table 2.9. Multizonal space camera MKF-6

Parameters	Estimate
Height of survey, km	200–400
Number of channels	6
Spectral range, nm	480–840
Objective	Pishanar 4/125
Shutter	Central, with rotating discs
Film width, mm	70
Overlapping, %	20; 60; 80

To obtain from three (or four) narrow-zonal image of one object taken with a multizonal camera and processed on a transparent slide, a real-colour or false-colour (spectrozonal) image, one uses projectors that can combine the colours, i.e. multispectral projectors. By choosing the respective combinations of illumination filters one can obtain a colour IR image. To process and combine the black-and-white zonal images taken with the MKF-6, a multispectral projector MSP-4 has been constructed in Germany (Kronberg, 1988; Soyuz-22..., 1980).

The optical scheme of two MSP-4 channels is shown in Fig. 2.20. In MSP-4 one can place up to four transparent positive (or negative) frames and obtain an adequate real- or false-colour image of the location in different versions with a high geometrical resolution and a small overlapping uncertainty. Relatively low contrasts of initial black-and-white MSP-4 frames can be transformed into contrasting colours of a false-colour image. An increase in the information content of the image obtained is an important means of decoding the materials of an aerospace survey of vegetation cover and agricultural crop fields.

To provide a high-quality survey, the MKF-6 camera should be supplied with a system to compensate for an image blurring caused by the motion of spacecraft during the exposition. The measuring instrumentation to determine the compensation speed is shown in Fig. 2.21.

2.4 THE USE OF THERMAL INFRARED SCANNERS FOR SOLVING ENVIRONMENTAL PROBLEMS

The optico-mechanical IR scanners, thermal scanners, are now widely used in solving the Earth's resources and ecological problems (Kronberg, 1988; Shilin, 1982). They are often used during the IR aerosurvey.

The thermal scanner is an optico-mechanical survey system which during flight receives the IR emission from landscape objects, forms an image of the location beneath, in which different radiation temperatures of the object and types of

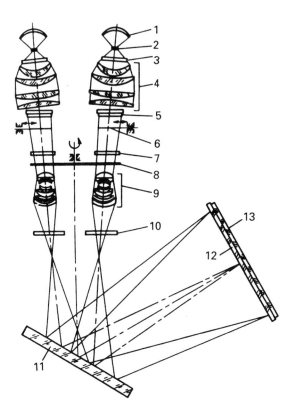

Fig. 2.20. Optical scheme of two channels of MSP-4: 1—concave mirror; 2—halogen projection lamp; 3—thermal filter; 4—condenser lenses; 5—negative holder; 6—shutter; 7—colour light filter; 8—sector shutter; 9—projection objective; 10—neutral light filter; 11—deviating mirror; 12—screen; 13—Fresnel lens.

landscape, that is, the spatial resolution of temperatures, are presented in various tints of grey. Usually the scanner consists of an optico-mechanical unit, detector units and an image recorder. The principle of the survey with the thermal scanner is illustrated in Fig. 2.22.

A monograph by B. Shilin (1982) is dedicated to an application of the thermal aerosurvey to study the Earth's resources. Recommendations on the choice of optimal conditions for the thermal survey have been given in this publication.

The practical and scientific significance of the development of the instruments and techniques to study the IR radiation from aero- and space-platforms is determined by the fact that the state of numerous natural and man-made objects on the Earth's surface depends on changes in the temperature field. The thermal images obtained of the underlying surface provide information on the state of water areas and vegetation, make it possible to solve hydrological and geological as well as reclamation problems, and to study the snow and ice cover. The technical description of concrete modifications of airborne thermal scanners can be found elsewhere (Kronberg, 1988).

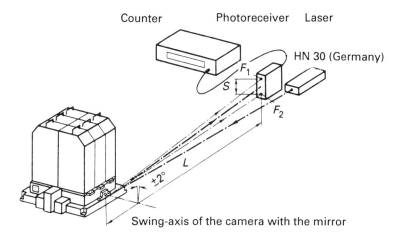

Fig. 2.21. Measuring complex to measure the rate of compensation for blurring an MKF-6 image.

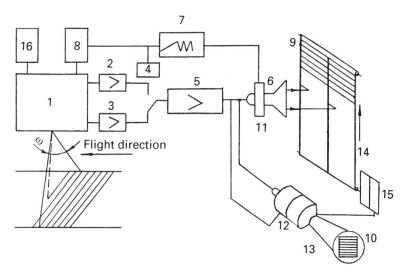

Fig. 2.22. The principle of the thermal scanner survey: 1—optico-electronic system; 2, 3—
pre-amplifiers; 4—fast-operation switch; 5—video-amplifier; 6—photorecorder's tube; 7—
pulse generator; 8—synchro-sensor; 9—image on the film; 10—videocontrol tube; 11, 12—
deviating bobbins of line-by-line sweep; 13—frame sweep; 14, 15—electric drive.

In Russia, a two-channel (3–5; 8–13 μm) thermal scanner "Vulkan", whose parameters are listed in Table 2.10, is the most widely used airborne thermal scanner. At present there is an improved thermal scanner "Malakhit", whose parameters are given in Table 2.11. Information about the basic parameters of various home-made and foreign systems of thermal aerospace survey is listed in Table 2.12.

Table 2.10. Thermal scanner "Vulkan"

Parameter	Estimate
Spectral ranges, μm	3.2–5.3 (4.2–5.3) and 8–13 (10–13) μm
Thermal resolution at 20°C (flight altitude 1000 m):	
— 3.2–5.3 μm channel	0.5° C
— 8–13 μm channel	0.2° C
Spatial resolution	2 mr
Viewing angle	80° C
Speed of response	0.015–0.3 s^{-1}
Maximum weight, kg	200
Simultaneous record of two channels on 19-cm photographic film	
Cooling of sensors by liquid nitrogen	
The scanner is designed for aircraft and helicopters	

Table 2.11. Thermal scanner "Malakhit"

Parameter	Estimate
Spectral band, μm	8–13
Thermal resolution at 20° C (flight altitude 1000 m)	Better than 0.2° C
Spatial resolution	1.5 mr
Viewing angle	120°
Speed of response	0.02–0.4 s^{-1}
Weight, kg	65
Record on 8-cm film	
Closed cooling system	
Designed for aircraft and helicopters	

Table 2.12. Main parameters of thermal aerospace survey systems

System type (country)	Field of view, grad	Swath width, km (in flight altitude H)	Resolution angle, mrad (line resolution m)	Spectral range, μm (spectral channels)	Sensitivity, K	Additional data
RS-700, Texas Instruments (USA)	120	(3.4 H)	0.5–1.5	8–13	0.2–0.3	Airplane
Bendix LN-3 (USA)	120	(3.4 H)	2.5	0.38–0.6 0.2–0.6 3–5.3 8–13	0.2	Airplane
Reconofax XVI, HRB—Singer (USA)	120 140	(3.4 H)	2 3	3.5–5.3 8–13	0.2–0.3	Airplane
AADS-1260, Deadalus (USA)	86 43	(2 H)	2.5 1.25	10 channels in the range 0.38–1.1; 10.4–12.5	0.3	Airplane, thermal channel calibration

Matra M867 (France)	90	(2 *H*)	3	4 channels in the range 0.3–1.1	0.2	Airplane, thermal channel calibration
				2 channels in the range 8–13	0.5–0.2	
Vulkan, AOMZ, (Russia)	90	(2 *H*)	1.5	3–5.3 8–13	0.1	Airplane
ATL-80, HG-H Infrarouge Ing. Syst. (France)	45–60	(1.15 *H*)	1.5–3.5	3–5.3 8–13	0.1–0.3	Airplane, calibration
TIMS, IPL (USA)	76.5	(1.6 *H*)	2.5	8.2–8.6 8.6–9 9–9.4 9.4–10.2 10.2–11.2 11.2–12.2		
Jashma, AOMZ (Russia)	80	(1.17)	2.8	8–13 9.5–10.5 10–11 10.5–11.5 11–12 11.5–12.5	0.1	Airplane, calibration
TM (USA)	—	185	(30)	5 channels in the range 0.45–1.75;	0.5	Landsat satellite type, calibration
			(120)	2.08–2.35 10.4–12.5		
AVHRR (USA)	—	2700	(1100)	2 channels in the range 0.58–1; 3.55–3.93 10.5–11.5 11.5–12.5	0.12	NOAA satellite type, calibration
MSU-CS (Russia)	—	600	(170)	4 channels in the range 0.5–1.1;		"Kosmos-1939" satellite
			(600)	10.4–12.6	0.5	
Thermscan (Russia)	—	600	(1800)	0.5–1 8–13	0.5	Scanner for the inter-planetary station "Fobos"
Malackit, AOMZ (Russia)	120	(3.4 *H*)	1.2	8–13	0.1	Airplane, helicopter
Termez M2 (Russia)	45–60		0.5; <0.1	8–13	0.02–0.3	Ecological satellite (system in elaboration stage)

2.5   SATELLITE TELEVISION SYSTEMS

Spaceborne TV systems operate in the same range of the electromagnetic spectrum as photographic systems (0.4–0.9 μm). Cameras of the type "Vidicon" are used mainly in remote sounding. An image is drawn as a pattern of charges on a flat light-sensitive screen and read out by a sweeping electronic beam. The brightness of the image points is transformed into respective voltage, coded in frequency and amplitude, transformed into a digital form of the pulse and transmitted to the ground. On the ground it is, again, transformed into the perspective brightness of the image elements and taken from the screen onto the film.

The advantage of the TV method, compared to photography, is that the videosignal is transmitted to the Earth as a voltage value, which makes it possible to use the automatic processing through further electronic–digital conversions of the signal. This serves as the basis for computer preparation of data and image processing. The space-borne TV systems are carried by the orbital and geostationary meteorological satellites to perform the global-scale meteorological observations (Currant, 1985; Kondratyev, 1980a; Trifonov, 1981). The space-borne TV system includes cameras carried by the satellites "TIROS-ESSD", "Nimbus", "NOAA", "METEOSAT", and "Meteor".

The basic shortcomings of TV systems carried by meteorological satellites have been their low spatial resolution—from several hundreds of metres to several kilometres. However, this resolution can be used not only to observe weather and the global state of the environment, but also in some cases to solve concrete ecological problems. For example, from the data of the Meteor-18 TV system the distribution of the types of trees in the mid-latitude forest of Russia has been studied (Fig. 2.23). Figure 2.24 shows the pattern of tracing the distribution of the slow-melting edge (Vetlov, 1980). However, the spatial distribution from hundreds of metres to several kilometres is, of course, insufficient to solve numerous problems of soil use as well as to perform detailed observations of the state of vegetation and agricultural crops in individual regions.

The space-borne TV system of the well known American Earth's resources satellite, Landsat (initially called ERTS), has a higher spatial resolution. For example, apart from multispectral scanners (Kronberg, 1988) Landsat-1 and Landsat-2 carried multizonal survey TV systems consisting of three RBV Vidicon cameras (Fig 2.25). From an altitude of 917 km, each camera covers an area of 185 $\times$ 185 km^2. The cameras operate in three spectral zones: 0.48–0.58; 0.58–0.68; 0.69–0.83 μm. Individual frames of three TV cameras were superimposed and transformed into the false-colour image of the Earth's surface site under study. The spatial resolution of the RBV image was about 20 m. The Landsat-1,2 TV images were taken simultaneously with the survey using the MSS multizonal scanner carried by these satellites. The survey ranges with the RBV cameras are shown in Fig. 2.26.

The Landsat-3 satellite launched in March 1978 carried an RBV TV system consisting of two similar TV cameras operating in the range 0.50–0.75 μm. The principle of the Landsat-3 RBV survey is shown in Fig. 2.27. It surveyed two adjacent locations 98 $\times$ 98 km^2 in size, with an overlap up to 14 km by the side. The

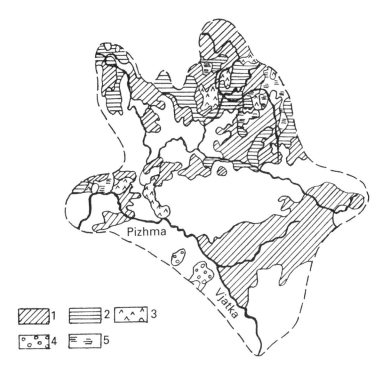

Fig. 2.23. Scheme of distribution of the types of trees in the mid-latitude forests from TV images of the river Viatka basin obtained from "Meteor-18": 1—middle- and south-taiga fir forests; 2—birch and aspen forests; 3—middle- and south-taiga pine forests; 4—broad-leaved forests with some coniferous trees; 5—marshes.

spatial resolution on the TV image was about 30 km. The use of two similar cameras operating in a wide spectral range made it impossible to transform two synchronous TV images into a false-colour image, which is very important when vegetation cover is observed. Therefore the satellites Landsat-4 and Landsat-5, again, carried a TV system consisting of three RBV cameras.

2.6 MULTICHANNEL SCANNING SYSTEMS

At present the principal method for obtaining information above the environmental state is by obtaining scanned images. The survey is made in a wide spectral range (0.3–14.0 μm)—from UV to thermal IR. Electromagnetic emission reflected or emitted by landscape objects is caught by the optical scanning system and fixed-on detectors. They transform the incident radiation into an electric signal, which is recorded on magnetic tape in either analogue or digital form. Owing to this registration technique, the spectral data from the scanners are easily reproduced, that is, duplicated and distributed among the users.

Of decisive importance for the wide use of scanned images for the Earth's

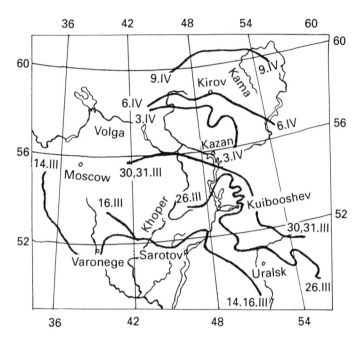

Fig. 2.24. Propagation of snow melting edge from TV images.

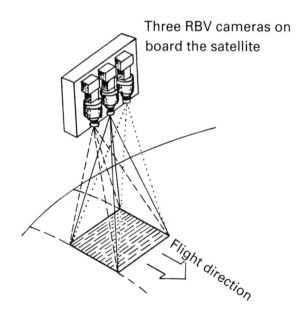

Fig. 2.25. Scheme of arrangement of multizonal TV systems of three RBV cameras.

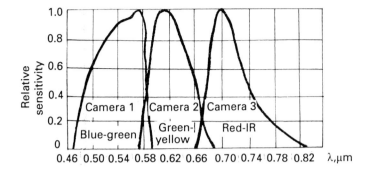

Fig. 2.26. Spectral ranges of survey with RBV cameras.

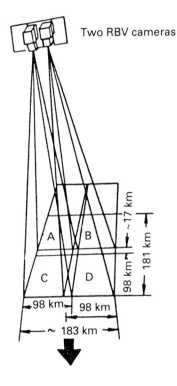

Fig. 2.27. TV system of two RBV cameras on Landsat-3.

resources and ecological studies with the remote sounding from space-borne platform is the expediency with which the spectral data recorded with electronic devices can be transmitted to the Earth either in the direct transmission (DT) regime in the zone of radiovisibility of the receiving station or upon being recorded on magnetic tape in the memory regime (MR), when the satellite is outside the FOV of the receiving station. The record of multispectral data on magnetic tape has opened up wide prospects for preliminary processing, presentation of multizonal images with the use of the programming of computer processing, including such systems as "Pericolour" and personal computers.

The main shortcoming of space images as well as TV, IR and microwave image is the ambiguity of results obtained from their interpretation. This is connected with the fact that only the data on the spatial distribution of the brightness field in any spectral region characterized as an image are not enough for a definite indication of the observed objects and determination of their properties.

The absence in most cases of absolute calibration has resulted in the space photos being mainly used for the qualitative analysis and interpretation of natural formations (Beregovoi et al., 1972a; Grigoryev, 1975; Grigoryev and Kondratyev, 1989). The development of multispectral scanners (American satellite..., 1974; Avanesov et al., 1981a,b; Selivanov et al., 1977, 1981) has been a considerable progress. The Earth images obtained from them, due to the videosignal referencing (Beregovoi et al., 1982b; Price, 1987; Space opportunities..., 1987), should bear the quantitative information about the brightness of the objects and be automatically computer-processed.

In Russia, two systems have been created, providing information about the Earth's resources in the interests of the national economy. One of them is based on photography and supplies high-quality photographs of slowly varying processes and phenomena (Kienko, 1987). The other system is based on the use of multichannel TV scanners and provides prompt information via a telemetric channel (Selivanov and Tuchin, 1981; Selivanov et al., 1977, 1981).

The multichannel scanners (MS) of optical range measure the spectral brightness of natural objects simultaneously in several narrow spectral intervals. Such systems have been used on Skylab (Kondratyev, 1980a), satellites Landsat (American satellite..., 1974; Kondratyev, 1980a; Kronberg, 1988), Seasat (Space based..., 1977) and "Meteor-Priroda" (Kozlov et al..., 1981; Trifonov, 1981; Vetlov, 1980), SPOT (Kronberg, 1988; Space based..., 1987). They have also been mounted on some aircraft laboratories (Ziman et al..., 1976). The MS serves the basis for the operational system "Resurs-0" and "Okean-0". An extensive programme of studies accomplished with their help has made it possible to demonstrate the efficient application of MS in the interests of the solution of scientific and economic problems.

The first specialized satellite to study the Earth's resources—the American satellite ERTS-1 (Landsat) (American satellite..., 1974; Kondratyev, 1980a; Kronberg, 1988)—was launched on 27 July 1972 in the Sun-synchronous orbit with the following parameters: apogee—920 km, perigee—901 km, angle of inclination to the equator plane—99.12°, orbital period—103.27 min. Landsat was created on the basis of the meteorological satellite Nimbus (Kondratyev, 1980a; Kozlov et al..., 1981). The ERTS-1 satellite carried a multispectral scanning system MSS with four spectral channels: 0.5–0.6; 0.6–0.7; 0.7–0.8; 0.8–1.0 μm. From an altitude of 910 km it ensured the survey of a band 185 km wide with a field resolution of about 80 m. The Sun-synchronous orbit made it possible to perform a multiple survey of the same region of the Earth with the same angle of Sun elevation with an 18-day repeatability. The information content of the radioline constituted 1.6×10^7 bit/s. In the DT regime the ERTS-1 MSS operated over several years, having shown high economic efficiency. Landsat-2 (ERTS-B) was launched on 22 January 1975, and Landsat-3 on 5 March 1978. In construction and instrumentation they are similar to ERTS-1. However, the payload has been modified. For example, the MSS camera, in addition to four channels (0.5–1.1 μm), also has a fifth channel (10.4–12.5 μm) to improve assessments of the state of crops and the yield forecast, as well as to determine the thermal characteristics of soils and rocks (Space based..., 1977).

The Russian experimental programme to study the Earth's resources with the use of automatic satellites "Meteor-Priroda" was started in 1977 by launching an experimental satellite "Meteor", equipped with a multispectral radio–TV complex (RTVC) (Kozlov et al..., 1981; Vetlov, 1980), including two multichannel scanners of low (MSU-L) and moderate (MSU-M) resolution. This made it possible to adjust the regime of the experimental exploitation of the operational Earth natural resource system (ENRS) and a relatively regular distribution of information among the users.

A detailed description of MSU can be found in the literature (Selivanov and Gektin, 1982; Selivanov and Tuchin, 1981; Selivanov et al..., 1977, 1981). The scanners are optico-mechanical systems with 1-line sweep and 1-element receivers, the frame sweeping being realized due to the satellite's motion. The MSU-L operates in four spectral ranges, and the MSU-M in two ranges. The scanners' parameters are given in Table 2.13, and their spectral characteristics are shown in Fig. 2.28.

In MSU-L the scanning is made with the help of the swaying mirror driven by the cam mechanism, and in MSU-M with the help of the rotating mirror pyramid. An image is formed with the help of the objective OKS-4-75SA with a focal length of f = 75 mm and an entrance pupil diameter of 18.75 mm. The optical schemes of the scanners of MSU-L and MSU-M have been described elsewhere (Selivanov and Tuchin, 1981; Selivanov et al..., 1977, 1981).

On the basis of experience from RTVC exploitation an experimental board information complex (BIC-E) was developed (Selivanov et al., 1981). It also has a wide-angle scanner with a narrower (up to 600 km) viewing band and a 1.5-fold higher spatial resolution. The number of channels is now four, and the light fluxes are measured with a higher accuracy. The BIC-E complex supplements the "Meteor" RTVC instruments.

The BIC-E includes two instruments to transmit the spectrozonal images: an optico-mechanical mid-resolution scanner with a conical sweep MSU-CS and an optico-electronic high-resolution scanner with a plane sweep MSU-E. The scanners operate simultaneously. In this case the information content of the colour flux constitutes 7.68 Mbit/s. The transmission is made at a carrier frequency of 466.5 MHz using the dual relative phase manipulation technique.

The multi-channel high-resolution scanner (MSU-E) includes the use of the lines of receivers based on CCD instruments with 1024 elements in one line.

The underlying surface is projected onto three lines of CCD elements, each operating in its own spectral range. The lines are arranged normal to the flight direction. The line is swept electronically, and the frame due to the satellite's motion.

The slant sounding of the surface (at an angle of 39°), characteristic of the conical

Table 2.13. Multizonal scanning device parameters

| System of instruments | Type of device | Resolution on the Earth's surface (nadir) | | Scanning angle, degree | Swath width at altitude $H = 650$ km | Spectral channels | Radiation detectors | Number of elements in the active part of the line | Rate of scanning | Incl. angle |
		In flight direction (in frame) km	In line direction, km		km	μm			$\dfrac{\text{N lines}}{\text{s}}$	grad
	MSU-L	1.7	1.0	106	1930	0.5–0.6	PEM-114	1880	4	0
						0.6–0.7	PEM-114			
						0.7–0.8	PEM-114			
						0.8–1.0	PEM-112			
RTVC	MSU-M	0.142	0.240	90	1380	0.5–0.7	Photodiodes	5700	48	0
						0.7–1.0				
	MSU-CS	0.243	0.175	66.5	600	0.5–0.6	Photodiodes	3614	48	38.9
						0.6–0.7				
						0.7–0.8				
						0.8–1.0				
BIC-E	MSU-E	0.045	0.045	2.5	45	0.5–0.6	CCD instr.	1024	218	0
						0.65–0.75				
						0.8–1.0				
EIIC	MSU "Fragment"	0.080	0.080	15	185	0.4–0.5	PEM-114			0
		0.080	0.080			0.5–0.6	PEM-114			
		0.080	0.080			0.6–0.7	PEM-114			
		0.080	0.080			0.7–0.8	PEM-114			
		0.080	0.080			0.8–1.1	PEM-112			
		0.240	0.240			1.2–1.3	PD-8			
		0.240	0.240			1.5–1.8	PD-8			
		0.480	0.480			2.1–2.4	FS-2AN			

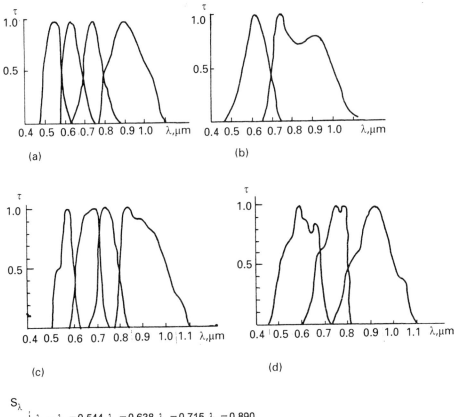

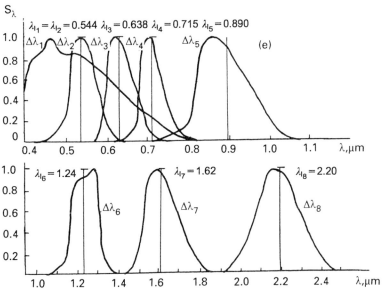

Fig. 2.28. Spectral characteristics of multispectral scanning systems: (a) MSU-L; (b) MSU-M; (c) MSU-CS; (d) MSU-E; (e) MSS "Fragment".

scanning technique, helped information about the water surface state to be obtained (Selivanov and Gektin, 1982).

According to the "Meteor-Priroda" programme (Kozlov et al., 1981), the satellites "Meteor" (apart from RTVC and BIC-E) carried a multizonal scanning system "Fragment" (Avanesov et al., 1981a,b), with a system digital transmission of information (Bogomolov et al., 1981). The latter forms an experimental information-measurement complex EIIC). The complex includes: (I) a multizonal system of optical scanning "Fragment"; (II) a system of digital transmission of multizonal video information; (III) a system of receiving and recording magnetically; (IV) a system of digital processing.

The system "Fragment" ensures the sweeping of the Earth's surface image across the flight route in the band about 85 km simultaneously in eight zones of the visible and near-IR spectral ranges (see Table 2.13).

G. Avanesov and his group (1981a,b) note that when developing the system "Fragment", the emphasis has been placed on the process of measuring the brightness of natural formations, the comparison of the obtained electric signal with the reference one, and the coding of the signal. The coded signal is more noise-proof compared with the analogue presentation of video information. In the "Fragment" video-tract the conversion of measured brightness into equivalent digital values is realized via successive operations in the following converters: optical linear converter (receiving optical system); spatial–temporal optical converter (scanning element and analysing diaphragm); optical selector (fibre-optical ramifier and band spectral filters); photoelectric linear scale converter (radiation receiver and direct current amplifier), and analogue-to-digital converter.

The optical selector in the "Fragment" system is based on the scheme with a separate spectral and spatial selection, for which the fibre-optical ramifier is used, the entrance ends of light-guides forming the matrix of the analysing diaphragms.

Some authors (Avanesov et al., 1981a,b; Bogomolov et al., 1981) believe that the measurement accuracy of the "Fragment" system makes it possible to automatize the processes of processing the space video information by using the serial computers. The "Fragment" system enables one to obtain high-quality multi-spectral images of only individual fragments of the Earth's surface. Therefore, to solve such practically important economic problems as assessing the states of vegetation, soil, crops in large regions, and yield forecast over the country, and others, it is necessary to improve all the MSUs enumerated above that serve the basis for the operative Earth natural resources system.

Analysis of the existing and developed MSUs of the optical range suggest some conclusions and recommendations on their further improvement.

The functional capabilities of MSU are determined by the following parameters:

— field resolution for each measurement channel;
— viewing spectral and scanning geometry;
— radiometric measurement accuracy in each channel (relative and absolute errors);
— the number of working spectral zones, their width and location in the spectral range of the instrument's operation;

— brightness range of natural formations, recorded by each measurement channel;
— threshold sensitivity of measurement channel.

Most of the enumerated parameters are interdependent. Therefore, when developing new instruments, it is necessary to choose optimal values for each of them, with a given accuracy of radiometric measurements. However, for the successful optimization of the parameters of MSU used in the government space Earth resource system, it is necessary: (i) to enumerate and get agreement on scientific and economic problems ranked by their importance, which can be solved with the MSU; (ii) to speed up the work on compiling a catalogue of the spectra of natural formations, considering possible temporal and seasonal variations.

The multichannel scanning systems have been widely used in studies of the environment. Figure 2.29 is an image of Neva Bay in three spectral intervals obtained from the space apparatus "Kosmos-1939". Possibilities of using the multichannel scanners in the analysis of the state of vegetation cover are well illustrated by Fig. 2.30 (Rock et al., 1986).

The successful use of the MSU data for the remote measurements from space of the parameters of natural objects is much determined by the level of metrological support that includes a certification of geometrical parameters and calibration of measuring and bearing channels against wavelengths, energetic brightness, and energetic irradiance. For the energetic calibration of the MSU spectral channels, the checking schemes should be used. Each checking scheme should be based on the respective State reference.

2.6.1 Composition and basic characteristics of scientific complexes carried by the satellites of the Russian space system

The Earth-resources satellites of the "Resurs"
This series shown in Fig. 2.31 carries a complex of instruments, the basic parameters of which are given in Table 2.14.

1. MSU-E—high-resolution instrument. Field resolution is 45 m. Width of the covered band: 45 km, three spectral channels: 0.5–0.6; 0.6–0.7; 0.8–0.9 μm. When two instruments are switched on, the viewing band broadens to 80 km. The optical axis shifts within $\pm 30°$ in the plane normal to the plane of the orbit, with the help of a revolving mirror.
2. MSU-CS — mid-resolution instrument. Field resolution is 175 m in channels 1–4 and 590 m in channel 5. Swath width is 600 km. Five spectral channels: 0.5–0.6; 0.6–0.7; 0.7–0.8; 0.8–1.0; 10.3–11.8 μm. The survey can be made simultaneously in four channels (1, 2, 3, 4, or 1, 2, 4, 5). A synchronous operation is foreseen of both MSU-CS and MSU-E. The MSU-CS survey is made in channels 2 and 4.

Fig. 2.29. Image of Neva Bay in three spectral intervals obtained from Kosmos-1939: (a) 0.5–0.6 μm; (b) 0.6–0.7 μm; (c) 0.8–0.9 μm.

Fig. 2.29. (b) 0.6–0.7 μm

Fig. 2.29. (c) 0.8–0.9 μm

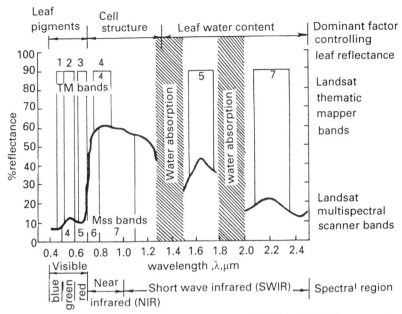

Fig. 2.30. Typical vegetation reflectance curve acquired with JPL field spectrometer. Landsat MSS and TM bands are indicated. Gaps in the spectral curve at 1.4 and 1.9 μm are caused by atmospheric water absorption (data were not plotted at these points).

Table 2.14. Characteristics of the space system "Resurs–0": Sun-synchronous orbit; height 650 km; mass of satellite 1840 kg; mass of instrumentation 600 kg; lifetime in orbit 2 years; accuracy of the orientation 30′. Basic parameters of the on-board instruments

Parameters	MSU-E (multichannel high-resolution scanner on CCD structures)	MSU-CS (multichannel mid-resolution cone-sweeping scanner)	SLR (side-looking radar with the synthetic aperture antenna)	Microwave radiometer
Swath width, km	2 × 45	600	100	1200
FOV, km	± 350	600	100	1200
Number of spectral channels	3	5	1	4
Spectral range, μm	0.5–0.6 0.6–0.7 0.8–0.9	0.5–0.6 0.6–0.7 0.7–0.8 0.8–1.1 10.4–12.6	9.2 cm	0.8 cm 1.35 cm 2.2 cm 4.5 cm
Resolution near the surface, m	45 × 45	240 × 170 (0.5–1.1 μm) 500 (10.4–12.6 μm)	200 × 200	17 km
Speed of data transmission, Mbites/s	7.68	7.68	15 Mbites/s (without on-board processor) 200 Kbites/s (with on-board processor)	80 Kbites/s

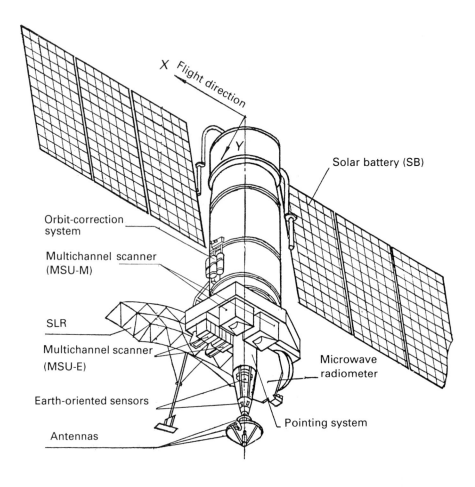

Fig. 2.31. The space system "Resurs-0", general view.

Oceanographic satellites of the "Okean" series

1. MSU-L low-resolution instrument. Field resolution is 1 km. Swath width is 1930 km. Four spectral channels: 0.5–0.6; 0.6–0.7; 0.7–0.8; 0.8–1.0 μm.
2. MSU-M mid-resolution instrument. Field resolution is 345 m. Swath width is 1360 km. Two channels: 0.5–0.7; 0.7–1.1 μm.
3. SLR side-looking radar. Working wavelength is 3.2 cm. Field resolution is about 2 km. Swath width is 450 km.
4. RMO8 scanning radiometer. Working wavelength is 0.8 cm. Field resolution is 15 km. Swath width is 550 km.
5. MSU-CS mid-resolution instrument. Field resolution is 500 m. Swath width is 950 km. Scanning at 39° forward and backward, in the direction of the satellite's flight. One spectral channel in each of the front and rear zones (0.6–0.8 μm).

The regime of synchronous switching-on of MSU-L, SLR, and RMO8 is foreseen with video information on a single frame. The survey with MSU-E, MSU-CS, MSU-L, SLR, and RMO8 can be made over any land and ocean area in the memory regime with subsequent transmission to the receiving station.

Meteorological satellites of the type "Meteor-2"
The basic parameters of the system "Meteor" (Fig. 2.32) are listed in Table 2.15.

1. MR-900B—scanning telephotometer. Low-field resolution—2.5 km in nadir. Swath width is 2100 km. One spectral channel—0.5–0.7 μm.
2. MR-2000B—scanning telephotometer. Low-field resolution—1 km. Swath width is 2650 km. One spectral channel—0.5–0.7 μm.
3. BCh-100—IR scanning radiometer. Low-field resolution—8 km. Swath width is 2850 km. One spectral channel—8–12 μm.
4. 174K—IR scanning radiometer. Angular resolution is 2°. Swath width is 1000 km. Ten spectral channels.

Meteorological satellites of the type "Meteor-3"

1. MR-900B—scanning telephotometer. Low-field resolution—3 km. Swath width is 2600 km. One spectral channel—0.5–0.7 μm.
2. MR-2000B—scanning telephotometer. Low-field resolution—2 km. Swath width is 3000 km. One spectral channel—0.5–0.7 μm.
3. "Klimat"—IR scanning radiometer. Field resolution is 3–5 km. Swath width is 3000 km. One spectral channel — 10.5–12.0 μm.
4. 174K—IR scanning radiometer. Angular resolution is 2°. Swath width is 1000 km. Ten spectral channels.

2.6.2 Composition and basic characteristics of scientific instrumentation of foreign meteorological satellites

1. NOAA – AVHRR instrument
The operating regime, APT: field resolution in nadir is 4 km over the whole image area. Swath width is 3000 km. Spectral ranges : TV-inform.—0.725–1.100 μm, IR-inform.—10.5–11.5 μm. Periodicity repeated survey with two satellites, daily—4 times. Information is transmitted to the information-receiving station (IRS) and automated IRS (AIRS).

The operating regime, HPPT: field resolution nadir is 4 km over the whole image area. Swath width is 3000 km. Spectral channels—0.55–0.90; 0.725–1.100; 3.55–3.93; 10.5–11.5; 11.5–12.5 μm. Information is received by the IRS in Moscow.

2. Geostationary meteorological satellites
METEOSAT—Earth coverage by 0° meridian with a radius of 70°. Surface resolution in nadir: TV—2.5 km; IR—5 km; water vapour—5 km. Spectral ranges: TV—0.4–1.1 μm; IR—10.5–12.5 μm; water vapour—5.7–7.1 μm. Periodicity of repeated survey for TV and water vapour—once a day; IR-inform.—twice a day.

Table 2.15. The space-borne system "Meteor": height of the orbit 720 km; total mass of satellite 2400 kg; mass of scientific complex 700 kg; lifetime in orbit 2 years; accuracy of orientation 30'. Basic parameters of the on-board information complex

Characteristics	TV-complex	IR high-resolution radiometer	IR spectrometer	UV backscattering spectrometer	Ozone-M (multichannel UV spectrometer)	TOMS (total ozone content rapper)	ERBE (to measure radiation budget)	RMC—radiation metrological complex
FOV, km	3100	3100	1000	200	To measure on slanted routes	3100	3000	Flux record: protons —1-600 MeV; electrons—0.15-3.1 MeV. Total sums of electrons and protons: 2 MeV and 30 MeV, respectively
Number of spectral channels	1	1	10	8	4	6	4	
Spectral ranges, μm	0.5-0.8	10.5-12.5	9.4-19.68	0.25-0.38	0.25-0.29 0.37-0.39 0.6-0.64 0.99-1.03	0.3125 0.3175 0.3313 0.3398 0.36 0.38		
Resolution near the Earth's surface, km	0.7 × 1.4	3 × 3 1° for $t = \pm 40°C$; 3° for $t = -50°C$	42	3-5 vertically	2 vertically	47 × 47 in nadir 62 × 62 for all other frames	50 in nadir	

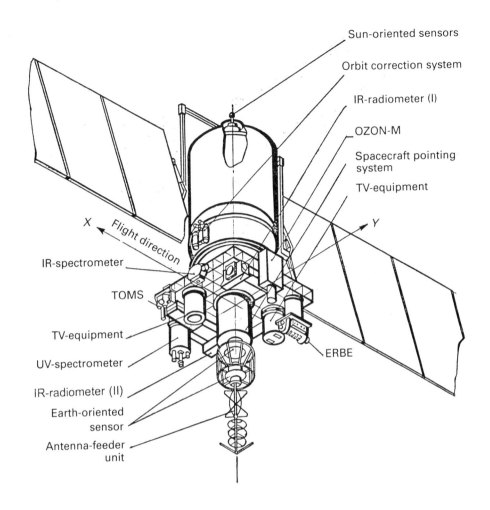

Fig. 2.32. The space system "Meteor", general view.

Information is received by the IRS in Moscow.

GOES—Earth coverage by the 75° W meridian with a radius of 70°. Spectral range for IR-inform.—10.5–12.5 μm. Periodicity of repeated survey—once a day. Information is received by the IRS in Moscow. Field resolution for IR-inform.—8 km.

GMS—Earth coverage by the central meridian is 140° W with the radius 70°. Field resolution for IR-inform. In nadir is 5 km. Spectral range is 10.5–12.5 μm. Periodicity of repeated survey is twice a day. Information is received by the IRS in Moscow and Khabarovsk.

P. Kronberg (1988) gives the technical specifications of the space survey systems in the interests of land use (see Table 2.16).

Table 2.16. Technical requirements for space survey systems in the interests of land use (Kronberg, 1988)

Sphere of application	Local resolution, m	Periodicity	Types and intervals of survey (channels, wavelengths, μm)	Geometrical accuracy	Scales used
Soil science	30	2–4 times a year	Channels, MSS: 4–7; 0.4–1.1; 1.55–1.7; 10–12		1:50000 to 1:200000
Agricultural inventory, harvest assessment	10–30	Every 7–9 days annually	Panchromatic channels 4–7; 0.4–1.1; 1.55–1.7; 10–12	±1 pixel	1:100000 to 1:250000 1:100000 1:50000
Forest inventory	10–30	4–10 times a year	Panchromatic channels 4–7; 0.4–1.1; 1.55–1.7; 10–12	-1 pixel	1:100000
Hydrology	30–60	Depending on the problem	Channels 5; 0.3–0.9; 10–12	-1 pixel	1:100000 1:250000
Land use	30–100 20–30	4 times during vegetation period	Panchromatic channels	±1 pixel	1:250000 1:50000
Oceanography Ice observation Coastal navigation	500–1000	Twice daily	Channels 11; 0.3–0.9; 10–12; + altimeter, passive microwave radiometry	±2 pixels	1:500000 to 1:100000

2.7 MANNED ORBITAL STATIONS

Thirty-five years have passed since the space flight of the first cosmonaut Yu.A. Gagarin on the spacecraft "Vostok". During these years space exploration has made considerable progress manifested through:

— creating technically perfect space vehicles which can carry and ensure operation of large complexes of scientific instruments;
— accomplishing extensive programmes of scientific studies, both national and international.

Experience in manned space flights has illustrated a high efficiency of instrumental and visual observations by the astronauts (Beregovoi et al., 1972a,b; Buznikov, 1980a,b, 1981, 1982, 1983a,b,c, 1986, 1987; Buznikov et al., 1984; Kondratyev and Buznikov, 1984), application and testing of various scientific complexes; accomplishment of scientific studies, and solution of economic problems (Beregovoi et al., 1972a; Kondratyev et al., 1972a; The expedition..., 1989). The flight of the first orbital station "Salut" launched on 19 April 1971 has marked a new stage in space exploration (Beregovoi et al., 1972a; Glushko, 1987). Systematic flights of the Russian orbital stations "Salut" with changeable crews have promoted the mastering of space according to plan. By 1990 the total time spent by Russian astronauts in orbit had reached 13 years. Manned orbital stations (MOSs) have become scientific orbital laboratories to carry out a complex of experimental and production work (Beregovoi et al., 1972a; Glushko, 1987; Kondratyev et al., 1978).

They have opened up wide possibilities to study the Earth's surface and the atmosphere by making use of remote sounding with the help of visual (Beregovoi et al., 1972b; Buznikov et al., 1984; Grigoryev and Kondratyev, 1989), optical (Beliajev et al., 1978; Beregovoi et al., 1972a; Buznikov, 1980a,b, 1983a,b,c, 1986, 1987; Kondratyev and Buznikov, 1981; Zümnich, 1989), radar (Armand, 1960; Kondratyev et al., 1990; Lakhtanov and Piotrovskaya, 1983; Salganik et al., 1990), and other observational means. In the space programmes for MOS, of much importance are investigations into the interests of land sciences, studies of its resources, and global ecological studies.

Accumulated experience has made it possible to make one more important step within the programme of space studies—the MOS "Mir" was launched on 20 February 1986. It became the basic unit for the permanent manned complex of the module type (Grigoryev and Kondratyev, 1989; Permanently..., 1990). Figure 2.33 shows one of the intermediate stages of equipping the complex "Mir" with the modules, when, apart from the basic unit and transport vehicles, it contains the astrophysical module "Kvant" and one of the sample scientific modules.

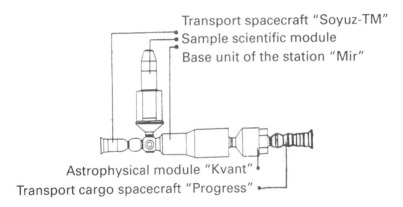

Transport spacecraft "Soyuz-TM"
Sample scientific module
Base unit of the station "Mir"

Astrophysical module "Kvant"
Transport cargo spacecraft "Progress"

Fig. 2.33. Scheme of the intermediate stage of equipping the orbital complex "Mir" with scientific modules.

The orbital complex "Mir" includes: the basic unit, transport vehicles "Soyuz-TM", transport cargo vehicles "Progress", and scientific modules. The basic characteristics of the orbital complex "Mir" are given in Table 2.17. In the period of exploitation in orbit, both the number of docked modules and the general configuration of the complex can be changed. The module design of the MOS "Mir" has made it possible to substantially broaden the objectives of manned space flights by equipping the MOSs with specialized modules, which enable one, on the one hand, to expand the scientific programme and, on the other hand, to make it goal-oriented at various stages of the flight.

When choosing concrete experiments for the MOS "Mir" or the space module ENRS, of primary importance are: (i) the scientific and practical value of the experiment; (ii) advantages of the MOS in this experiment compared to automatic

Table 2.17. Basic characteristics of the orbital complex "Mir"

Parameter	Estimate
Orbit inclination, deg.	51.6
Height of orbit, km	300–400
Period of rotation, min.	90.3–93.4
Accuracy of orientation:	
— conventional, deg.	1.5
— precise, min.	15
Total mass of the complex, t, max.	130
Volume of pressurized bays, m^3	400
Total length of the base unit of the module "Kvant" and two spacecraft, m	32.9
Maximum transverse size by solar batteries, m	29.7
Number of modules	up to 5
Number of spacecraft "Soyuz"	0–2
Number of spacecraft "Progress"	0–1
Size of crew, people:	
— basic	2–3
— visiting	2–3

space vehicles, such as "Meteor-2", "Meteor-Priroda", "Okean-0", "Resurs-0" in the near-polar mid-altitude orbits.

The main element of the station is the orbital (basic) unit of the complex "Mir", which provides the conditions needed for the work and rest of the crew and controls the operation of all the elements of the station, including power supply, transmission to Earth of telemetric information about the results of scientific studies and experiments, etc. The characteristics of the basic unit of the complex "Mir" are listed in Table 2.18. The scientific modules are designed to mount the scientific instrumentation and life-support systems. The basic characteristics of a sample scientific module are listed in Table 2.19.

Table 2.18. Characteristics of the base unit of the complex "Mir"

Parameter	Estimate
Mass, t	21
Length, m	13.13
Length of working bay, m	7.67
Maximum diameter, m	4.2
Diameter of the passage bay, m	2.2
Type of carrier-rocket	"Proton"

Table 2.19. Basic characteristics of a sample scientific module

Parameter	Estimate
Mass in orbital complex, kg	20600
Length of body, m	12.5
Payload, kg	5000
Type of carrier-rocket	"Proton"

Table 2.20. Basic characteristics of the transport spacecraft "Soyuz-TM"

Parameter	Estimate
Mass of spacecraft, kg	7070
Mass of the landing module, kg	3000
Length of the spacecraft body, m	6.98
Maximum diameter, m	2.72
Span of solar batteries, m	10.6
Size of crew, people	3
Flight time, days:	
— autonomous	3.2
— as part of the complex	180
Type of carrier-rocket	"Soyuz"

The manned transport vehicle "Soyuz-TM" is to deliver a crew to the station and take the crew and the cargo containing the results of studies and experiments back to the Earth (see Table 2.20). The characteristics of the transport cargo vehicle "Progress" delivering fuel to the station, scientific equipment, elements of the life-support system and other systems are given in Table 2.21.

Owing to the orbit's inclination of 51.6°, the on-board complex makes it possible to observe 95% of the Earth's surface. The basic regime of the orientation of the

Table 2.21. Basic characteristics of the cargo spacecraft "Progress"

Parameter	Estimate
Mass of spacecraft, kg	7240
Payload, kg	Up to 2400
including:	
— in cargo bay	Up to 1400
— in filling-up bay	Up to 1200
Length of the body, m	6.98
Flight time, days:	
— autonomous	Up to 3
— as part of the complex	Up to 90
Type of carrier-rocket	"Soyuz"

complex is the gravitational stabilization (with the longitudinal axis of "Mir" in nadir), with solar batteries oriented towards the sun. The regime of orientation is foreseen with the longitudinal axes of the station and the modules in the orbital system of coordinates (along and across the flight trajectory) as well as in the inertial system of coordinates.

The on-board computer information complex, which includes seven computers, performs numerous operations in the automatic regime on the complex maintenance, and also helps to control the state of the systems by using displays containing data.

2.7.1 Composition of the equipment of the "Mir" complex
The orbital unit includes a:

1. Multichannel spectrometer MKS-M (Zümnich, 1989) to measure the brightness of the "Earth surface-atmosphere" system in the visible and near IR of solar radiation reflected by the Earth. Control is realized either in automatic regime or from the control panel inside the pressurized bay. Information is transmitted via telemetry channels and recorded on the MCS MGF.
2. Hand-operated spectrometer "Spektr-256" to study the spectral characteristics of natural formations, the dynamics of colour coordinates of natural formations, the study of the structure and dynamics of the terrestrial atmosphere. Operation control is in the instrument itself.
3. Hand-operated spectrograph RSS-3 for spectrographic measurements of natural formations on the Earth's surface, of the atmosphere near the twilight and daytime horizons, and of the Sun's disc through the atmospheric layer on slanted optical paths. It is also used for synchronous spectrographic measurements of the test areas during the synchronous sub-satellite experiments within the programme "Kuban". The spectrograph is an autonomous device and can be mounted on one of the windows of the station with the help of a special holder (Fig. 2.34).
4. Photographic complex of the station, which is represented by the cameras KATE-140, "Sever", and hand-operated camera "Hassel-blood".
5. "SKIF" complex, which makes it possible to record the spectra of emissions of the Earth's surface and atmosphere with simultaneous photographic and subsequent visual display of the data obtained (Pliuta et al., 1984). The control is either autonomous, from the control panel of the SKIF-NO unit, or manual, with the help of the SKIF-OM unit. It can be fastened to any window of the station 230 mm in diameter supplied with special holders.

2.7.2 Composition of the equipment of the scientific research module-1
1. Remotely controlled videospectrometric TVC complex. It is mounted on the observation platform, which can operate in the automatic regime of guidance and monitoring the objects with the coordinates known. The second regime of operation of the platform is the real-time control of the TVC from the Centre of Flight Control. The third regime is the semi-automatic regime of control from the operator's place in the orbital station "Mir". The TV and spectral equipment is

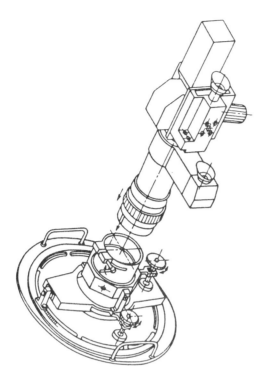

Fig. 2.34. Mounting of the RSS-3 spectrograph on a window of the orbital complex "Mir".

mounted on the remotely controlled platform. The accuracy of the measuring of the platform position in space is not worse than 0.5′. The orientation of the TVC depends on the orientation of the platform; in this case either the 3-axis orbital or the inertial orientation of the complex is needed.

The TVC incorporates:

— a multichannel spectrometer MKS-M2 to measure the brightness of the "atmosphere-surface" system in the visible and near-IR;
— a spectrometer ITS-7D to measure absolute values of the spectral brightness of the Earth–atmosphere–space transition zones and the underlying surface in the spectral interval 4–16 μm;
— TV-cameras KL-140ST and KL-103 to reflect the position of the object under study on the operator's TV screen.

2. Teleradiometer "FAZA" to measure absolute spectral brightness of the Earth–atmosphere–space transition zones and underlying surface in the spectral interval 0.4–2.2 μm.

3. A multizonal photocamera MKF-6MA (Soyuz-22..., 1980) to take photos of the underlying surface in 6 spectral intervals.

2.7.3 The measuring complex of the specialized scientific module "Priroda"

The scientific complex "Priroda" makes it possible to realize with the help of a special scientific module of the orbital complex "Mir":

— radiophysical methods of the environmental studies;
— IR spectroradiometric methods to study the spatial structure of the reflected and scattered radiation in the "atmosphere–surface" system.

The complex incorporates the following instruments:

— microwave radiometric system "Mir", including the route polarization radiometers for nadir measurements R-30, R-80, R-135, R-225P, RP-600, two panoramic lines of three polarization radiometers RP-600 operating at 40° to nadir, "IKAR-II", a unit of scanning polarization radiometers "Delta", and scanning radiometer R-400 "IKAR-D" also operating at an angle of 40° to nadir;
— 64-channel IR spectroradiometric system "ISTOK-1";
— 17-channel spectroradiometric system in the visible and near-IR—MOZ-Obzor;
— TV camera of the viewing arrangement "ISTOK-1";
— 2-frequency synthetic-aperture side-looking radar—SAR;
— Precision radioaltimeter—PRV;
— a system of information collection to study the atmospheric transparency "Ozone-Mir".

The characteristics of scientific instrumentation of the complex "Priroda" are given in Table 2.22. The general view of the specialized module "Priroda" together with the scheme of the instrument's arrangement is shown in Fig. 2.35.

2.7.4 The occultation sounding of the atmosphere from manned spacecraft

Developments of methods and instruments for continuous global-scale monitoring of the distribution of some trace gases, such as water vapour, ozone, nitrogen oxides, etc., are important for practical application of some sections of the WCP (Kondratyev, 1980b). This is connected with the fact that the state of the atmosphere (especially its upper layers) is largely determined by solar radiation absorption for which the atmospheric trace gases are responsible. Interest in their distribution has been raised by increasing atmospheric pollution, the importance of studies of photochemical processes in the stratosphere and mesosphere, a search for dependences between the spatial and temporal variations in the gas and aerosol components of the atmosphere, and present climate change (Kondratyev, 1980c; Marchuk, 1979). A change in the concentration of trace gases can break various natural processes taking place in the atmosphere, as well as the ecological equilibrium. For example, an increase in the water vapour content will change the albedo of the surface–atmosphere system. Information about the vertical distribution of water vapour is also important to develop a theory of the thermal regime of the stratosphere and the mesosphere. So far, there is no adequate theory of the appearance and distribution of water vapour in the stratosphere and the mesosphere.

Table 2.22. Composition and characteristics of the scientific instrumentation of the complex "Priroda"

Instrumentation	Weight, kg	Power supply, W	Wavelength, cm	Directional diagram width, deg.	Fluctuation sensitivity for $t=1$ s, K	Spatial resolution ($h=400$ km), km	Information content, Kbytes/s	Swath width ($h=400$ km), km	Viewing angle from nadir, deg.	Country
					I. Microwave radiometric system "IKAR"					
1. Set of nadir route indicating radiometers	70	130	—	—	—	—	0.4	—	—	Russia
R-30			0.3	9	0.15	60		60	0	
R-80			0.8	9	0.15	60		60	0	
R-135			1.35	9	0.15	60		60	0	
R-225P			2.25	9	0.10	60		60	0	
R-600			6.0	9	0.15	60		60	0	
2. Set of scanning radiometers "Delta"	50	100	—	—	—	—	0.8	400	40	Russia
R-30			0.3	1	1.5	5				
R-80			0.8	1.5	0.5	8				
R-135			1.35	2	0.4	15				
3. RP-225 (panoramic)	20	40	2.25	12	0.15	75	0.1	750	40	Russia (3 radiometers)
4. R-400 (scanning)	35	30	4.0	5–7	0.15	50	0.2	400	40	Bulgaria Russia (5 radiometers)
5. R-600 (panoramic line)	20	30	6.0	12	0.15	75	0.3	750	40	Bulgaria Russia (5 radiometers)
					II. IR spectrometric system "ISTOK-1"					
6. "Istok-1"	100	60	3.6–16 μm (64 chann.)	12' × 48' (viewing angle)	0.12	1 × 6 (4 km—slant)	0.8	6	0–90 scanning 0–90 orbital plane	Russia, Poland Czech Republic Romania

III. Spectrometric system in the visible and near-IR										
7. "MOZ-Obzor"	120	220	0.415–1.01 (17 chann.)			0.6	16/256	85	0	Russia Germany
IV. TV camera										
8. "Istok-1" TV-camera	3	5	0.4–0.75 μm	15	0.5 lux	0.3	6.5	90	0	Russia
V. Precision radioaltimeter										
9. PRV	90	450	2.25	1.15	—	0.1	8.0	2	0	Russia
VI. Side-looking synthetic-aperture radar										
10. SAR	470	750 × 2	92 / 23	1 × 4 / 2.5 × 4	—	0.1–0.15	—	70–100	30–40	Russia
VII. Instruments to measure the concentration profile of ozone and other trace gases										
11. "Ozone-Mir" (occultation measurements)	70	200	4 ranges within 0.26–0.12 μm	—	—	15 km vertically	50	—	—	Russia
VIII. Multichannel scanning instruments										
12. MSU-CS	56	300	0.5–0.6 / 0.6–0.7 / 0.7–0.8 / 0.8–1.1 / 10–12.5 μm	—	0.5	120 m	11.5×10^3	350	39	Russia
13. MSU-E	27	150	0.5–0.6 / 0.6–0.7 / 0.8–0.9		0.5	300 m	11.5×10^3	2 × 27	—	Russia
IX. Lidars										
14. "Alisa"	250	2650	5270 Å	3′	—	150 m vertically 1000 m horizontally	40 Mbites/ cycle	—	0	Russia, France

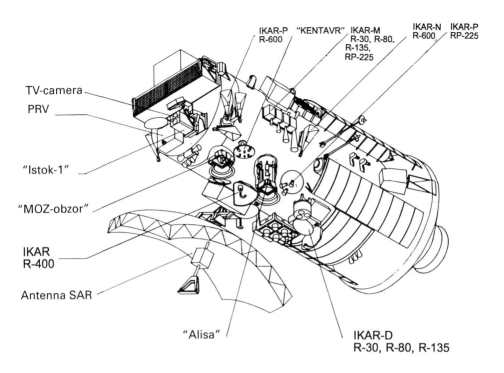

IKAR-P   "KENTAVR" IKAR-M   IKAR-N IKAR-P
R-600   R-30, R-80.   R-600   RP-225
                       R-135,
                       RP-225

TV-camera

PRV

"Istok-1"

"MOZ-obzor"

IKAR
R-400

Antenna SAR

"Alisa"   IKAR-D
                                     R-30, R-80, R-135

Fig. 2.35. Schematic general view of the specialized scientific module "Priroda" of the orbital complex "Mir".

The global character of this problem has required new measurement techniques with the use of space-borne means which make it possible to accomplish a systematic monitoring of the state of the atmosphere on global scales. Here the occultation sounding of the atmosphere on slanted optical paths during sunrise and sunset (with respect to the space vehicle carrying the spectrometer) records the solar radiation absorption in the most informative absorption bands for the atmospheric gas under study provides a gradative assessment of the attenuation (Kondratyev et al., 1974d, 1976, 1978).

The scheme of an experiment realization on slanted optical paths at sunrise and sunset with respect to the spacecraft is shown in Fig. 2.36. At the moment of measurement the input slit of the spectrometer must be parallel to the Earth's horizon, since only in this case is it possible to record the atmospheric absorption of solar radiation with a good vertical resolution and to estimate the true altitude of the optical trajectory corresponding to the recorded absorption spectrum. Analysis of the information support to spectral measurements of stratospheric and mesospheric humidity, making use of the occultation sounding technique, has been made in Kondratyev et al. (1974d).

For the first time, the technique of occultation sounding of the atmosphere to study the water vapour vertical profile has been realized in 1975 during the flight of

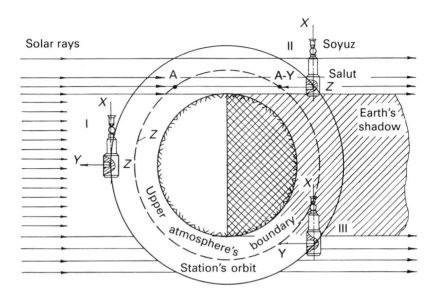

Fig. 2.36. Scheme of an experiment on occultation sounding.

the orbital station Salut-4 (Kondratyev et al., 1976), carrying a complex of solar spectrometers CSS-2—a 2-channel specular fast spectrometer based on the vertically symmetrical scheme, with the photon electric measurement of parameters and the solar servosystem. The servosystem directed the input slits of the spectrometers to the geometric centre of the solar disc to an accuracy of 1' and kept them in this position during the period of measurements. At the moment of measurements the input slits of the spectrometers were parallel to the Earth's horizon owing to the orientation of the station, moving by its own momentum.

Figure 2.37 shows the optical-kinetic scheme of CSS-2. The CSS-2 unit was mounted outside the pressurized bay of the station Salut-4 and included the IR spectrometer with the spectral channel 3800–3825 cm^{-1} and half-width of the apparatus function 0.8 cm^{-1} to measure the absorption in the 2.7-μm band of water vapour, and the UV spectrometer with the spectral range of measurements 400Å in the interval 2000Å – 3600Å with the spectral width of the slit 2Å.

The spectrometer was fast-operating. When measuring the absorption by water vapour in the 2.7-μm band, each spectrum 3800–3825 cm^{-1} wide together with the standard, is recorded over 1.75 s, and the contour of the basic information line 3816.07 cm^{-1} over 0.09 s.

Figure 2.38 exemplifies a record of the water vapour absorption spectra at sunrise. Measurements of the water vapour mixing ratio in the stratosphere and the mesosphere made with CSS-2 in winter over the Marshall Islands testify to a dry stratosphere with the mixing ratio $q_{H2O} = 1$–2×10^{-6} g/g at altitudes of 30 to 60 km (Kondratyev et al., 1976). Comparison of the results of occultation measurements on Salut-4 and on meteorological rockets has shown that an

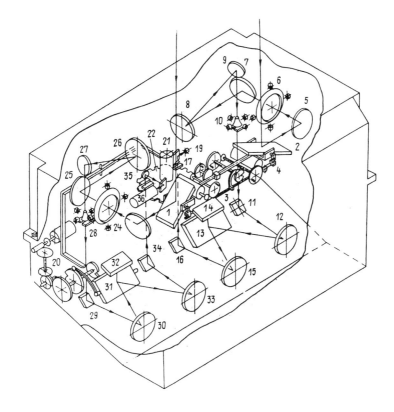

Fig. 2.37. The optico-kinematic scheme of the complex of solar spectrometers.
Servosystem: 1, 2—tracking mirrors, 3, 4—electric motors of azimuth and inclination; 6, 24—sensors of rough tracking.
IR channel: 8—focusing objective (extra-axis parabola $f = 278$ mm; $\alpha = 19°$); 10—input slit with sensors for precise tracking; 12—collimation objective; 14—diffraction grating $N = 300$ lines/mm; 15—camera objective; 17—output slit; 19—receiver FS2AN; 20—mechanism for output slit motion; 5, 7, 9, 11, 13, 16, 18—flat mirrors.
UV channel: 26—focusing objective (extra-axis parabola $f = 278$ mm, $\alpha = 19°$ input slit with sensors of precise tracking; 30—collimation objective; 32—diffraction grating $N = 1200$ lines/mm; 33—camera objective; 35—output slit; 36—receiver PEM-ozone, 23, 25, 27, 29, 31, 34—flat mirrors.

increased moisture content of the stratosphere obtained with rocket soundings is explained by omitting the parasite moisture introduced by the carrier and remaining in the instrument (Kondratyev et al., 1978).

The measurement of the spectra of solar radiation absorption by the atmosphere following the scheme shown in Fig. 2.38 at each sunset and sunrise makes it possible, because of the orbit's precession, to obtain the vertical profiles of the atmosphere over different geographic regions. The orbital station makes 17 rotations round the Earth per 24 hours. If measurements are made twice in each orbit, one can obtain 34 vertical profiles of the atmosphere during 24 hours, which makes it possible to make

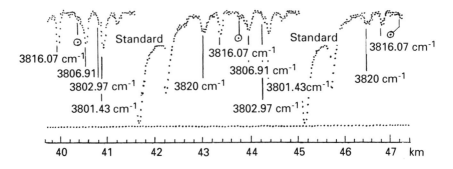

Fig. 2.38. An exemplified record of the spectra of solar radiation absorption by water vapour in the 2.7-μm band at slanted optical paths with the CSS-2 carried by Salut-4.

predictions about the global distribution of water vapour in the stratosphere and the mesosphere. To solve this problem, the IKAR spectrometer has been developed, the technical characteristics of which are given in Table 2.23, and the optical scheme in Fig. 2.39.

Experience from occultation measurements on Salut-4 has shown the possibility of their use to create an operational system of monitoring the gas composition of the atmosphere on a global scale.

Table 2.23. Technical characteristics of the spectrometer "IKAR"

Parameter	Estimate
Angles of following the Sun:	
— azimuth	$+9°$
— elevation	$+7.5°$
Rate of Sun following	$5° \text{ s}^{-1}$
Accuracy of pointing at the centre of the Sun's disc	$\pm 1'$
Spectral range of measurement	$3800–3825 \text{ cm}^{-1}$
Reverse linear dispersion, dv/dl	$1,66 \text{ cm}^{-1} \text{ mm}^{-1}$
Spectral resolution, Δv	0.37 cm^{-1}
Light-power of the instrument by the flux	$9.10^{-4} \text{ cm}^2/\text{cm}^{-1}$
Illumination and collimation objectives	Extra-axis paraboloidal mirrors $f = 505 \pm 3$ mm, $\varphi = 11° \, 45'$
Dispersing element	Flat diffraction grating $N = 300$ lines mm^{-1}, Angle of glitter 52°; working order $K = 2$
Rate of scanning, dv/dt	$15 \text{ cm}^{-1} \text{ s}^{-1}$
Receiver	Non-cooled photoresistor PS2AN with germanium filter

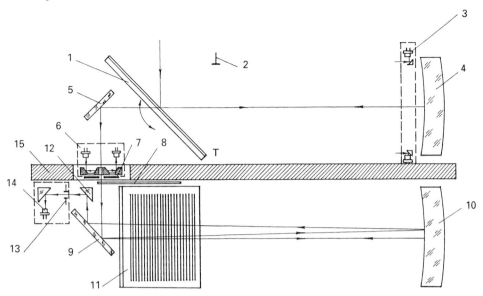

Fig. 2.39. Optical scheme of the spectrometer: 1—mirror of the servosystem; 2—diaphragm; 3—sensors of preliminary tracking; 4—illumination objective; 5—flat mirror; 6—sensors for precise tracking; 7—input slit; 8—disc of modulator; 9—flat mirror; 10—collimating and camera objective of the spectrometer; 11—diffraction grating; 12—flat mirror; 13—output slit; 14—radiation receiver; 15—plate.

2.7.5 On reconstruction of water vapour profile in the upper stratosphere and lower mesosphere using the occultation sounding in the 2.7-μm absorption band

In connection with the solving of problems of global ecology, of great interest is the problem of monitoring the gas composition of the middle atmosphere. Here the satellite remote sounding systems are the basic means of observations. The technique of occultation sounding on slanted paths is most useful to monitor the gas and aerosol composition of the upper stratosphere and lower mesosphere in the altitude interval 30–70 km (Kondratyev and Pokrovski, 1989b). For aerosol, ozone, and some other trace gases this method has proved to be useful (Kondratyev and Pokrovski, 1989b; Kondratyev et al., 1987). The H_2O 2.7-μm band can be used to determine the vertical profile of water vapour. For the first time, an attempt has been made (Kondratyev et al., 1976) to retrieve the H_2O profile in the stratosphere based on the CSS-2 data obtained on Salut-4 over the Marshall Islands on 21 January 1975. Later on, similar studies were undertaken by American scientists using the SAMS instruments carried by Nimbus-7 (The stratosphere..., 1981).

A publication by A. Buznikov, O. Pokrovski and T. Pchelova (1991) was dedicated to processing the data of measurements made with CSS-2 using an alternative conversion method.

Setting the problem

There are four strong lines in the H_2O 2.7-μm absorption band: 3801.43; 3806.91; 3816.07; 3820 cm^{-1}. Each can be used to record the vertical profiles of atmospheric transparency which, in turn, can be used as initial data to retrieve the water vapour concentration profiles.

This inverse problem is non-linear in view of an almost exponential dependence of atmospheric transparency on the reduced water vapour mass along the optical path in the atmosphere, which is determined by the viewing line. The setting of the problem and basic formulas have been given in Kondratyev et al. (1976). In view of the non-linear dependence mentioned above, to solve the inverse problem, one needs the iteration algorithms requiring multiple calculations of atmospheric transmission for different H_2O masses at every observation height. In this case, the line-by-line calculation technique for transparency functions is not worth while because of the much needed computer time. For practical realization of the inverse problem, more useful are various approximations in calculations of transmission functions for spherical geometry.

The algorithm LOWTRAN-5M (Robertson et al., 1981) which ensures calculations with a resolution of 5 cm^{-1} and accuracy 1–2%, was used to approximate the transmission functions. Since the input spectra were made with a higher resolution, they were reduced to a 5 cm^{-1} resolution through convolution with a triangular apparatus function. Both calculated and measured transmission functions $\tau_{\Delta v}(v,h)$ and $\tilde{\tau}_{\Delta v}(v,h)$ depend on frequency v, spectral interval half-width Δv, and viewing line height h. Besides, calculated values of transmissions $\tau_{\Delta v}(v,h)$ depend on the vertical distribution of water vapour $q(h')$ ($h' \geq h$). Thus, $\tau_{\Delta v} = \tau_{\Delta v}(v,h,q,(h'))$, $h' \geq h$. Practically, one has to use a discrete set of recorded transmission values $\tau_{\Delta v}(v, h_i)$ ($i = 1,\ldots, n$). Calculations are also made for a finite number of tangential observation heights $\{h_i\}$. This determines the possibility of retrieving the water vapour profile only in a finite number of layers confined to altitudes $\{h'_j\}$ ($j = 1,\ldots, N$). At each tangential height, h_i, the observed transmission contains certain observation errors $\tilde{\tau}_{\Delta v}(v, h_i) = \tau_{\Delta v}(v, h_1 + \varepsilon(h_i))$. Suppose, the observation errors $\varepsilon(h_i)$ are random and have zero means and known dispersions $\sigma^2_{\varepsilon(h_i)} = \sigma^2_\varepsilon(i)$. With observation uncertainties supposed to be independent at various heights, h_i, one can state that the covariance matrix of random vector $\varepsilon = (\varepsilon(h_1),\ldots,\varepsilon(h_n))^T$ (T is the transpose) has a diagonal form $\Sigma_\varepsilon = \text{diag}\{\sigma^2_\varepsilon(1),\ldots, \sigma^2_\varepsilon(n)\}$. In the presence of correlated errors of observations the matrix Σ_ε can have a free structure. The latter circumstance is the more substantial that in solving the inverse problem the values $\varepsilon(h_i)$ should also include an error of approximation of transmission functions. Introduce the vectors formed from the values of measured transmissions at fixed v and Δv: $\tilde{\tau} = (\tilde{\tau}_{\Delta v}(v,h_1), \ldots, \tilde{\tau}_{\Delta v}(v,h_n))^T$, the respective calculated transmissions $\tau = (\tau_{\Delta v}(v,h_1,q(h')),\ldots,\tau_{\Delta v}(v,h_n,q(h')))^T$, and the values sought $q(q(h'_1),\ldots,q(h'_N))^T$. Now the inverse problem of the determination of the water vapour vertical profile is reduced to the solution of the minimization problem

$$\min_q ||\tilde{\tau} - \tau(q)||^2_{\Sigma_s}, \tag{2.23}$$

where the notation of energy norm $||a||_{B^2} = (a,Ba)$ is used.

Before solving problem (2.23), it is necessary to consider some methodical problems.

Analysis of the direct problem solution

The vertical profiles of atmospheric spectral transparency on slanted paths serve as initial data for water vapour retrieval. In the spectral region considered, these profiles depend on the vertical profiles of water vapour, aerosol, temperature, atmospheric pressure, and other characteristics. Studies of the sensitivity of atmospheric spectral transmission to changes in the atmospheric characteristics mentioned above serve the basis for solution of the inverse problem. Such studies make it possible to obtain recommendations on the choice of the most informative spectral intervals and to determine the altitudinal range of sounding.

The calculation of the transmission on slanted paths based on the data on the vertical profiles of basic atmospheric parameters is a direct problem. At the first stage, the calculated and measured values of transmission have been compared. Calculations were made with the vertical distributions of atmospheric parameters corresponding to the 1962 US model (Kneizys et al., 1983). A comparison of experimental and calculated values of transmission for two lines, 3801 and 3816 cm^{-1} (Fig. 2.40), demonstrates different agreements of the data for different observation heights. The differences (curves 1 and 2) in the middle stratosphere (30–45 km) reach tens of per cent. In the lower mesosphere and upper stratosphere (45–65 km) the difference between experimental and calculated values constitutes several per cent. One of the reasons for these difference is an exponential decrease with height of the weight concentration of water vapour and other optically active components. Therefore possible deviations of real vertical distributions of atmospheric components from the model ones (used in calculations) manifest themselves most at low altitudes, corresponding to large optical masses of water vapour and other components. However, other reasons for the differences should also be considered. One of the major reasons consists in the difference between the spectral resolution of the data. The resolution of the CSS-2 complex is $0.8 \, cm^{-1}$ (Kondratyev et al., 1976). A reduction in the measured spectra to a resolution of $5 \, cm^{-1}$ according to the calculation scheme (Robertson et al., 1980) (Fig. 2.40, curve 3) makes it possible to reduce the differences between calculated and experimental profiles of atmospheric transmission. Another source of possible differences is connected with inaccurate vertical referencing of spectral data. The point is that during a complete record of the spectrum in the H_2O band the height of observations changes by about 3.75 km. Curve 1 (Fig. 2.40) was obtained based on vertical referencing of spectral data for the end of the recorded spectrum. An account of real height of observations (curve 4) makes it possible to reduce by a quarter the difference between calculated and experimental data.

Thus, owing to correction for the two factors mentioned above, the difference almost halves. Then, studies were made on the inter-model variability of the vertical profiles $\tau_{\Delta v}(v,h)$. Along with the basic model of the H_2O distribution, two alternatives were considered (Kneizys et al., 1983): tropical and mid-latitudinal.

Besides, variations in $\tau_{\Delta v}(v,h)$ caused by inter-model variability of other atmospheric characteristics were considered: vertical profiles of aerosol attenuation, temperature and pressure. Calculations have shown that the inter-model variations in aerosol (tropospheric, oceanic, volcanic, etc. (Kneizys et al., 1983)) lead to variations some 20–30 times less than those due to the inter-model variability of water vapour. The inter-model variations in temperature and pressure also have a small effect. The range of variations in $\tau_{\Delta v}(v,h)$ at each height of viewing was compared with the interval of differences between experimental and calculated values. For altitudes below 30 km the inter-model scatter of transmission values was less than the difference with experimental data. At altitudes of 40 km and higher the interval of the inter-model variability exceeds the difference between the experimental and calculated transmissions. Both this and the earlier analysis of the data in Fig. 2.40 make it possible to substantiate the possibility of using this method of interpretation to inverse the vertical profiles $\tau_{\Delta v}(vh)$ at $h \geqslant 40$ km.

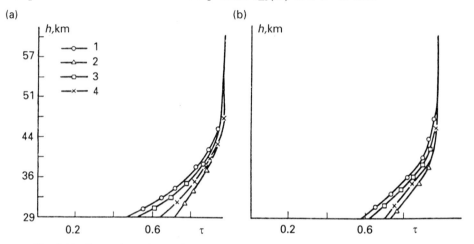

Fig. 2.40. Comparison of experimental and calculated vertical profiles of transmission $\tau_{\Delta v}(v,h)$: (a) $v = 3801$, (b) 3816 cm^{-1} (1—initial experimental values, 2—calculated values for "middle" heights of observations, 3—experimental data reduced to the 5-cm^{-1} resolution, 4—calculated values for specified observation heights).

Studies of the information content of the method
With this aim in view, studies were made of the sensitivity of calculated transmission values to variations in the optically active atmospheric components. Water vapour is the basic optically active component of the atmosphere within the 2.7-μm absorption band. Information about the sensitivity of this method with respect to the profile $qH_2O(h')$ is contained in the operator for partial derivatives $\partial\tau_{\Delta v}(v,h)/\partial q_{H_2O}(h')$ depending on three derivatives: spectral interval Δv, viewing height h, and level h' at which the water vapour content should be retrieved. To make the solution of the inverse problem easier, the profile of the volume mixing ratio $q(h')$ presented in 10^{-6} (ppm) is considered as the distribution sought. Figure 2.41 shows the plots of altitudinal dependences

$$\left.\frac{\partial\tau_{\Delta v}(v,h)}{\partial_q(h')}\right|_{h=40\text{ km}}$$

for five values of Δv. The strongest sensitivity of observations to H_2O concentration

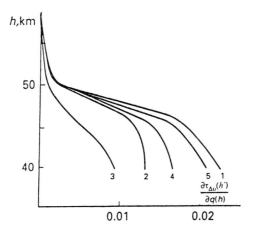

Fig. 2.41. Vertical profiles of sensitivity $\partial\tau_{\Delta\upsilon}(\upsilon,h)/\partial q(h')$ for five frequencies of sounding at $h = 40$ km: 1—$\upsilon = 3801$ cm^{-1}, 2—3806 cm^{-1}, 3—3801 cm^{-1}, 4—3816 cm^{-1}, 5—3820 cm^{-1}.

is observed at an altitude h' equal to the height of viewing, h. The sensitivity of the four lines considered is markedly stronger than for any other spectral intervals. Figure 2.41 exemplifies a spectral interval centred at $\upsilon = 3810$ cm^{-1}. At a height of $h = 40$ km the lines $\upsilon = 3801$ and 3820 cm^{-1} dominate in sensitivity.

For a more adequate study of the information content of the method the authors studied the statistical characteristics of the relationships between measured and retrieved values. Bearing in mind the dominating effect of water vapour on the formation of the profile of spectral transmission $\tau_{\Delta\upsilon}(\upsilon,h)$ in the 2.7-μm band, a statistical modelling of an ensemble of vertical distributions $q(h')$ was made in the interval of altitudes 40–70 km with a 5-km step. As an initial distribution, the 1962 US standard model was taken. Then, Gauss "disturbances" with zero averages and dispersions $\sigma_q^2(h')$ equal to $\alpha\bar{q}(h'))^2$ ($0 < \alpha < 1$) non-correlated in h' were superimposed on $q(h')$ using the standard procedure. Thus, the statistical ensemble of H_2O distributions

$$H_2O \; \{q^j(h'_i)\}^N_{i=1} \; k$$

was formed from prescribed k (N is the number of vertical profiles). To make it easier, we shall denote this ensemble $\{x_i\}^N_{i=1} \; k$. The profile of transmissions $\{\tau^j_{\Delta\upsilon} \; (\upsilon,h_i)\}$ $s_{\Delta\upsilon=1} \; n_{l=1} \; k_{j=1}$ can correspond to each distribution of H_2O $x^j = \{x^j_1,\ldots,x^j_N\}$ (n is the number of viewing heights, s the number of spectral lines under study). Superimpose the model observation errors $\varepsilon_{\Delta\upsilon}(h_l)$ on the calculated values $\tau^j_{\Delta\upsilon}(\upsilon,h_l$. Consider $\varepsilon_{\Delta\upsilon}(h_l)$ to be Gauss non-correlated random values with zero average and dispersions $\sigma_\varepsilon^2(l)$ equal to $(\beta\bar{\tau}_{\Delta\upsilon} \; (\upsilon,h_l)^2)$ where

$$\bar{\tau}_{\Delta\upsilon} \; (\upsilon,h_l) = \sum_{j=1}^{k}\tau^j_{\Delta\upsilon}(\upsilon,h_l)/k, \quad 0 < \beta < 1.$$

From an ensemble of output variables $\{y^j_{\Delta\upsilon}(h_l)\}$ s, n, k proceeding from the equation

$$y^j_{\Delta v}(h_l) = \tau^j_{\Delta v} \left(v h_l + \varepsilon^j_{\Delta v}(h_l) \right).$$

Apply to a pair of ensembles $\{x^j_i\}^N_{i=j}\, k$ and $\{y^j_{\Delta v}(h_l)\}s_{\Delta v=1},\, k_{j=1}$ (l is fixed) the method of canonic correlations. Such an approach makes it possible to relate fluctuations of the vertical distribution of H_2O with respective oscillations of spectral transmission at a fixed viewing height $h = h_l$. Figure 2.42 shows in a diagram form pairs of vector of canonic correlations for the vertical distribution of water vapour and spectral measurements of transmission at $h = 40$ km. The results indicate not only the most "sensitive" information zones at a height h and frequency in an occultation experiment but also their correlations. For example, it follows from the data in Fig. 2.42a,d that the measurements in the lines at $v = 3806$ and 3801 cm^{-1} are not only most informative through the whole 2.7-μm band but also most sensitive to oscillations in the concentration of water vapour in a layer adjacent to the middle of the viewing line. Figure 2.42b,e demonstrates the fact that the difference in the values of transmission obtained for the two lines mentioned above enables one to distinguish between the H_2O concentrations in two atmospheric layers lying above. Then follows the line 3816 cm^{-1}, the measurements in which is given information for the 45–50-km layer (Fig. 2.42c,f). These preliminary conclusions are suggested by the results of statistical analysis of the information content of this occultation experiment.

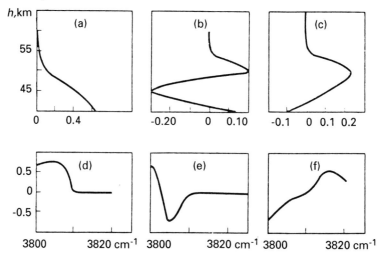

Fig. 2.42. Pairs of vectors of canonical correlations: (a)–(c) vertical modes of presentation of the profile $q(h')$; (d)–(f) spectral modes of presentation of fluctuations $\tau_{\Delta v}(v,h)$ ($h = 40$ km).

Examples of retrieving the water vapour vertical profile
The major objective here is to develop a method of inversion of the vertical profiles of transmission to estimate the water vapour content in the stratosphere and the mesosphere. This inverse problem is reduced to a minimization of functional (2.23). Note should be taken of the special character of problem (2.23). One special feature of (2.23) is determined by the fact that $\tau_{\Delta v}$ depends non-linearly on q. Another feature is

that the operator $\tau_{\Delta v}(q)$ has a "triangular" structure. It means that each of its components $\tau_{\Delta v}(v,h,q(h'))$ depends only on the water vapour concentration $q(h')$ at $h' \geqslant h$.

The features of (2.23) mentioned above make it possible to formulate the method of layer-by-layer inversion. Consider the case when the grids of heights $\{h_i\}_{i=1}^n$ and $\{h'_j\}_{j=1}^N$ coincide (when $N = n$). For $h_n = h'_n$, instead of (2.23), we have a scalar minimization problem

$$\min_{q(h_n)} (\tilde\tau_{\Delta v}(v,h_n) - \tau_{\Delta v}[q(h_n)])^2 \qquad (2.24)$$

to solve on which one can use the methods of Newton type (Kondratyev and Pokrovski, 1989b). In case of simultaneous use of several spectral lines we have instead of (2.24)

$$\min_{q(h_n)} \sum_{\Delta v=1}^s (\tilde\tau_{\Delta v}(v,h_n) - \tau_{\Delta v}[q(h_n)])^2. \qquad (2.25)$$

Denote the result of the solution of (2.24) and (2.25) by $q^*(h_n)$. Thus, at the first stage of the layer-by-layer inversion we obtain the H_2O concentration in the very upper layer of the atmosphere.

At the ith stage of the method of the layer-by-layer inversion ($i = 2, 3,...$) one can determine the H_2O concentration in the ith layer (starting from the upper one) of the atmosphere by solving the scalar optimization problem

$$\min_{q(h_{n-i})} (\tilde\tau_{\Delta v}(v,h_{n-1}) - \tau_{\Delta v}[q^*(h_n), q^*(h_{n-1}),..., q^*(h_{n-i+1}), q(h_{n-i})])^2. \qquad (2.26)$$

The multispectral problem is written similarly to (2.25). The solution of (2.26) results in an estimation of $q^*(h_{n-i})$. By solving a problem of the type (2.26) $(n-1)$ times, we obtain the required profile of the parameters $q^*(h_n),...,q^*(h_1)$.

The results of the water vapour profile retrieval in the interval 40–80 km are discussed and compared to other data (Fig. 2.43). The following models were used as initial distributions of water vapour (Kneizys et al., 1983): the 1962 US standard model, the tropical model, and the mid-latitude models for summer and for winter. Choosing, in turn, each of these models as a profile of initial approximation in minimization problems (2.24) and (2.26), we studied the stability of the method of layer-by-layer inversion for this problem. Though the inter-model differences reached 80–100%, the retrieved profiles $q^*(h_i)$ differed by not more than 30%. This testifies to the relative stability of this method. Then we studied the dependence of the solution of the inverse problem $q^*(h_i)$ on the spectral information used. Maximum differences were observed in the 40–50-km layer (Fig. 2.43, curves 4 and 5), which is explained by a different structure of information supply of a given experiment when measurements in the strong line 3801 cm^{-1} and in the weak line 3816 cm^{-1} are used. This difference is determined by the structures of the first and the third modes in Fig. 2.42.

The profiles obtained (curves 4 and 5) differ substantially from the retrieval results (Fig. 2.43, curve 2) described in Kondratyev et al. (1976). The conclusion has been drawn (Kondratyev et al., 1978) that the stratosphere is "dry". As seen from

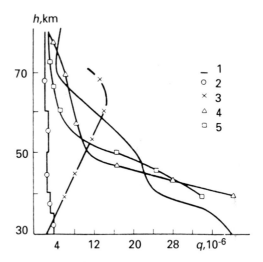

Fig. 2.43. Comparison of the water vapour vertical profiles in the upper stratosphere and lower mesosphere: 1—the 1962 US standard model, 2—retrieved from CSS-2 data (Kondratyev et al., 1976, 1978) (orbital station Salut-4), 21 January 1975, tropical zone, 3—retrieved from Nimbus-7 SAMS data. (The stratosphere..., 1981) 4 April 1979, mid-latitudes, 4—retrieved by the layer-by-layer inversion method from CSS-2 data for $v_1 = 3801$ cm^{-1}, 5—the same for $v_2 = 3816$ cm^{-1}.

the data in Fig. 2.43 (curve 1), the existing atmospheric models assume the stratosphere to be "humid". The results of our retrieval are in better agreement with the model profiles than with the results of the retrieval made earlier (Kondratyev et al., 1976, 1978). An averaged distribution for the area of mid-latitudes (Fig. 2.43, curve 3) and that obtained by Kolbek (The stratosphere..., 1981) from processing the 5-channel measurements made with the Nimbus SAMS complex is intermediate between the results given in Kondratyev et al. (1976, 1978) and those obtained here. In the lower and middle stratosphere the results given in Kondratyev et al. (1976, 1978) and in the WMO project (The stratosphere..., 1981) agree. In the upper stratosphere and lower mesosphere the results of American studies are in better agreement with our results.

The aforesaid suggests the following:

1. Studies have been made of the factors which determine the variability of the vertical profiles of atmospheric spectral transmission for basic lines in the H_2O 2.7-μm absorption band: (a) distribution of water vapour, aerosol, temperature, pressure; (b) altitude referencing; (c) spectral resolution.
2. An analysis has been made of the information content of the occultation sounding of water vapour in the stratosphere and the lower mesosphere. The role of various spectral lines has been established between the data of optical measurements and the H_2O concentration in some layers of the atmosphere.
3. The layer-by-layer inversion method has been realized to retrieve the water vapour profiles. The stability of the method has been studied. The results of solution of the inverse problem have been analysed.

2.8 COMPLEX OF AIR-, SURFACE- AND SPACE-BORNE INSTRUMENTS FOR THE INTERDISCIPLINARY PROJECT "KUBAN"

The satellite data alone are not enough to assess the state of vegetation cover and to carry out ecological studies. Virtually all of the investigators who deal with both applied problems (e.g. the LACIE experiment (Kondratyev et al., 1986b)) and fundamental scientific problems (e.g. the ISLSCP project (Buznikov and Kondratyev, 1989; Kondratyev, 1987a)) face the problem of satellite data validation. In this connection, complex sub-satellite experiments first carried out in the Soviet Union in 1969 (Kondratyev et al., 1971a,b) have become a major kind of Earth's resources and ecological studies, for example, CENEX (Kondratyev, 1990d), FIFE-89, and HAPEX (Becker et al., 1987). Naturally, when studying the vegetation cover, forests, agricultural crops over large territories, airborne studies can be quite independent. Large complexes of aircraft studies are carried out by making use of the MGO IL-18 aircraft laboratory (Fig. 2.46a) (Beregovoi et al., 1972a), CAO aircraft, the measuring complexes of which have been described above. At present, in Russia the most extensive studies of vegetation cover (first of all, crops) are carried out by the specially setup firm "AIUS-Agroresurses". Its main objective is to create an automatic information system to control the agricultural resources of Russia. This system is based on the information obtained with the instruments carried by ten aircraft TU-134 SH, one of which is shown in Fig. 2.44b, collection and processing of aircraft information.

The measuring complex carried by these aircraft has been used in accomplishing the interdisciplinary complex project "Kuban". The project foresees a complex of scientific, test-production and adoption works to study possibilities of practical application of available space-borne means, including the MOS "Mir" and automat satellites, as well as airborne platforms together with synchronous and quasi-synchronous surface observations in the problems of assessing the state of agri-ecological systems and their control. The experiment was carried out in the territory of Krasnodarski Krai, which is one of the most developed regions with an intensive agricultural production, with an extremely high level of exploitation of agriclimatic resources. The "Kuban" project makes use of the capabilities of the MOS "Mir", satellites of the sub-systems "Resurs-F" and "Resurs-O", aircraft TU-134SH, AN-2, helicopters KA-26, MI-2 equipped with technical means for the remote sounding of agricultural areas, forests, reclamation systems, water basins and other natural resources.

Technical support was realized through the following instrument, with which the MOS "Mir" was equipped:

— cameras "Sever" and KATE-140;
— spectrometric microprocessing system SKIF-M;
— spectrograph RSS-3;
— Bulgarian spectrometer "Spektr-256".

The automatic satellite of the sub-system "Resurs-F" carried a K-1000 camera; satellite "Resurs-01" No. 2 was equipped with multichannel scanning systems MSU-

Fig. 2.44. (a) The MGO IL-18 aircraft laboratory. (b) The TU-134SH aircraft in the service of agriculture.

M and MSU-E. The remote sounding means were mounted on the high-altitude aircraft TU-134SH and low-altitude aircraft AN-2, and helicopters MI-2 and KA-26. The TU-134SH carried:

— multichannel scanning system MSS "MATRA" (M-867) with six channels in the range 0.5–14.0 μm;
— multichannel cameras MSK-4 (MKF-6 m);
— topographic instruments TAFA-10;
— side-looking radar "Nit" at λ = 2 cm at two polarizations;
— passive microwave radiometer at λ = 30 cm.

   The small airborne platforms (AN-2, MI-8, KA-26) carried:

— spectrometric microprocessing system SKIF-M;
— spectrograph RSS-3;

— spectroradiometer SR-4000 (spectral range 0.48–1.10 μm; resolution $\Delta\lambda$; = 10 nm);
— spectrometer BSK;
— microwave radiometer for λ = 25; 18; 31 cm;
— colour TV camera;
— spectropolarimeters developed in LETI (Buznikov, 1993b) and the Institute of Physics, Belorussia Acad. Sci. (MSS-2P).

Surface means of background information review were located at test sites and moving laboratories they included:

— 4-channel surface radiometer "MATRA";
— field photometer developed in the Institute of Agricultural Meteorology (wavelength range 400–800 nm);
— neutron water gauge VNTs-1;
— spectropolarimeter MSS-2P.

The instruments enumerated above are planned to solve the following functional problems within the project "Kuban":

(a) land use:

— land inventory;
— control of land protection and use;
— determination of periodically flooded, covered with water and oversaturated lands;

(b) soil cover:

— soil mapping;
— revealing and assessing the dynamics of water and wind erosion of lands;

(c) vegetation cover:

— assessment of the state of major agricultural crops;
— forecast of the yield of major crops (with winter wheat as an example);
— assessment of the state and use of alpine pastures;
— revealing the areas of soil under crops oversaturated with pesticides and fertilizers;
— inventory of aforestation belts;
— assessment of the state of natural forests;

(d) water resources:

— the state of the hydrographic network;
— the degree of overrunning with algae of the lagoons bordering the Azov Sea;
— the state of irrigation systems;

(e) ecology:

— determination of the zones of maximum atmospheric pollution with industrial wastes;

— assessment of erosion processes on hillside land;
— assessment of pollution of the Black Sea coastal zone and determination of the zones of propagation.

2.9 THE USE OF SYNTHETIC APERTURE RADAR (SAR) FOR ENVIRONMENTAL INVESTIGATIONS

Despite the numerous advantages of optical techniques of the remote sounding of the environment from space (visual, easy to decode; experience in interpretation, etc.), the optical means cannot be used to study the surface of the Earth and the World Ocean in conditions of continuous cloudiness and lacking illumination. In this connection, the techniques of the radar sounding of the Earth in the interests of ecological and Earth's resources studies are put into practice (Armand, 1960; Bogomolov et al., 1981; Marchuk, 1964).

Initially, a large number of studies has been carried out with the help of aircraft radar (the experiment "Bering"..., 1989); then studies were made using the SLR carried by satellites of the type "Kosmos-1500" (Information capabilities..., 1988). First of all, radar systems have been widely used to study the ocean and the ice (Chelomei et al., 1990; Shestopalov et al., 1984, 1985).

Radar studies from space are usually carried out with the help of three types of system.

Scatterometers (Grishin, 1987) with a wide viewing band (about 600 km) but low spatial resolution (about 50 km) are used, mainly, to study the large-scale fields of near-water surface winds.

The SAR (Salganik et al., 1990; Jorgensen, 1988) have a high resolution near the Earth's surface (tens of metres) but narrow swath band (from several to 100 km). This makes it possible for them to solve the problems connected with studies of the characteristics of meso- and macro-scale formations of the ocean surface and in the ice (Grishin, 1987), but opens up wide possibilities for the Earth's resources and ecological studies (Kondratyev et al., 1989, 1990; Salganik et al., 1990).

SLRs of the type "Kosmos-1500" with $\lambda = 3$ cm, swath band about 500 km and resolution 1–3 km are widely used to estimate the near-water wind speed from the scattered signal intensity, to observe the zones of non-stationary roughness, to study the ocean and ice.

Table 2.24 lists the basic parameters of the SLR type "Kosmos-1500". Information is transmitted to the Earth via decimetre and metre channels. Information via the decimetre channel (range 460 MHz) goes to the Centre for Data Collection and Processing in Moscow and to regional centres in Novosibirsk and Khabarovsk. This is of high quality, but users receive it 1–2 weeks later (Information capabilities..., 1988). For the prompt transmission of information the metre channel (range 137 MHz) is used. The points of receiving this information are simple and they are distributed among more information users. The quality of information via the metre channel is lower, but, on the other hand, the information is transmitted promptly. This is important for studies of the dynamic processes in the ocean and ice, and for steering ships in a stormy ocean, through ice fractures, etc.

Table 2.24. Basic parameters of the Kosmos-1500 SLR

Parameter	Estimate
Distance to Earth's surface (orbital altitude), km	649–679
Orbital inclination, deg.	82.6
Radiation wavelength, cm	3.15
Polarization of radiation and data receiving	Vertical
Length of pulse, μs	3 (5)
Repetition rate, Hz	100
Number of stored signals	8 (16)
Width of antenna directional diagram by the 3-dB level, deg.	
— azimuth (flight)	0.15
— local angle	30
Range of incidence angles, deg.	22–52
Average resolution in swath band by the 3-dB level, km	
— data transmission via decimetre line	0.8 × 2.5
— via metre line	2 × 2.5
Swath band (on the Earth's surface), km	
— storage regime	475 × 2500
— direct transmission regime	475 × 400

Apart from the speed, which largely determines the practical value of the information obtained with SLR (Kosmos-1500, Kosmos-1602, Kosmos-1766), on these satellites the SLR information is combined with the low-resolution optical scanner MSU-L (Shestopalov et al., 1984) and scanning radiometer (Shestopalov et al., 1985). This ensures a synchronous sounding of natural formations in different ranges of electromagnetic waves. This is quite valuable, since, for example, when the ocean–atmosphere system is investigated, the optical range is rather efficient to study the processes in the atmosphere, but gives much less information about the ocean in view of the low albedo of its surface. At the same time, radar enables one to study the surface practically without atmospheric interference. It follows (Shestopalov et al., 1984) that combined optical and radar observations have made it possible to distinguish between surface and deep-water phenomena in the glaciers when studying the Antarctic. The accuracy of determining the parameters of the wind field from the Kosmos-1500 SLR images constitutes 10–30% by module and 20–30° by wind direction. The technique developed (Information capabilities..., 1988) serves the basis for assessing the energetic characteristics of tropical cyclones.

The SAR has opened up wide possibilities to apply the radar techniques to topological and Earth's resources studies from space (Salganik et al., 1990; Woodwell et al., 1988). In contrast to the non-coherent SLR, in the SAR the azimuthal resolution is determined not by the horizontal size of the antenna but by the length of the section of the carrier's trajectory along which the aperture of the artificial antenna synthesized. In this case a coherent-pulse SAR is used, the reflected signals being stored in memory (with their amplitude and phase) in each period of sounding, with their subsequent weighted summing in the interval of synthesizing

(Salganik et al., 1990). The SAR resolution is much higher than that of the non-coherent SLR.

According to Kondratyev (1990b), the idea of using the SAR in the space-borne complexes was suggested in the USSR as far back as 1962. Between 1960 and 1970, samples of space-borne SAR as well as their airborne analogues, were constructed for preliminary tests. However, at that time, the launching of an SAR-carrying satellite was considered inexpedient, and it was not until 1987 that the SAR-carrying satellite Kosmos-1870 was launched. By this time, the USA had launched Seasat (1978), SIR-A (1981), and SIR-B (1984), with the SAR parameters close to those of the Kosmos-1870 SAR.

2.9.1 Results from radar observations of the Earth's surface from Kosmos-1870 and prospects of further studies

The use of SAR for the sounding of the Earth from space improves the quality of observations and provides additional possibilities in the studies of natural resources and assessments of the environmental state (Bogorodski et al., 1981; Salganik et al., 1990). The space-borne radar—an active system with a source of electromagnetic emission of its own—is completely independent of the illumination and meteorological conditions in the regions of observation. Note should be made of the high sensitivity of radars to the state of the observed surface (composition of the soil layer, roughness, local slopes, vegetation character, sea surface roughness, etc.) and to the moisture content of soil, vegetation and snow.

Widely variable frequency ranges and emission polarizations, as well as resolution compatible with the optical systems, make the SAR quite popular among satellite information users (Kosmos-1870..., 1990).

Kosmos-1870 is the first multipurpose space-borne platform of the series "Almaz". It was launched in July 1987 and functioned for more than two years. Its SAR produced a lot of radar images of different areas of the land and the ocean with a resolution of 25 m.

Basic characteristics of Kosmos-1870

A general view of Kosmos-1870 is presented in Fig. 2.45. The space apparatus (SA) of the series "Almaz" is a multipurpose platform carrying scientific complexes below 4 t in weight. The complex is mounted on the outside shell of the pressurized bay and inside it. The pressurized bay, 90 m^3 in volume, is filled with air or nitrogen at normal atmospheric pressure. Its temperature can be fixed within 15–35°C and is maintained with an accuracy of ± 1°C with the help of an efficient system of thermal regulation.

The complex units are scavenged with air by making use of fans. Electric power supply is realized from the on-board direct-current system 27.5 ± 0.5 V by two-wire scheme, isolated from the body.

The complex is controlled by prescribed cyclograms and orders from the on-board computer and from the Earth.

Scientific information is transmitted to the receiving panel via a broad-band radio-line either directly or via the retranslating satellite.

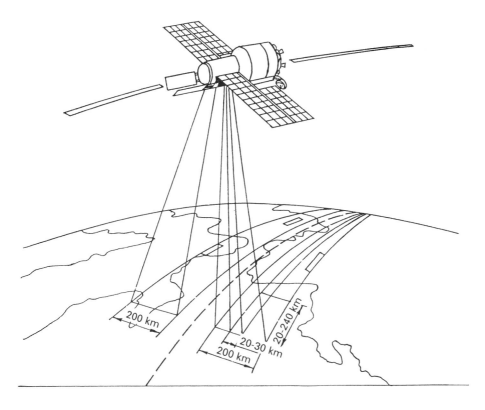

Fig. 2.45. Scheme of survey from Kosmos-1870.

If needed, the complex may have an individual transmission channel. The basic characteristics of Kosmos-1870 are given in Table 2.25.

The flight is accomplished in the Earth-oriented regime with an accuracy of 10′. The SA is stabilized with inertial electromechanic aggregates. The working orbit is maintained through periodic pulses of correction of the sustainer rocket.

Characteristics and viewing scheme of the Kosmos-1870 SAR
Table 2.26 shows the characteristics of the Kosmos-1870 SAR. The SAR can operate with antennas of either left or right board within the 350 km swath width. Thus, with an orbital inclination of 72°N the SAR can cover the band 78°N–78°S, that is, virtually the whole planetary surface.

The SAR has two operating regimes: survey with the simultaneous transmission of information to the receiving station; survey and record of information on the on-board magnetic tapes with subsequent output when the SA is in the zone of direct visibility of the receiving station. During the two-year experiments through use of Kosmos-1870, a radar survey has been made in various regions of the globe (Kosmos-1870..., 1990).

Table 2.25. Basic characteristics of space complex "Kosmos-1870"

Parameter	Estimate
Carrier-rocket	"Proton"
Parameters of the working orbit:	
— height, km	270–300
— inclination, deg.	71.9
Mass of spacecraft in orbit, kg	18550
Mass of scientific instruments, kg	400
Volume of the pressurized bay, m^3	90
Characteristics of power supply:	
— source power	Solar batteries and buffer accumulators
— voltage, V	27 ± 0.5
— mean power, W	2500
— peak power (15–20 min), W	2500–10000
Active lifetime, years	2

Table 2.26. Characteristics of the "Kosmos-1870" synthetic-aperture radar (SAR)

Parameter	Estimate
Local resolution, m	25–30
Swath width, km	20–30
Length of route, km	20–250
Angles of observation from nadir, deg.	30–60
Viewing band, km	2×200 (350)
Antenna system:	
— number of antennas	2 (left and right sides)
— type	slotted guide
— size, m	15×1.5
Wavelength, cm	10
Polarization	HH
Length of sounding pulses, μs	0.1
Repetition rate, Hz	3000
Pulse power, kW	190
Radiometric resolution (by 30×30 m pixel), dB	5
Form of the SAR output signal	Analogue radiohologram
Operating regime:	
— direct transmission	In the zone of receiving station
— the on-board magnetic tape record	Drop in the zone of receiving station
Size of the slotted-waveguide antenna unfolded in orbit, m	15×1.5
Information processing	Optical on the ground
Information storage	On-board 6-GHz tape recorder

2.9.2 Scientific and applied value of high-resolution radar information

During the flight of Kosmos-1870 a number of scientific and applied studies were made aimed at determining the possibility of the practical use of high-resolution radar information (Salganik et al., 1990).

In the interests of oceanology, studies have been made of wind-driven sea surface roughness and ripples, hydrological fronts, vortices and rings, flow dynamics, surface manifestations of inner waves and bottom relief, sea surface pollution, boundaries of flooded rivers and water basins (Kondratyev et al., 1990; Kurbatkin et al., 1974). In the interests of geology, data have been obtained on the structure of geological formations for descriptive and dynamic geology.

Radar mapping of the fields and ploughed soils has been made as applied to the problems of agriculture and land use, to obtain data on the state of crops, to assess the soil moisture content, waterlogged areas, to specify the boundaries of the fields and forests.

The possibility has been assessed to use the SAR to draw maps, to renew the topographic maps and to draw them for the regions difficult to assess.

The subsequent launchings of SAR-carrying platforms of the "Almaz" series were aimed at obtaining new data for statistical studies, which broadened the application of high-resolution radar information. Even at this stage it is clear that the information obtained can be used for:

1. Obtaining images of the Earth's surface in the regions difficult to access and where the cameras cannot be used because of continuous cloudiness.
2. Prompt all-weather delivery of reliable information at any time when determining the scale of disasters such as floods, typhoons, volcanic eruption; the use of this information in rescue works.
3. Control of sea surface pollution caused by drilling oilwells, as well as oil terminals, and other places of possible waste, determination of oil slicks.
4. Assessment of the ice cover state and the steering of ships in heavy ice situations, etc.

2.9.3 Examples of radar survey from Kosmos-1870

Below are given fragments of sample SAR images.

1. The Bushir peninsula in the Persian Gulf. The shelf relief is clearly seen. The coastal zone is about 10 m deep. One can see a ship-canal leading to the port; the canal is marked with buoys.
    The bottom relief survey is probably connected with tidal currents, resulting in the relief being slightly reflected on the water surface but clearly seen on the radar image (Fig. 2.46).
2. The image of the Sea of Marmara shows the vortices caused by deep-water currents. However, the surface micro-relief is determined by a considerable amount of plankton and pollutants in the upper water layer (Fig. 2.47).
3. The possibility to survey a region of disaster is illustrated with the image of a region of the Persian Gulf where the size of an oil slick caused by a damaged large ship is clearly identified (Fig. 2.48).

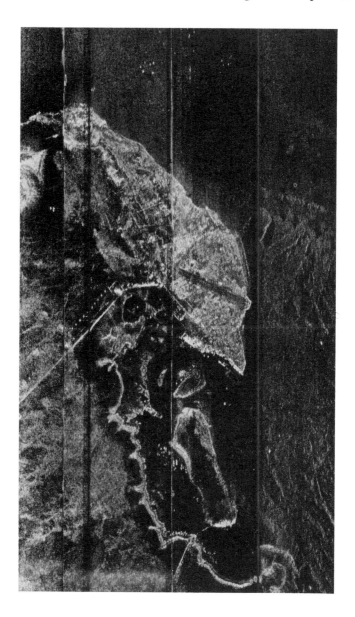

Fig. 2.46. Radar image of Bushir peninsula in the Persian Gulf.

Fig. 2.47. The 8 April 1989 radar image of the Sea of Marmara.

4. The image of a region of the Volga delta demonstrates the radar capabilities to identify various structures of land surface, specifically, desertification of agricultural soils in bottom land. Areas under rise, a zone of irrigation and the boundary of sands are clearly seen (Fig. 2.49).
5. The possibility to observe the regions in the Far North to perform the ecological control of the regions of oil and gas extraction is shown in the image of Pechora delta (Fig. 2.50).
6. The image of the region of Spitak (Armenia) in the epicentre of the powerful earthquake shows a geological fracture determining the seismic danger of the region (Fig. 2.51—a negative).
7. The SAR image of agricultural land on the Taman peninsula, its demolished coastline, and the Kerch Strait waters are shown in Fig. 2.52.
8. The image of the central part of the European territory, Russia (Voronezh), demonstrates the possibility to observe the state of agricultural areas. The difference in the brightness of individual fields is explained by various crops and their vegetation phases (Fig. 2.53).

2.9.4 Some results from processing the SAR images

Radar studies of the ocean surface from space are based on selective scattering of radiowaves by the sea roughness spectrum constituents.

The character of interaction of the sounding electromagnetic radiation with the surface and natural objects is determined by the wavelength, its polarization and angle of incidence. The technique of radar sounding of the ocean surface is most developed at present (Information capabilities..., 1988; Chelomei et al., 1990). All the techniques of space-based radar sounding of the ocean surface making use of scatterometer (SAR, SLR) operation in the microwave range are based on a two-scale model of selective scattering (Woodwell, 1989). Ripples reflect microwaves.

Fig. 2.48. Radar image of a burning tanker, the rescuing ships, and oil slicks on the surface of the Persian Gulf.

Large waves modulate the parameters of the ripple-scattered signal.

Determination of the water-surface wind field is connected with the spectral density of scattering ripples. This grows with increasing wind speed (Information capabilities..., 1988). The effect of azimuthal anisotropy of scattering by a ripple in the presence of large waves makes it possible to determine the direction of large waves, which in most cases coincides with the direction of the wind.

The sensitivity of radar reflections of signals at centimetre waves to high-frequency constituents of the sea roughness spectrum determines the possibility of map-drawing and assessing the parameters of oceanic currents from the aerospace platforms (Salganik et al., 1990; Chelomei et al., 1990). Depending on the relationship between wind speed direction and current velocity, the intensity of the ripple spectrum varies differently, which enables one to identify this phenomenon on

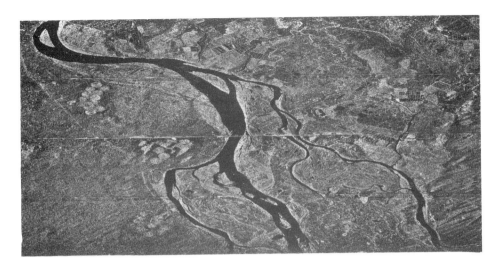

Fig. 2.49. Radar image of the Volga delta (the river Achtuba region) and the bordering territories. Slant distance 313 km.

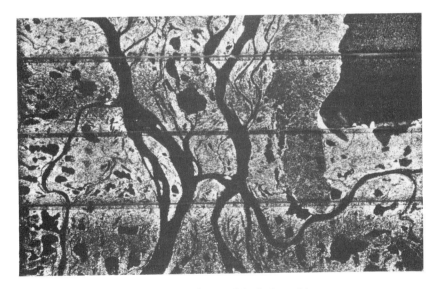

Fig. 2.50. Radar image of the Pechora delta.

Fig. 2.51. Radar image of the region of Spitak (Armenia) (negative).

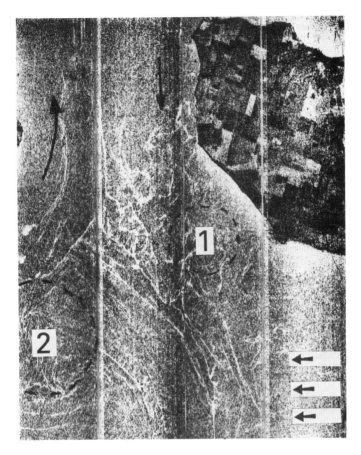

Fig. 2.52. The 9 September 1987 radar image of Taman peninsula. ← E–N–E wind, 3 m s^{-1}; → direction of currents;—location of the port soil heaps: 1—Sajenko shoal; 2— experimental heap.

a radar image. Similarly, the radar image shows the exits of the inner wave observed as shift currents.

The image of Neva Bay obtained from Kosmos-1870 illustrates the possibilities to use radar image for identifying the areas contaminated with surface-active substances (SAS), which efficiently damp the high-frequency ripple. This manifests itself through a decrease in the reflected signal by 20–15 dB compared to SAS-free water areas. The sub-satellite measurements have shown that such contrasts make it possible to detect the SAS-films 0.1 μm or more thick.

In their work dedicated to high-frequency radar observations of the sea surface from Kosmos-1870, V. Chelomei and his group (1990) give the results of using the 10-cm SAR for oceanographic studies. They discuss in detail the problem of using SAR to indicate surface and inner waves. A comparison of satellite and ship observations in the Atlantic and Pacific oceans gives an accuracy of $\pm 20°$ in the

Fig. 2.53. Radar image of agricultural areas in the region of Voronezh.

measurements of the direction of propagation of wind-driven waves and ripples.

The conclusion is drawn about the high quality of space-derived SAR images from Kosmos-1870. Possibilities are shown for their use to study the wind-driven roughness (the energy carrying component) and ripple, hydrological fronts, current dynamics, surface manifestations of inner waves, vortices and rings of various scale, slick strips, and elements of bottom relief at different depths. However, the theoretical solution to the problem of the effect of surface manifestations of the intra-oceanic or atmospheric processes on the characteristics of measured signals cannot be considered satisfactory, so far, because of the difficulties that appear in solving the electrodynamic part of the problem and in connection with the absence of adequate physical models of roughness.

In interpreting the SAR images of natural formations on the Earth's surface obtained from space, specialists also face a difficult prodlem (Kondratyev et al., 1990).

The processing of the SAR images of the Earth's surface natural formations obtained from Kosmos-1870 revealed the necessity for their decoding and assessing the possibility of their use to solve the Earth's resources and ecological problems. For this purpose several SAR images of various regions of the country have been chosen: ploughed lands and natural formations of the Voronezh region (16 May 1989); the Taman peninsula, Kerch Strait, and the adjacent region of the Black Sea (9 September 1987); and the lake Ladoga basin (13 February 1989).

These images illustrate the following natural formations in different seasons: ploughed soils in the spring and in the autumn; tree-planting areas, meadows, river valleys, seawater surface of free-water basins; lake ice cover; forests in winter and other mesoscale structures. Physical features of SAR signals reflected from the Earth's surface have been studied well (Kronberg, 1988; Mel'nik et al., 1980). The following parameters are known to from a reflection form the surface: complex dielectric penetrability, surface roughness (prolile), sub-surface layer inhomogeneity. The enumerated parameters determine the spectral and polarization characteristics of the reflected SAR signal and, thereby, characterize the surface properties. So, for example, the efficient dielectric penetrability of soil depends on the moisture content. The moisture content in plants often depends on the vegetation phase, which opens up potential possibilities to control the development of crops. Surface roughness is an important factor determining the properties of the reflected signal, which also makes it possible to identify the natural formations from SAR images. The presence of several factors governing the backscattering signal seriously hinders the decoding of SAR images, and broadens the decoding of SAR images. The creation of a high-resolution SAR system broadens the decoding of SAR images, and broadens the perspectives of applying radars to study the Earth's resources and ecology.

An attempt has been made (Kondratyev et al., 1990) to relate the natural-landscape characteristics of the location under study to the persistent statistical characteristics of the respective areas of high-resolution SAR images. Studies were aimed at revealing possibilities to use a space-borne SAR system operation in the centimetre range in ecologo-geographic investigations. In this connection, an exact geographic referencing of SAR images was carried out. Then the surface sites' images were digitized by making use of "Pericolor-2000", which made it possible to apply conditional gradations of brightness to photomaterials (from zero to 256).

Based on results of sub-satellite surface observations, areas were selected on a digital image. Their analysis has shown that the radar survey gives a clear reflection of the surface objects (agricultural fields and their boundaries, relief inhomogene-ities, household constructions, coastlines, sharp changes in relief, etc.). In the case of the water surface, the image corresponds to real dynamics of water masses. For example, an analysis of the state of water masses of Kerch Strait was made with an account of data on the temperature and salinity of water, wind speed and direction, obtained during the flight of Kosmos-1870 and over a period of 2–3 days before the survey. The data of the marine hydrometeostation (HMS) in the Opasnoye settlement (analysis of water samples to characterize the environmental pollution, and results of aerovisual observations) enabled one to trace the dynamics of water masses. The SAR image (Fig. 2.52) reveals zones of shore abrasion, shallow waters, current direction, oil film up to 30 mg/m^2 thick, zones of secondary pollution. The results of SAR image decoding agree well with the data of aerovisual observations of this region.

The decoding of agricultural fields in the Voronezh region is based on a comparison of an SAR image (Fig. 2.53) with the scheme of land use as well as characteristics of soil and vegetation from the data of agronomists in this region. These data and the digital processing of SAR images using a Pericolor-2000 serve as the basis for the analysis of the materials obtained.

The use of traditional methods of classification of natural objects by their false-colour images and dividing their brightnesses into 256, 32, 16 or 8 gradations with the help of a Pericolor-2000 is inadequate for the diversity of crop soils and natural objects. In this connection, average, maximum and minimum values of brightness were selected for each of the chosen areas. To reveal persistent statistical features of the objects under observation, ordinal statistics and quantiles were used, which ensured the stability of statistical conclusions in conditions of a priori uncertainty and noise (Mel'nik et al., 1980).

Based on the use of ordinal and rank statistics, standard assessments have been obtained of location (shift) and scatter (scale) of conditional brightness on the images (Mel'nik et al., 1980; Application..., 1981). These assessments, with their nonparametric and robust properties, have ensured the reality of statistical conclusions, which was confirmed by the field data. For further analysis the Tjuki technique (Tjuki, 1981) was used which foresees: (i) 1-D presentation of average and extreme values of brightness for different objects—"Tjuki boxes"; (ii) 2-D presentations in the coordinates "average-span" and other "parallel Tjuki diagrams"; (iii) construction of variational series of the brightness of various objects with confidence intervals, or spans.

Such a technique ensures a reliable "search analysis" and a vivid presentation of observation data, and makes it possible to discover the inner regularities manifested in observational data. For example, the use of this technique ensured a division of the obtained data base into individual groups of objects (fallow, winter crops, maize, grass) and revealed a possible inhomogeneity within the groups of fields under

Table 2.27. The state of fallow ground in the Voronezh region from the data for 16 May 1989

Number of field	Culture	Description of the state	Location
B7	Fallow ground	Dark with weeds	State farm "Burliajevski"
B8	"	Sandy loam	"
H1	"	Fresh-ploughed (left side, probably, not ploughed)	State farm "Novohoperski"
H3	"	On saline lands, disked, harrowed	"
H5	"	On black soil	"
K1	"	Cultivated after winter crops	Coll. farm "Krasnoje"
K2	"	"	"
K3	"	Light sand field	"
K4	"	Sand field	"
K6	"	Darker sandy soil	"
K7	"	White sand	"
K8	"	Sandy soil	"
K9	"	"	"
K10	"	"	"
K12	"	Darker sandy soil	"
K21	"	Sandy loam	"
B5	"	Black soil	Coll. farm "Vostok"
B8	"	"	"
B9	"	Black soil with weeds	"
07	"	Black soil	State farm "Novy"
08	"	"	"
09	"	Non-ploughed with sun-flower stalks, occasional saline land	"

consideration (Fig. 2.54, Table 2.27, Fig. 2.55). Maximum values of average brightness with the least scatter correspond to the driest fields and crops with the moisture volume content at a minimum. These are mainly sandy soils and crops on them. Maximum variability and minimum average brightness are characteristic of most soils and crops. Saline lands are characterized by strong dielectric penetrability and are put into a separate class (Fig. 2.55).

Thus, the preliminary analysis of data for selected areas of SAR images has shown potential possibilities to use the present robust statistical procedures in studies of natural resources and ecology from space. Note also that a more detailed "varifying" analysis (using Tjuki's terminology) enables one to substantiate the supposed possibilities to discover the laws and to discriminate the samples due to a more thorough statistical processing using multidimensional data bases (multidimensional regressive factor, quantile analysis). However, this requires an improved programme support to the current computer complexes.

For example, an analysis of the distribution of probabilities for individual crops making use of various procedures of constructing the distributions revealed an additional possibility to identify objects on SAR images and an apparent inhomogeneity of the image areas chosen for analysis. The decoding of areas under crops on the image of the Taman peninsula using variational series of brightness

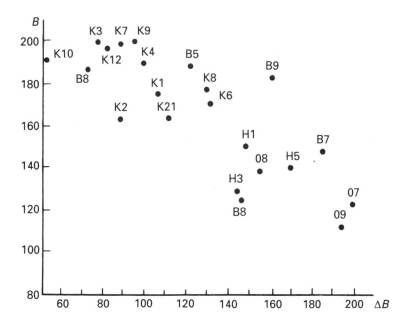

Fig. 2.54. A 2-D presentation of the brightness characteristics of the soils of the Novokhoperski district of the Voronezh region: in coordinates *B*—average brightness; Δ*B*—the field brightness span (for notations of the fields, see Table 2.27).

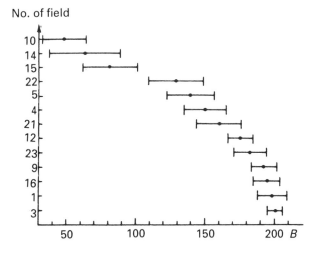

Fig. 2.55. Variability of average brightness and brightness dispersion of SAR images for individual natural objects of Taman peninsula for 9 September 1987.

with non-parametric confidence intervals (Deidvid, 1979) has confirmed the real presence of inhomogeneity (Fig. 2.52). For example, one managed to detect on SAR images the vineyards of different age, saline land. The test statistical analysis of SAR images making use of the current stable procedures of processing has demonstrated their usefulness, an expediency of development and application of the present robust procedures of the multidimensional analysis to assess the ecological state of natural objects from the results of radar survey from space.

In the course of decoding the high-resolution SAR images, a detailed "confirming" multidimensional analysis is planned on the basis of spectral–zonal images in the optical and IR ranges. This will ensure the complex use of techniques of multidimensional, regressive, factor analysis and multidimensional classification. Such an approach will make it possible to select significant factors and parameters, retrieval of which (based on solution of respective inverse problems) will make it possible to carry out the quantitative monitoring of the objects in an ecologically dangerous state. An important condition for progress in this field is to create a highly efficient set of applied programmes of the multidimensional analysis of images functioning in an interactive regime. Also important is the development of a measuring apparatus and peripheral complexes of new generation on a multi-processor basis.

Thus, an experimental processing of high-resolution SAR images obtained from space revealed wide prospects for an application of the mathematical technique of SAR data processing and prospects for their use to solve Earth's various resources and ecological problems.

2.9.5 Examples of radar survey from the space-borne platform "Almaz-1"

A space vehicle "Almaz-1" was launched in a satellite's orbit on 31 March 1991 via a launching rocket "Proton". Almaz-1 is a stabilized platform with a constant precise orientation towards the Earth with an orbital inclination of 72.9° and a period of rotation round the Earth of 90 minutes. The height of the working orbit was maintained in the 250–300-km range. In March 1993, following a command from the Earth, Almaz-1 ceased to function.

Almaz-1 was equipped with an advanced SAR operating at the 9.6-cm wavelength, and a scanning microwave radiometer. An advanced system of transmission, collection and processing of information made it possible to distribute the data among the users in a digital form, as well as in the form of photos and records on magnetic tape, or to transmit the information directly to the receiving stations of the users. The use of a satellite-retransmitter has made it possible to perform a survey and to transmit signals from any region of the globe. The radar images obtained permitted a detailed all-weather survey of the Earth's surface with a horizontal and azimuthal resolution of 10–15 m.

The use of radar with the decimetre wavelength range and horizontal polarization for emission and receiving ensures highly informative radar images of geological formations on the Earth's surface, the structure of sea surface roughness, vegetation cover, soil moisture, and ice reconnaissance.

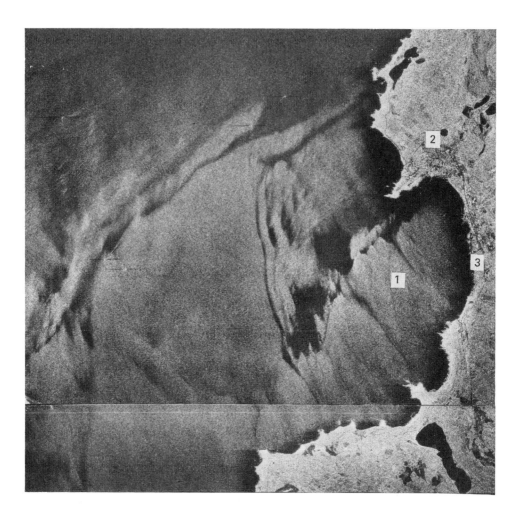

Fig. 2.56. Radar image of the surface of the Gulf of Finland in the region of Koporye Bay:
1—Koporye Bay; 2—Sosnovy Bor; 3—Leningrad AES.

Figure 2.56 exemplifies a radar image of the Gulf of Finland in the region of the Koporye Bay (1), a town of Sosnovy Bor (2), and Leningrad AES (3). The image was obtained on 12 May 1991. It enables one to study the state and structure of the water surface, largely determined on that day by the direction and spread of the surface wind. The wind direction is marked with an arrow, its speed, from meteodata, was not more than 3–5 m s^{-1}.

Figure 2.57 demonstrates the ice situation in the Antarctic on 27 July 1991 in the region where the motor-ship "M. Somov" had been beset. In the figure one can see a white point (1). White patches (2) are images of large icebergs.

Figure 2.58 shows a radar image of the Bosporus between Europe and the Asia

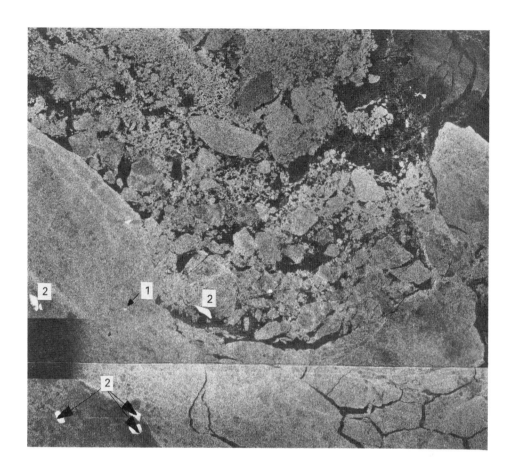

Fig. 2.57. The 27 June 1991 radar image of the ice situation in the Antarctic: 1—motor-ship "M. Somov". 2—large icebergs.

Minor peninsula. The image was obtained on 27 July 1991 in the 1877th descending orbit of Almaz-1. The time was 02:21:47 GMT. The viewing angle was 40.43°. The range was 385 km. The Bosporus connects the Black Sea and the Sea of Marmara. Its length is about 30 km; the width is 750 m to 3.7 km. The largest Turcic city, Istanbul, located at foothills on both shores of the Bosporus near the Sea of Marmara is well seen on the image. The districts and the buildings are identified from geometrically regular streets. The European part, which is the largest part of the city, is divided into two zones by the Golden Horn, and is connected with the Asiatic part through a bridge 1560 m long and ferry boats, clearly seen on the image. The bridge, ferry boats and port structures in the Golden Horn Bay are also cleary seen. In the Sea of Marmara basin, on the roadstead, near the port, the ships are seen as points of bright light. Motor-roads and rail-roads can easily be identified. The sea surface reveals the wind-driven inhomogeneities, slickwise strips and ship traces.

Fig. 2.58. The 27 July 1991 radar image of the Bosporus.

During the survey over the sea basin a weak variable wind was blowing, which was responsible for the appearance of patches and strips on the sea surface (ripple patches, smoothing effects, zones and boundaries of intensified winds, and, respectively, wind-driven waves—ripple).

Films of SAS on the sea surface were formed here owing to plankton vital functions. These slicks are driven by winds and prevailing currents. The data on the motion of surface slicks can be used to control the general circulation of water masses in closed seas and water basins. This is illustrated by the image of the Sea of Marmara shown in Fig. 2.59.

Figure 2.60 presents a radar image of agricultural crops in the "Gazyr" region of the Krasnodar Krai obtained on 25 May 1991 in the 880th descending orbit of Almaz-1. The time is 13:02:14 GMT. The viewing angle is 49°. The range is 435 km. Different reflectivities of plants and their changes under the influence of various factors make it possible to use the radar survey to observe the state of natural and man-made vegetation cover.

Fig. 2.59. Films of SAS on the surface of the Sea of Marmara.

Fig. 2.60. The 25 May 1991 radar image of agricultural crops in the region Gazyr of the Krasnodar Krai.

During the flight of Almaz-1 an experiment was carried out at the "Gazyrskoye" test farm on assessing the effect of nitric feeding of plants on the reflective properties of vegetation cover. The experiment was made over an area of about 5 ha divided into 49 sites 32 × 32 m in size. To obtain different levels of provision of plants with nitrogen, seven doses of it were introduced to the early springtime extra-feed: 0; 30; 60; 90; 120; 150; and 180 kg ha^{-1}. The extra-feeding was made by hand on 21 March 1991. The survey from Almaz-1 was carried out on 25 May 1991. In sample plants the total nitrogen content was estimated and a rapid analysis was made to determine the indices of provision of plants with nitrogen. An approximating function to determine the total nitrogen content has the form:

$$N = 1.14 + 1.638e^{-L},$$

where L is the value of the reflected processed signal.

The mean deviation in determining the total nitrogen content in plants both theoretically and experimentally constituted 4.4%. Indices of the nitrogen content were determined from the formula:

$$N = 0.23 + 2.145e^{-L}.$$

The mean deviation in the indices of nitrogen content in the winter wheat calculated from the data of remote sounding from space was 21%.

Thus, the experiment carried out during the flight of Almaz-1 has confirmed the possibility to determine the index of provision of winter wheat with nitrogen using the radar remote sounding technique.

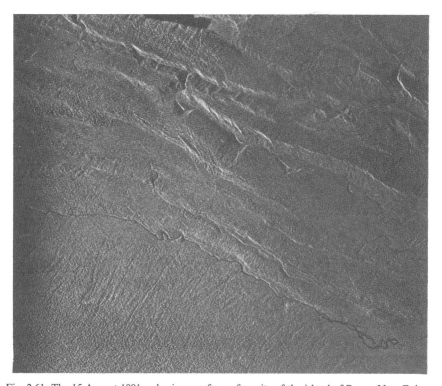

Fig. 2.61. The 15 August 1991 radar image of a surface site of the island of Papua New Guinea.

Figure 2.61 demonstrates a radar image of a surface site of the island of Papua-New Guinea obtained on 15 August 1991 in the 2180th orbit of Almaz-1. The viewing angle is 35.84°. The range is 375 km. The time is 00:31:45 GMT. The character of the image is closely connected with the peculiar features of the geological structure. One can clearly see fractures connected with folded structures, with a large dip angle (40–50°). The geological decoding of the radar image of the site of the island of Papua-New Guinea made it possible to identify the sites with similar features of geological structure. From relationships between the forms of relief one can identify a tectonic structure in the west-north-western direction and a flat descending structure in the north-north-eastern direction (monoclinal structure). This radar image demonstrates a unique sensitivity of the radar sounding to the

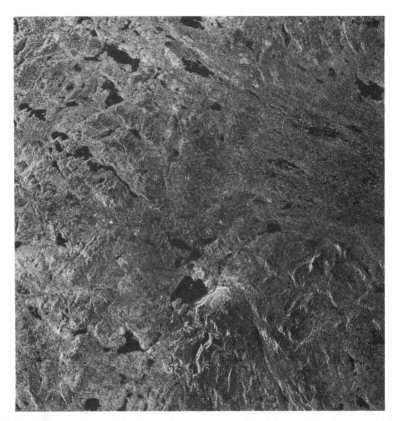

Fig. 2.62. Radar image of an area in the north-western part of the Murmansk region near the boundary with Norway.

surface relief, makes it possible to reproduce the pattern and the mechanism of the formation of the present geological structure of the locality.

Figure 2.62 shows a radar image of an area in the north-western part of the Murmansk region, near the boundary with Norway. In this area the relief is the sloping hills with an overstepping of 100–150 m. The south-eastern part is characterized by small hills with relatively sloping hillsides. Analysis of the geological structures shows the main part of the region to be Archaean rocks (3.6–2.1 billion years old) suffering changes close to magmatic. In the lower part of the image a nickel-ore quarry can be identified. The infrastructure of the quarry is clearly seen:

— light half-rings of the empty-rock moulding;
— dark cavity of the quarry itself;
— road system;
— east of the towns Lousari and Zapolarny there are two lakes transformed into slag-settlers; on the coastal water surface are seen pulp pipelines and in the central part of the water surface are alluvial pulp islands.

One can clearly see a tectonic fracture in the north direction from the second, smaller lake, to the left shore of the river Pachenga. This means the need for ecological control of this area to prevent the flow of contaminated waters from the lake to the river. Possibilities of the practical use of the information obtained are as follows:

— the retrieval of structures in the most ancient geological formations (usually this requires detailed surface observations making use of special techniques);
— the geoecological control of the mining regions.

Figure 2.63 presents a radar image of the coastline of the Abu-Dhabi emirate (the date: 13 July 1992. Orbit: no. 7466, descending. Time: 12:10:10 GMT. The viewing angle: 25.56°. The range: 380 km).

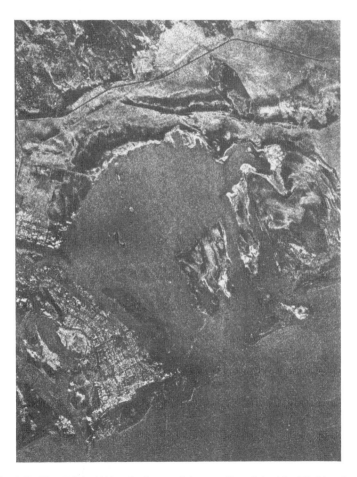

Fig. 2.63. The 13 July 1992 radar image of the coastline of the Abu-Dhabi emirate.

One can see the urban constructions of Abu-Dhabi and the transport network. In this region the coastline is characterized by the shore banks, spits and islands. The shore in this region is mainly low-lying, edged with sandy beaches. The coastline is strongly indented. This is a typical ingression shore, that is, flooded with sea water, which periodically covers the slightly lowered lands.

The tides, run-up and run-away waves result in the coastline often having no clear contours, and the adds reveal vast dried up places of silty–clayey and sandy materials. The dark background on radar images (a weak reflected signal) is the forms of relief affected by the sea, and saline hollows; the light background (a strong reflected signal) is sands with an aeolian (wind) small-scale relief. Such images make it possible to control and to forecast changes in the coastline and the shelf relief caused by marine processes, that is, to monitor the coastal zone.

Thus, the two-year period of radar functioning on board the platform Almaz-1 has made it possible to obtain a vast amount of experimental material on the Earth's resources and ecology studied from space and to develop some new approaches to use the results of respective radar survey.

2.9.6 Prospects of development of the space-borne system "Almaz"

During the last decade tendencies appeared in the development of Earth sciences, connected with their increasing interaction and the necessity to study the Earth as an integrated ecological system.

Study of the Earth as an ecological system requires a new stage of space-based investigations based on obtaining the global quantitative data base of the Earth, the state and the evolution of its atmosphere, hydrosphere, cryosphere, lithosphere, and biosphere. All spheres are integrated into one system and take place in the transformation and distribution of the incoming solar energy, energy and matter exchange among the spheres, in energy losses to outer space; that is in the processes over timescales of minutes and hours to centuries.

The present stage of global ecological studies of the Earth on the basis of remote sounding from space is aimed at a realization of such international programmes as "Global Change"—IGBP, WCR, WOCE, the Russian programme of studies of the role of the energy-active zones of the ocean in climate change "sections". To realize these programmes, the EOS system has been planned. For this system, special heavy space platforms are being developed. The space vehicle "Almaz" is a space-borne platform, the technical capabilities of which are listed in Table 2.28. In this connection, at the meeting of the Soviet–American Working Group "Earth Sciences" (Washington, 23–27 September 1991) the soviet side proposed to use the space system "Almaz" as an automatic space ecological laboratory (ASEL) on an international basis and to launch the stations "Almaz-1b" and "Almaz-2" in 1995 and 1998 (see Table 2.28). With this aim in view, the possibility is being developed to equip the ASEL "Almaz" with scientific instruments enumerated in Table 2.29.

An arrangement of Almaz-1b is shown in Fig. 2.64 and that of Almaz-2 in Fig. 2.65. The programme of creating a series of automatic space stations with a stage-by-stage increase of the complex for remote sounding of the Earth is illustrated by the diagram in Fig. 2.66.

Table 2.28. Basic characteristics of ASEL "Almaz-2"

Parameter	Estimate
Parameters of the working orbit:	
— height, km	600
— inclination, deg.	73
Carrier-rocket	"Proton"
Mass in the basic orbit, kg	21000
Mass of on-board scientific instruments, kg	6500
Mass of DU-fuel components, kg	3150
Characteristics of power supply:	
— mean-orbital, W	
initial	2840–3800
final	2200–3050
— maximum (peak), W	10000
Accuracy of orientation and stabilization during the remote sounding session:	
— orientation (bank, course, pitch), min	±5
— stabilization (bank, course, pitch), °/s	0.001–0.003
Transmission of remote-sounding information to the Earth	To IRS in Russian and abroad; via RS to IRS
Time of ASEL active functioning, years	5
Launch	1998

IRS—information receiving stations
RS—retransmitting satellite

Table 2.29. The automatic space ecological laboratory (ASEL) "Almaz-2"

Type of instrument	Technical characteristics
1. SAR	Number of channels—3; resolution—10–15 m or 50 m; swath width—75–100/500 km.
2. SAR	Number of channels—1; wavelength—120 cm; resolution— 20–200 m; swath width—200–300 km.
3. Microwave radiometer	Number of channels—7; wavelength range—0.3–21cm; resolution—3–20 km; swath width—1200 km.
4. Radar raingauge	Number of channels—2; wavelength range—1–2 cm; resolution—250 m; swath width—100 km.
5. Visible multichannel scanner	Number of channels—11; spectral range—400–100 nm; resolution—20 m; swath width—1000 km.
6. IR multizonal scanner	Number of channels—5; wavelength range—1600–12000 nm; resolution—60m; swath width—1000 km.
7. Microwave scatterometer	Swath width—450 km; measurement accuracy—2 m/s, 20°.
8. Altimeter	Measurement accuracy—10 cm.
9. Lidar	Number of channels—8; wavelength range—266–1064 nm.
10. IR spectrometer	Wavelength range—2.5–10.5 μm.
11. Extinction photometer	Number of channels—2; wavelength range—0.45–0.63 μm.
12. Spectrometer of millimetre range	Wavelength range—1.5–5 mm.
13. Solar spectrometer	Wavelength range—0.1–4.5 μm; spectral resolution up to 0.01 μm.
14. BEST measuring complex	Radar raingauge. Microwave radiometer, lidar, radiometer-correlator WINDMATIC.

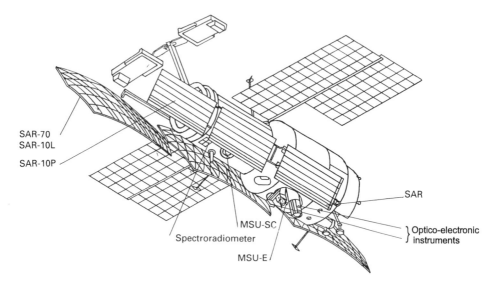

SAR-70
SAR-10L

SAR-10P

.SAR

| MSU-SC
Spectroradiometer

} Optico-electronic
J instruments

MSU-E /

Fig. 2.64. An arrangement of the space laboratory "Almaz-1B".

Analysis of the problems of fundamental scientific studies of the Earth and the possibilities of their realization with the help of space-borne means has led to the conception of the programme called "ECOS". The conception has been developed by the scientists of the institutions of the Russian Academy of Sciences (Armand at al., 1993). It includes two interconnected and supplementing sub-programmes—ECOS-A and ECOS-D. ECOS-D is a detailed programme of the Earth's resources and ecological studies from space planned to be realized on a heavy space platform—the automatic space laboratory ASEL. The ASEL should be launched in an orbit close to the polar one. It should be equipped with an extensive remotely sounding complex providing detailed studies in the optical and radio range of electromagnetic waves. One advantage of ASEL is the possibility to use the same instruments for various studies, whish raises the efficiency of both the instruments and the studies owing to information obtained from adjacent fields of observations.

To create an ASEL which would realize the ECOS-D programme, the space vehicle "Almaz" was suggested as the basis. The capabilities of "Almaz" (6.5 t payload, energy power 4 to 10 kW) make it possible to mount a unique complex of multi-wave high-resolution instruments, including the 4-frequency (3.5–120 cm) SAR (resolution near the Earth's surface 7–15 m), multichannel panoramic multi-beam microwave radiometer (3–21 cm), optical and IR multichannel scanner for detailed studies of the ocean and land surface, 2-wave rain radar, microwave, IR and UV optical spectrometers and lidars for detailed studies of the structure, composition and dynamics of the atmosphere.

The ECOS-A programme foresees the global studies survey of the Earth and its atmosphere with a simultaneous study of the effect of solar–terrestrial connections on the ecological system of the Earth (Avanesov et al., 1992). This programme is

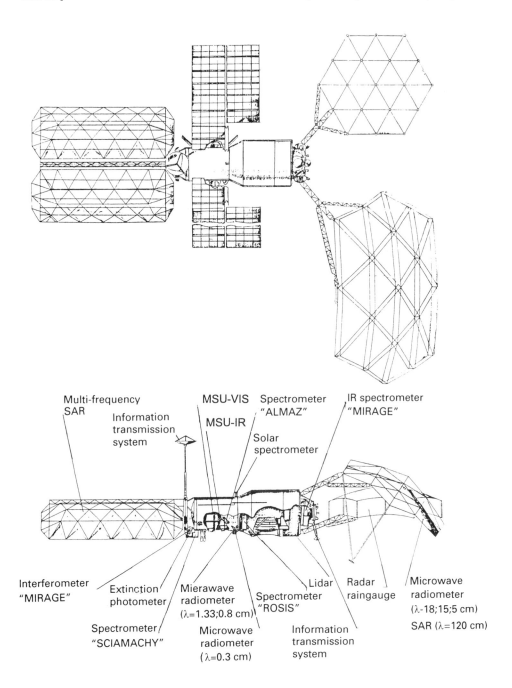

Fig. 2.65. An arrangement of the space laboratory "Almaz-2".

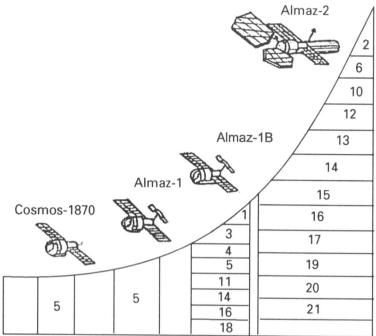

Fig. 2.66. The programme of creating a series of automatic space stations with a stage-by-stage increase of the complex for remote sounding of the Earth: 1—videospectrometer; 2—multizonal scanner; 3—SLR; 4—single-frequency SAR-70; 5—single-frequency SAR-10; 6—triple frequency SAR; 7—optico-electronic instruments; 8—MSU-CS multizonal scanner; 9—MSU-E multizonal scanner; 10—radar raingauge; 11—MSU-IR multizonal scanner; 12—ATMOS-complex; 13—MIRAS IR spectrometer; 14—multichannel microwave radiometer; 15—multi-frequency lidar complex; 16—radioaltimeter; 17—wind radioscatterometer; 18—MSU-VIS multizonal scanner; 19—extinction photometer; 20—solar spectrometer; 21—spectroradiometer for monitoring of the ocean from space.

based on the simultaneous use of two comparatively small space vehicles. One of these vehicles should be equipped with the instruments for the global sounding of the Earth's surface and its atmosphere. It should be launched in the near-Earth Sun-synchronous orbit. The second, carrying the complexes to measure the characteristics of the solar electromagnetic and corpuscular emission, will be in the orbit in the vicinity of the Lagrange point.

The structure and composition of the ASEL scientific complex on the basis of "Almaz" have been chosen following the conception of provision of a new stage of studies of the Earth as an ecological system including all its components: atmosphere, hydrosphere, cryosphere, lithosphere, and biosphere. The problems of studies were taken into account when estimating the accuracy of parameters, directions of sounding, zones of survey, etc. The problems of detailed studies of the

Earth as an ecological system solved with the multipurpose space-borne laboratory within the programme ECOS-D are listed in Table 2.30. The structure of the programme of studies of the Earth as an ecological system with the use of a space laboratory "Almaz-2" is shown in Fig. 2.66. Parameters of the scientific complex carried by "Almaz" are given in Table 2.29. The composition of the complex has been chosen so that it can be used on ASEL in 1995–1996 except for the complex BEST (France). The possibility of using it on ASEL (to be launched in 1997–98) is to be decided (Armand et al., 1993).

Table 2.30. Problems of detailed space studies of the Earth as an ecological system (programme ECOS-D) solved by the multipurpose space laboratory

Objectives, parameters	Instruments	Application
1. Radiation budget 1.1 Parameters of solar radiation 1.2 Parameters of reflected radiation	MSU-VIS., MSU-IR Solar spectrometers	Climatology
2. Atmosphere 2.1 Determination of basic atmospheric parameters 2.1.1 Cloudiness and its parameters: — mapping — thickness — cloud particles' size distribution — upper boundary — temperature — water supply — velocity — direction — albedo 2.1.2 Rain rate 2.1.3 Determination of vertical profile — temperature — humidity 2.1.4 Wind: — speed — direction 2.1.5 Mid-atmospheric turbulence 2.1.6 Integral parameters: — mean temperature — water vapour — droplet moisture 2.1.7 Observation of typhoons, hurricanes	 MSU-VIS, MSU-IR, lidar Lidar, MR Lidar, MR, AMAS (ATMOS) spectrometer Lidar MSU-IR, MR Lidar, MR WINDMATIC (BEST) MSU-VIS Radar raingauge mm-radar, spectrometer Lidar Lidar, scatterometer (above water), WINDMATIC (BEST) MR Extinction photometer MR Lidar Lidar, MR MSU-VIS, MSU-IR, MR	Climatology meteorol. forecast Climatology, meteorol. forecast Radiation budget Radiation budget Met. forecast agriculture Climatology, met. forecast Meteorology Met. forecast Climatology Met. forecast
2.2 Determination of trace gases content. 2.2.1 Record of CO_2 concentrations	MIPAS interferometer, lidar AMAS spectrometer, ROSIS spectrometer, MIRAS IR spectrometer, SCIMACHI spectrometer	Environmental control, climatology Study of greenhouse effect

Objectives, parameters	Instruments	Application
2.2.2 Record of trace gases (SO_2, $C10$, NO_2)	MIPAS interferometer, lidar, AMAS spectrometer, ROSIS spectrometer, MIRAS IR spectrometer, SCIMACHI spectrometer	Environmental control
2.2.3 Record of aerosol content	MIPAS interferometer, lidar, AMAS spectrometer, ROSIS, spectrometer, MIRAS IR spectrometer, SCIMACHI	Environmental control
2.2.4 Spatial and temporal distribution of ozone	MIPAS interferometer, lidar, AMAS spectrometer, ROSIS spectrometer, MIRAS IR spectrometer, SCIMACHI spectrometer	Control of the state of ozone layer

3. Water surface		
3.1 Study of the World Ocean global circulation		Oceanology, oceanography, climatology, meteorol. forecast
3.2 Study of the structures of surface roughness: gravitational waves (GW), gravitational-capillary waves (GCW), ripples, inner waves (IW), correlation with currents	MSU-VIS, MSU-IR, SAR, MR	Oceanology
3.2.1 Mapping sea surface temperature fishery,	MSU-IR, MR	Oceanography, climatology, environmental protect.
3.2.2 Record of near-water wind fields	MR, MSU-IR, scatterometer	Met. forecast, climatology
3.2.3 Record of surface currents and their parameters	SAR, MR, radioaltimeter	Oceanography, oceanology
3.2.4 Record of fronts, vortices, zones of upwelling and inner waves	MR, MSU-IR, SAR	Oceanography, oceanology, fishery
3.2.5 Record of variations of water surface height with respect to the Earth's geoid	Radioaltimeter	Oceanology
3.2.6 Mapping the sea ice surface and its parameters (dynamics of the state)	MR, MSU-IR, MSU-VIS, SAR	Oceanography, met. forecast
3.3 Study of currents	MR, MSU-IR, SAR, radioaltimeter	Oceanology
3.4 Study of sea ice surface: — boundary — solidity— thickness — hummocking	MR, MSU-IR, SAR, MSU-VIS	Oceanology
3.5 Study of biological productivity		Oceanology, biology
3.5.1 Study of regional–seasonal variability of primary production in a water column (by colour and other parameters)	MR, MSU-VIS, SAR	
3.5.2 Discovering the laws of phytoplankton formation	MR, MSU-VIS, SAR	Oceanology, biology
3.6 Study of anthropogenic pollution		
3.6.1 Estimation of concentration of suspended matter and biomass	MSU-VIS, SAR	Oceanology, environmental protection
3.6.2 Estimation of concentration of dissolved organic matter (yellow substance)	MSU-VIS, SAR	Oceanology, environmental protection

Objectives, parameters	Instruments	Application
3.6.3 Detection of oil slicks	MR, MSU-VIS, SAR, MSU-IR	Environmental protection
3.6.4 Discovering relationships between pollution and biologic activity	MR, MSU-VIS, SAR	Oceanology, environmental protection

4. Land		
4.1 Mapping the surface		
4.1.1 In the interests of geology	MR, MSU-VIS, MSU-IR, SAR	Geology
4.1.2 Vegetation	MR, MSU-VIS, MSU-IR, SAR	Geography
4.1.3 Type of soils	MR, MSU-VIS, SAR, MSU-IR	Geography, soil science, agriculture
4.1.4 Study of the zones of disaster and strong geodynamic phenomena affecting the environment, including active fractures	MR, MSU-VIS, SAR, MSU-IR	Geology, environmental protection, emergencies
4.2 Assessment of soil parameters		Soil science, agriculture
4.2.1 Temperature (profile)	MR, MSU-IR	
4.2.2 Moisture content (profile)	MR, MSU-IR, SAR	Environmental protection
4.2.3 Content of humus, fertilizers,	MR, MSU-VIS, SARchemicals	
4.2.4 Salinity	MR, MSU-VIS, SAR, MSU-IR	Environmental protection
4.2.5 Control of erosion processes	MSU-VIS, SAR	Environmental protection
4.3 Assessment of the state of agricultural processes		Biology, agriculture
4.3.1 Identification of the types of plants	MSU-VIS, MSU-IR, SAR	
4.3.2 Determination of the biomass vegetation phases	MSU-VIS, MSU-IR, SAR	
4.3.3 Estimation of moisture content	MR, MSU-VIS, SAR, MSU-IR	
4.3.4 Damage by pests, weeds, diseases	MR, MSU-VIS, SAR, MSU-IR	Environmental protection
4.3.5 Anthropogenic damage	MR, MSU-VIS, SAR, MSU-IR	Environmental protection
4.4 Control of desertification	MR, MSU-VIS, SAR, MSU-IR	Geography, environmental protection
4.5 Study of the state of forests		Forestry, environmental protection
4.5.1 Identification of the types of trees	MSU-VIS, MSU-IR, SAR	
4.5.2 Damage by pests, diseases	MSU-VIS, MSU-IR, SAR	Environmental protection
4.5.3 Anthropogenic damage	MSU-VIS, MSU-IR, SAR	Environmental protection
4.6 Control of the state of reclamation constructions and assessment of their efficiency	MR, MSU-VIS, SAR, MSU-IR	Hydrology, agriculture, environmental protection
4.7 Assessment of the state of snow cover		Meteorology, agriculture, environmental protection
4.7.1 Temperature (profile)	MR, MSU-IR	
4.7.2 Thickness (snow supply, water equivalent)	MR, SAR	
4.7.3 Snow cover structure (the presence of layers of different density)	MR, SAR	
4.7.4 Surface contamination (extent, zones)	MR, MSU-VIS, SAR, MSU-IR	
4.7.5 Mapping of seasonal snow line	MR, MSU-VIS, SAR, MSU-IR	
4.8 Assessment of the state of ice cover		Climatology, meteorology
4.8.1 Mapping the ice edge on land and on water	MR, MSU-VIS, SAR, MSU-IR	

Objectives, parameters	Instruments	Application
4.8.2 Height of glaciers' surface	MSU-VIS radioaltimeter, SAR	
4.8.3 Mapping the edge of ice and firn (determination of the zones of glaciers' water supply)	MSU-VIS, SAR	
4.8.4 Microrelief of mountain glaciers	MSU-VIS, SAR	
4.8.5 Ice thickness	MR, SAR	
4.8.6 Temperature (profile)	MR, MSU-IR	
4.8.7 Humidity	MR, SAR	
4.8.8 Density, crystalline properties of ice and firn	MR, SAR	
4.8.9 Cracking	MSU-VIS, SAR	
4.8.10 Surface contamination (extent, zones)	MR, MSU-VIS, SAR, MSU-IR	Environmental protection
4.9 Study of the zones of permafrost	MR, MSU-VIS, MSU-IR, SAR	

MSU—multizonal scanning unit
SAR—synthetic-aperture radar
MR—microwave radiometer

2.10 CONCLUSION

In conclusion the following should be mentioned:

1.   Two principal approaches have taken shape in the development of quantitative spectral techniques to study the Earth's resources and the environment. The first is multichannel scanning TV systems, multizonal cameras and trace spectro-telephotometers, which make it possible to obtain images of the underlying surface and the optical characteristics in several, relatively narrow spectral intervals. The second is the spectral measuring complex to record the whole continuous spectrum in a given spectral range from a comparatively small surface area. The first techniques are characterized by a high spatial resolution with a large volume of spectral information loss; the second techniques are characterized by a high spectral and comparatively low spatial resolution. Each technique is used in the field to its advantage. Their usefulness has been demonstrated in several space-based experiments.

   Both techniques of spectral studies are mutually supplementing. For example, the data on continuous spectra of reflection, absorption and scattering of solar radiation by natural formations are needed to develop and apply to their advantage the multichannel scanning instruments and multizonal cameras and, first of all, to make an optimal choice of the most informative spectral intervals.

   Further development of space-borne spectral studies of the state of the Earth's environment and resources depends both on the development of the on-board measuring instruments which would make it possible to obtain the spectral distribution of the brightness fields in different wavelength regions—from the UV to the radio range, and on the creation of fast-operating spectrometers with high spectral and spatial resolutions, to record a continuous spectra. Spectrometers with a continuous recording of spectra play the basic role here: they provide data to solve the fundamental scientific problems—study of spectral optical characteristics of natural formations, their dependence on the state of objects; accumulation of data needed to compile the catalogues of the spectra of natural formations. The use of multichannel scanning systems and multizonal cameras should be connected with the solution of concrete economic problems. The TV scanning system ensures the prompt obtaining of space information, and the cameras mounted on automatic space platforms and manned stations provide with the high-quality information from space about slowly varying natural processes and phenomena transmitted to the Earth together with the returned photomaterials.

2.   The multichannel scanning units (MSUs) of the optical range serve the basis for an integrated ENRS system and therefore need special attention. All the MSU parameters enumerated above should be strictly optimal. This is difficult at present in view of:

   — the absence of a list of economic problems placed in order of priority to be solved through a systematic spectral survey from space;
   — the absence of adequate reliable information about the spectral characteristics of natural formations, from which one can assess their state at the moment and forecast their state in the future;
   — the absence of a clear technique for an operational account of the effect of the atmosphere on the results of a spectral survey from space.

   All this requires systematic spectral studies of the optical properties of natural formations from space, aircraft and near the Earth's surface. Only a combination of spectral studies of natural formations from MOS, MSU, aircraft and near the surface with the global survey from space making use of space-borne TV and photo instruments will be able to ensure the efficient use of the space-borne ENRS system to solve concrete economic problems.

3.   Development of radar methods of the remote sounding of the environment has made the space-borne observations all-weather and independent of illumination conditions in the region of observations. The creation of SARs has increased substantially the spatial resolution and opened up wide possibilities for their use to solve various Earth's resources and ecological problems. The progress in global ecological studies depends much on a reasonable combination of optical and radar methods.

4.   In most cases, studies of global ecological processes require detailed Earth's resources investigations made simultaneously with a large remote-sensing complex. This complex can be carried only by a heavy space platform which would ensure its launch into orbit, its functioning and precise spatial orientation. Russia suggests an automatic space ecological laboratory (ASEL) be used as a heavy platform. It will be launched in a near-polar orbit and equipped with a large measuring complex for detailed studies in both the optical and the radio range of electromagnetic waves. An advantage of the heavy ASEL is the possibility of using the same instruments for different studies, which increases substatially the efficiency of both the applied instruments and the studies themselves owing to additional information from adjacent fields.

Table 2.31. Programme of studies of the Earth as an ecological system using the space laboratory "Almaz-2"

Fundamental problems	Problems to be solved
1. Development of an atmospheric general circulation model	1. Record of cloudiness, measurements of its parameters.
2. Study of global circulation of the World Ocean waters	2. Drawing the profiles of temperature and humidity.
	3. Assessment of the ozone layer thickness.
	4. Record of trace gases concentration.
	5. Mapping the sea surface temperature to $\Delta T \sim 0.5$ K
	6. Record of the ocean surface pollution.
3. Development of the model of the ocean–atmosphere energy exchange	7. Study of the upwelling, inner wave fronts.
	8. Study of surface roughness (GW, GCW, ripples).
4. Impact of the land energy balance on planetary climate	9. Record of the fields of near-water wind.
	10. Record of currents, measurements of their parameters.
5. Global dynamics of the biosphere	11. Mapping the seasonal snow line and ice edge.
	12. Control of the mountain ice formation.
	13. Measurement of soil temperature and moisture.
	14. Control of erosion processes.
6. Geological aspects of global change	15. Control of reclamation consequences.
	16. Control of changes in marine bioproductivity.
	17. Control of desertification, lands becoming boggy, salty.
	18. Study of the Earth's crust tectonic activity.
	19. Study of permafrost.
	20. Control of volcanic activity.

3

Optimization of observing systems

At present there are broad possibilities to accomplish observations of the environment. For this purpose, numerous ground-based networks can be used, as well as ship- and airborne observational means. Space-borne remote sounding systems contribute much to the information about the environment. On the one hand, the data of direct (*in situ*) observations principally differ from the results of remote observations, which are indirect data. On the other hand, interpretation of space-derived information without using data of *in situ* observations is very difficult. We shall consider the problem of synthesizing complex observational systems based on various criteria of information efficiency. Various models and techniques of observational systems' optimization will be discussed.

In Section 3.1 the information and information–economic models of the surface observational systems are considered. A combination of conventional and satellite observations is discussed in Section 3.2, with a case study of the analysis of hemispherical geopotential fields. The coupling of various kinds of information based on techniques of conjugated equations is given in Section 3.3. The multipurpose nature of the data of observations from space requires the solution of the problems of an optimal design of the remote sensing systems based on specific requirements defined by groups and classes of problems of the environmental monitoring to observational data. The information and economic approach to the solution of the problem of multipurpose planning satellite systems is substantiated in Section 3.4.

The information contained in this chapter gives us an idea about the diversity of approaches to the solution of the problem of optimization of observational systems.

3.1 AN INFORMATION MODEL OF THE SURFACE OBSERVATIONAL NETWORK

The problem of constructing a model for optimizing the system of hydrological and meteorological observations (SHMO) has been considered elsewhere (Pokrovski, 1984, 1987; Pokrovski and Malygina, 1986). This development was based on the schemes of an objective analysis, which ensure the retrieval of meteorological parameters at regular grid points.

In the publications mentioned, the MSD values at grid points served as a criterion for the location of observation network stations. However, for the users of hydrological and meteorological information (HMI), of great importance are also such properties as spatial and temporal resolution, completeness of the set of meteorological parameters, and the cost of observations. Thus, from the formal point of view, the problem of SHMO design is a multi-criterion optimization problem. Such a problem is posed in Section 3.1.1.

Bearing in mind the persistent relations between the spatial and temporal fluctuations of the principal meteorological parameters (temperature, geopotential, wind speed, etc.), the scheme of spatial and temporal analysis of the meteorological fields was used as a basis. A technique of a bi-orthogonal spectral expansion of the meteorological fields which ensures the most compact presentation of the spatial–temporal HMI has been chosen. This technique of meteorological fields filtration makes it possible to select certain characteristic temporal and spatial scales of fluctuations in solving the problem of analysis (Section 3.1.2). This ability of the technique enables one to develop an SHMO model as applied to the requirements of a concrete use for the spatial and temporal resolution of HMI (Section 3.1.3).

Section 3.1.4 describes the state of the problems of the multi-criterion optimization, based on the ideas of Boolean programming.

3.1.1 Mathematical basis of a multi-criterion problem to optimize a hydrometeorological observing system

3.1.1.1 Basic components of the problem

Let ξ be an SHMO. The SHMO ξ usually consists of several sub-systems $\xi = \Sigma \, \xi_i$. The sub-systems can be specialized observational networks, sub-systems of satellite, balloon, aircraft, ship, etc. observations. The objectives of collecting the HMIs define a list of the users, NC. The users, NC, formulate the HMI issue:

(a) in the form of a certain list of meteorological parameters—NE, or a list of transformed values—meteorological parameters—NP;
(b) with a certain accuracy, P;
(c) with a spatial distribution, SD or resolution, SR;
(d) with a certain temporal resolution, ST;
(e) with a certain periodicity of distributing to the user, PC;
(f) at a certain cost, M.

3.1.1.2 The structure of relationships

The parameters NE (NP), P, SD (SR), ST, PC, M are the principal criteria of the value of HMI from the user's point of view.

On the other hand, each of these parameters is function of SHMO, ξ. Therefore, $NE = NE(\xi)$, $NP = NP(\xi)$, $SD = SD(\xi)$, $SR = SR(\xi)$, $P = P(\xi)$, $ST = ST(\xi)$, $M = M(\xi)$.

3.1.1.3 The multi-criterion nature of the problem

The criteria enumerated above make it possible to introduce preference relationships among the alternative systems of observation, ξ. For example, the system ξ^1 is preferable with respect to NP compared to the system ξ^2 (let $\xi^1 > \xi^2$) if NP (ξ^1) > NP(ξ^2). Similarly, we can introduce preference relationships with respect to all other criteria, except M. In this case $\xi^1 > \xi^2$, if M(ξ^1) < M(ξ^2). Thus, when constructing the SHMO model, we face a multi-criterion problem denoted symbolically as

$$(NP, P, SR, ST, PC, M)$$

of an optimization of the structure and composition of ξ with the user's requirements met with respect to all the basic parameters; that is, the relationships NP $\geqslant$ NP*, P $\geqslant$ P*, etc. should be fulfilled. For M as specific condition, M $\leqslant$ M* should be fulfilled. For the optimization problem to be comprehensively posed, it is necessary to introduce an aim function, which must be maximized with account of limitations introduced by the HMI users. Let ϕ be the function of an HMI value.

3.1.1.4 The structure of the HMI value function

The criterion variables: NP, P, SR, ST, PC, characterizing the properties required of HMI, can be considered independent with regard to their preferences. However, each is connected with the HMI values, M. Therefore, based on the classic results of the decision-making theory, we come to the conclusion that the function of HMI value has the following structure:

$$\phi = \phi \, (NP,M) + \phi \, (P,M) + \phi \, (SR,M) + \phi \, (ST,M) + \phi \, (PC,M)$$

Each of the items on the right-hand side of this equation can be called the criterion function of an HMI value. Experts in both HMI numerical analysis and economics determine the criterion functions of the HMI value. Such functions relate the HMI value to the level of individual consumer properties of HMI: the set of parameters, accuracy, resolution, etc. The basis for such relations consists in counting the costs of broadening, re-equipment and renewal of the observation system needed to reach desired values for the criterion variables NP, P, SR, etc.

3.1.1.5 Optimization problems

(a) Each HMI user, NC, may determine the function of HMI value of its own, ϕ^{NC}, meeting his needs. Also, each user, NC, must specify the limits of acceptable values for every criterion of the problem: NP $\geqslant$ NP^{NC}, P $\geqslant$ P^{NC}, ..., PC $\geqslant$ PC^{NC}, M $\leqslant$ M^{NC}. Denoting a set of criteria $Y(\xi) = (NP, P, ST, SR, PC, M) \, (\xi)$, we determine the limitations in the vector from $Y(\xi) \geqslant Y^{NC}$. In this case the optimization problem for the HMI user, NC, is reduced to an assessment of SHMO (ξ), for which

$$\xi^{NC} = \arg \max_{\xi \, : \, Y \, (\xi) \, \geqslant \, Y^{NC}} \phi^{NC} \, [Y(\xi)]$$

(b) Of the most important practical interest is the problem of multipurpose planning of observation systems. The urgency of this problem is explained by the fact that SHMO should meet this requirement. This requires a respective modification of the aim function and limitations defined in a.

(c) When considering the economic aspects of the problem of providing both the national economy and its individual branches with an HMI of great interest is the following class of the SHMO optimization problems. The available SHMO supplies the user, NC, with the HMI with one of the criterion indices satisfied, for example, with an accuracy P = P* at a price of M = M*. Suppose the user is interested in increasing the accuracy of information by Δ (P^1 = P* + Δ). The optimization problem consists in the determination of the minimum additional observation means ensuring the level needed of P^1. Here a new value of HMI will be assessed as M^1 = M + δ based on analysis of the function ϕ (P, M). Such are the general schemes and the principles of SHMO planning.

3.1.2 Spectral decomposition techniques

3.1.2.1 Principal relationships
Let X (ω, t) be the meteorological field, ω the spatial coordinate, and t the time variable. The Fourier transformation in t in each point ω gives

$$X_s(\omega) = \int_{-\infty}^{\infty} e^{-ist} X(\omega, t)\, dt \qquad (3.1)$$

Suppose that $X(\omega, t)$ is the Gauss random field. Then X_s (ω) for each s is also a random Gauss field in ω. Hence, the respective covariance function $R_s(\omega^1, \omega)$ is Hermitian, that is, $R_s(\omega, \omega^1) = R^*_s(\omega^1, \omega)$ (where * denotes conjugation). It means the existence of a complete system of orthonormal eigenfunctions and non-negative eigenvalues of satisfying the equations:

$$\int_{\Omega} R_s(\omega, \omega^1)\, U_j^s(\omega^1)\, d\omega^1 = \lambda_j^s\, U_j^s(\omega) \qquad (3.2)$$

Note that for each value of s, corresponding to temporal fluctuations of a given scale, it is possible to obtain an orthonormal system of functions $U_j^s(\omega)$. This system of functions is an optimal basis according to Karhunen–Lojeve (Pokrovski, 1986) to present the respective fields $X_s(\omega)$ in the form

$$X_s(\omega) = \sum_j x_{sj} U_j^s(\omega) \qquad (3.3)$$

In (3.3) the coefficients x_{sj} are calculated using the formulas

$$x_{sj} = \int_{-\infty}^{\infty} \int_{\Omega} e^{-ist} [U_j^s(\omega)]^* X(\omega, t)\, d\omega\, dt \qquad (3.4)$$

Using the inverse Fourier transformation technique, as well as (3.2) and (3.3), we present the initial field $X(\omega, t)$ as

$$X(\omega,\, t) \;=\; \frac{1}{2\pi} \int\limits_{-\infty}^{\infty} \sum_j x_{sj}\, e^{ist}\, U_j^s\,(\omega)\, ds \tag{3.5}$$

Eq. (3.5) characterizes the bi-orthogonal spectral expansion of the field X in time frequencies s and spatial harmonics $U_j^s(\omega)$.

3.1.2.2 Sets of basic functions

In meteorology one often uses the basic systems of functions of the Karhunen–Lojeve type and such bases are called empirical orthogonal functions (EOF). The difference between the technique to construct a set of EOFs as in section 3.1.2.1 and the classical approach consists in that one can calculate the EOFs for the spectral random field $X_s(\omega)$ and not for the gridded field X, which in this case is usually assumed to be stationary. The approach suggested makes it possible to construct a system of 4-dimensional EOFs $e^{ist}\, U_j^s\,(\omega)$ depending on two variables ω, t and two indices j, s. This set of EOFs ensures an optimal approximation to represent the field $X\,(\omega,\, t)$.

3.1.3 A system of hydrometeorological observation models for a concrete user

The user is interested in HMI specified by parameters NE, P, SD(SR), ST, PC, M considered in section 3.1.1.1. The list of meteorological parameters characterizes an HMI archive to deal with when planning an SHMO. The accuracy P dictates the volume of resources of an observational system and its sub-systems needed for display. The spatial and temporal resolution of the output data SR and ST needed is put into the scheme of bi-orthogonal spectral expansion of meteorological fields (section 3.1.2.2), which enables one to operate with the transformed information. Suppose, the user is interested in the information about the meteorological parameter X with a temporal averaging corresponding to frequency s. In this case we shall operate with the transformed field $X_s(\omega)$ determined from (3.3). To design an observational system as applied to $X_s(\omega)$, it is necessary to have a certain archive of *a priori* information about special features of the probability distribution of $X_s(\omega)$. Assuming that the gridded field $X(\omega,\, t)$ is a Gauss field with the first and second moments known, we come to the conclusion that the transformed field $X_s(\omega)$ is the same. Below we shall omit the index, bearing in mind that everywhere we deal with a spectral component of the field X with frequency s in t.

3.1.3.1 Analysis of the archived information

Here we shall use archived observation information obtained with conventional observational means (aerological and meteorological network). Processing of this information, denoted as a data base $X = \{x_{ij}\}_{i=1}^{n}{}_{j=1}^{N} = \{x^j(\omega_i)\}$ (j is the number of realization, ω_i the coordinates of the ith station), consists in constructing the basis for EOF. In some studies the ways of EOF calculations have been considered. In planning the observation systems an approach can be used consisting in the presentation of EOF not on a grid but in the form of a linear combination of 2-D analytic functions, which form an orthonormal basis. This makes it possible to calculate EOFs at the points with arbitrary spatial coordinates ω, which is necessary when solving the problems of the optimal design of new observational systems. One can use the finite set of spherical harmonics $\{f_s(\omega)\}_{s=1}^k$ as the hemisphere basis. For limited rectangular regions the respective orthonormal systems of functions (trigonometric and polynomial, including splines) can be used.

Each realization of observations $x^j(\omega)$ ($j = 1, \ldots, N$) was transformed into the coefficients of expansion c^j_s ($s = 1, \ldots, k$) in orthonormal basic functions. Thus, the following spectral presentation is obtained:

$$x^j(\omega_i) = \sum_{s=1}^k c^j_s f_s(\omega_i) + \delta^j_k(\omega_i)$$

($i = 1, \ldots, n$; $j = 1, \ldots, N$) in which $\delta^j_k(\omega_i)$ denotes an approximation error for the jth realization in a point ω_i, determined by use of k-terms of expansion.

The latter equation can be rewritten as the following matrix:

$$X = F \cdot c + \Delta_k \qquad (3.6)$$

where

$$F = \{f_{is}\} = f_s(\omega_i)\}, \ c = \{c_{sj}\} = \{c^j_s\}$$
$$\Delta_k = \{\delta^k_{ij}\} = \{\delta^j_k(\omega_i)\}$$

To obtain the coefficients of expansion, one can use the Gauss quadrature formulas approximating integrals in expression for scalar products (Pokrovsky, 1984). The values of the meteorological parameters X in the Gauss knots of the quadrature formula should be preliminarily calculated by using the scheme of objective analysis. In this case one may suppose that $N > K$. Therefore the sample matrix $S_c = \frac{1}{N-1} c.c^T$ can be considered as that of full rank. Let U^s_c be the eigenvector of S_c with the number s. Then an EOF with the number s becomes

$$f_s(\omega) = \sum_{s'=1}^k U^s_c(s') f_{s'}(\omega)$$

Proceeding from (3.6) one can calculate the covariance matrix of the approximation error:

$$S_{\Delta_k} = \frac{1}{(N-1)} \Delta_k \cdot \Delta^T_k$$

Besides apparently, $F \cdot C$ and Δ_k are statistically independent in view of orthogonality Δ_k to a linear variety of the vector-columns of matrix F. Therefore $S_x = F \cdot S_c \cdot F^T + S_{\Delta_k}$.

In some cases it is expedient to suppose that the random vector of realizations from which the matrix $\Delta_k = (\delta^1_k \mid \ldots \mid \delta^N_k)$ is formed has statistically independent components. In this case one can find an estimate of the effective mean square deviation (MSD) $\sigma_{\delta k}$ of the approximation errors by solving the problem

$$\hat{\sigma}^2_{\Delta_k} = \underset{\sigma^2}{arg\ min} \sum_{i=1}^{n} (\sigma^2 - S^{ii}_{\Delta_k})^2$$

($S^{ii}_{\Delta_k}$ are the diagonal elements of S_{Δ_k}). Hence, we find that

$$\hat{\sigma}^2_{\Delta_k} = \sum_{i=1}^{n} S^{ii}_{\Delta_k} / n$$

This makes it possible to use the value found of $\hat{\sigma}^2_{\Delta_k}$ in other observation points.

3.1.3.2 Models of observation systems

Direct observations of a meteorological parameter X in an arbitrary set of points Ω_p can be presented as follows:

$$X(\Omega_p) = F(\Omega_p) \cdot c + \delta_k + \varepsilon(\Omega_p) \tag{3.7}$$

where $X(\Omega_p) = (x(\omega_1), \ldots, x(\omega_p))^{\mathrm{T}}$, $c = (c_1, \ldots, c_k)^{\mathrm{T}}$ $\varepsilon(\Omega_p)$ is the vector of errors of direct observations. Note that $c_s = (U_c^s)^{\mathrm{T}} \cdot c$. Indirect observations of the meteorological parameter X in an arbitrary set of points Ω_q can be presented as

$$Y(\Omega_q) = A \cdot F(\Omega_q) \cdot c + A \cdot \delta_k + \varepsilon(\Omega_q) \tag{3.8}$$

where A is the matrix whose rows are linear functionals of indirect observations, $\varepsilon(\Omega_q)$ are vectors of errors of such measurements. Apparently, the problem with the analysis in this case consists in obtaining the best statistical values of the vector c from the data of observations of either $X(\Omega_p)$ or $Y(\Omega_q)$. Therefore, through calculations of MSDs of analysis errors for different scenarios of the observation system, one can obtain quantitative estimates of their information contribution.

3.1.3.3 Characteristics of the information content of observation systems

The construction of the models of observation systems (3.7) or (3.8) is the basis for the quantitative estimates of their information content (IC). Using a statistical interpretation of that mentioned above, we face the problem of calculation of MSDs of the values of the vector of spectral coefficients which form the elements of the diagonal matrix

$$S_{\hat{c}} = S_c - S_c \cdot F^{\mathrm{T}} \cdot (F \cdot S_c \cdot F^{\mathrm{T}} + S_\eta)^{-1} \cdot F \cdot S_c \tag{3.9}$$

Here, $S_c = \mathrm{diag}(\lambda, \ldots, \lambda_k)$, where λ_i are the eigenvalues corresponding to the EOF with the number i, $S_\eta = S_{\Delta_k} + \Sigma_{\varepsilon_p}$. To simplify the calculations, more suitable is the (3.9) analogue in the form

$$S_{\hat{c}} = (S_c^{-1} + F^{\mathrm{T}} \cdot S_\eta^{-1} \cdot F)^{-1} \tag{3.10}$$

Variances of estimates over the grid can be obtained by an inverse spectral transformation (Pokrovsky, 1989b):

$$\Sigma_{\hat{x}} = F \cdot S_{\hat{c}} \cdot F^{\mathrm{T}} \tag{3.11}$$

Note that covariance matrices $S_{\hat{c}}$ and $\Sigma_{\hat{x}}$ through operators F, S_c and S_η depend on a set of observation stations Ω_p. For a system of indirect observations made in certain points and described with model (3.8) one can write an expression for the covariance matrix of errors in estimating the vector c:

$$S_{\hat{c}} = (S_c^{-1} + F^T \cdot A^T \cdot S_{\bar{\eta}} \cdot A \cdot F)^{-1} \tag{3.12}$$

in which $S_{\bar{\eta}} = A \cdot S_{\Delta_k} \cdot A^T + \Sigma_{\varepsilon_q}$.

Formulas (3.10) and (3.12) can be used to calculate the MSDs of an objective analysis from the data of any planned systems of observations. For this purpose it is necessary to use a spectral transformation (3.11) inversely.

The Shannon information measure for the system of direct observations described by model (3.7) is calculated using the formula (Pokrovski, 1972, 1989b):

$$J\,(X\,(\Omega_p),\, c) \;=\; \tfrac{1}{2}\, log\,|\,S_c^{-1} + F^T \cdot S_\eta^{-1} \cdot F\,|^{-1} \cdot \prod_{s=1}^{k} \lambda^2{}_s \tag{3.13}$$

For the system of indirect observations we have

$$J\,(Y\,(\Omega_q),\, c) \;=\; \tfrac{1}{2}\, log\,|\,S_c^{-1} + F^T \cdot A \cdot S_\eta^{-1} \cdot A^T \cdot F\,|^{-1} \cdot \prod_{s=1}^{k} \lambda^2{}_s \tag{3.14}$$

Formulas (3.13) and (3.14) enable one to obtain quantitative estimates of the information content of both existing and planned observation systems.

The approach discussed above makes it possible to assess the IC of both the whole system of an observations and its individual sub-systems. When assessing the IC of the existing ground-based observation networks, it is important to know the effectiveness of each station.

3.1.3.4 Characteristics of the efficiency of individual stations of the observation network

It was mentioned above that $\Sigma_{\hat{x}} = \Sigma_{\hat{c}}\,(\Omega_p)$. It should be added that $\Sigma_{\hat{x}}$ depends also on covariance matrices of the errors of measurement Σ_{ε_p} and approximation S_{Δ_k}.

3.1.3.5 Accuracy criterion

As a criterion connected with the MSDs of objective analysis, it is expedient to consider the trace of the covariance matrix $tr[\Sigma_{\hat{x}}(\Omega_p)]$ denoted by $E\,(\Omega_p)$. Besides, a relative characteristic of the effectiveness of objective analysis (Pokrovski, 1989a) is normally introduced:

$$R(\Omega_p) \;=\; tr[\Sigma_{\hat{x}}(\Omega_p)]\,/\,tr\,[\Sigma_x]$$

Now let us exclude station ω_i from the set of stations of the observation network Ω_p. Let us denote the resulting network $\Omega_{p/i} = \Omega_p - \omega_i$. For $\Omega_{p/i}$ it is possible to calculate the values $E(\Omega_{p/i})$ and $R(\Omega_{p/i})$. The parameter $DE(\Omega_{p/i}) = E\,(\Omega_{p/i}) - E(\Omega_p)$ characterizes changes in the variances of the estimates of an objective analysis, determined by the exclusion of observation data from the station ω_i. Let Θ be a null set of observation stations. Then the parameter $DE(\Theta) = E(\Theta) - E(\Omega_p)$ gives us some indication about changes in the MSD analysis with the data of all observation stations excluded simultaneously. Note that $E(\Theta) = \text{tr}[\Sigma_x]$ characterizes the standard deviation of natural fluctuations of the meteorological fields.

Now we can introduce a relative value, characterizing the efficiency of station ω_i:

$$DR(\Omega_{p/i}) = DE(\Omega_{p/i}) / DE(\Theta)$$

The parameter $DR(\Omega_{p/i})$ is connected with the criterion of accuracy in the list of parameters for the users presented above.

3.1.3.6 Criterion of spatial resolution

The parameter DR characterizes the effect of increasing the accuracy, which refers to the results of analysis averaged over the whole area analysed. However, a concrete user may be interested in the information on the parameter X for a given region and with the needed spatial resolution. It means that the concrete lth user of information can be interested in receiving data not on every component of the vector $x = (x_1, \ldots, x_N)^T$ presenting the results of objective analysis over a regular grid, but on certain linear functionals of the kind: $g_1(x) = g^T{}_l \cdot x$, $g = (g^1{}_l, \ldots, g^N{}_l)$ $(l = 1, \ldots, LN)$. Here LN is the total number of users, with $LN \ll N$. In this case as a criterion one should not use the function $E(\Omega_p)$ determined above but a criterion of the kind $E_{gl}(\Omega_p) = g_2{}^T \cdot \Sigma_{\hat{x}} \cdot g_l$ for a concrete user. Similarly, one can introduce the relative characteristics of an objective analysis:

$$R_{g_l}(\Omega_p) = g_l{}^T \cdot \Sigma_{\hat{x}}(\Omega_p) \cdot g_l / g_l{}^T \cdot \Sigma_x \cdot g_l$$

In the same way it is possible to determine the characteristics of an information contribution of station i in the interests of the lth user of information:

$$DE(\Omega_{p/i}) = E_{g_l}(\Omega_{p/i}) - E_{g_l}(\Omega_p)$$

and

$$DR(\Omega_{p/i}) = DE(\Omega_{p/i}) / DE_{g_l}(\Theta)$$

In these formulas

$$E_{g_l}(\Omega_p) = g_l{}^T \cdot \Sigma_{\hat{x}}(\Omega_p) \cdot g_l; E_{g_l}(\Theta) = g_l{}^T \cdot \Sigma_x g_l$$

Thus, the characteristics $Eg(\Omega_{p/i})$ and $DR(\Omega_{p/i})$ give us some indication about the efficiency of measurements from a concrete meteorological station in the interests of the lth user as to the needs of the spatial resolution.

The characteristics given above make it possible to assess the efficiency of individual stations of the network from the viewpoint of two, most important criteria—accuracy and spatial resolution (averaging)—of information in the interests of concrete users.

These parameters are input ones for the solution of the multi-criterion optimization problems discussed in Section 3.1.1. Some problems of this type will be given below.

3.1.4 Setting of discrete optimization problems

Along with the formulation of multi-criterion optimization problems (Section 3.1.1) based on the construction of respective additive aim functions, it is necessary to dwell on a broad class of problems solved by means of Boolean programming (Pokrovski, 1981, 1988). Each station of the observation network corresponds to a Boolean variable v_i, which can be either zero or unity. For the whole network, consisting of p stations, we introduce a vector with Boolean components $v(p) = (v_1, ..., v_p)^T$, each being related to certain station of the network. The zero value of v_i means that in an optimal design the station ω_i is absent. The "unity" means that the station ω_i is present in an optimal design. The vector $v^*(p)$ supplying a minimum of a certain functional with a set of limitations gives a solution for the problem of network optimization.

Consider some kinds of such functionals and characteristic limitations to the acceptable values of the vector $v(p)$.

3.1.4.1 Minimization of the number of network stations

This problem can be stated with limitations to the values of respective indices of efficiency of information (accuracy, spatial resolution, etc.). As in Section 3.1.3.4, let $DR(\Omega_{p/i})$ be the efficiency of a station in the accuracy of an objective analysis. In this case the simplest problem of multi-criterion optimization can be presented as

$$v^*(p) = arg\ min\ \{\sum_{i=1}^{p} v_i\} \tag{3.15}$$
$$v_i = \{^0_1$$

$$\sum_{j}^{p} DR(\Omega_{p/i})\, v_j \geqslant \alpha\, DR\,(\Theta) \tag{3.16}$$

Parameter α $(0 < \alpha < 1)$ characterizes the required threshold value of the network efficiency. Parameter $DR(\Theta)$ is the efficiency index of the whole network. $DR(\Theta) = 1$.

With an introduction of costs γ_i on the obtaining of information in the point ω_i and acceptable total costs Γ in addition to (3.16), it is possible to introduce limitations to costs in the form of an inequality:

$$\sum_{i=1}^{p} \gamma_i v_i \leqslant \Gamma \tag{3.17}$$

Limitations (3.16) and (3.17) are rather general. Let us use the efficiency indices DR_{g_l} $(\Omega_{p/i})$ for the spatial resolution of information for the lth user. In this case we can introduce an enumeration of the limitations in the form

$$\sum_{i=1}^{p} DR_{g_l}\,(\Omega_{p/i})\, v_l \geqslant \alpha_l \sum_{i=1}^{p} DR_{gl}\,(\Omega_{p/i}) \tag{3.18}$$

$(l = 1, ..., LN)$, determined by the needs of each user.

3.1.4.2 Maximization of the information efficiency of the network

Another approach to the rationalization of the observation network can consist in solving the problem of maximization of the total information efficiency of the network with a limited number of stations and limited relevant costs.

In this case the general aim function is

$$\sum_{i=1}^{p} DR\,(\Omega_{p/i})\,v_i$$

and the aim function of the lth user is $\sum_{i=1}^{p} DR_{g_l}\,(\Omega_{p/i})\,v_i$.

Introducing the weight factor β_l for the lth user $(0 \leqslant \beta_l \leqslant 1, \Sigma\,\beta_l = 1)$ we obtain an aim function for all users:

$$\sum_{l=1}^{\gamma N} \beta_l\,(\sum_{i=1}^{p} DR_{g_l}\,(\Omega_{p/i})\,v_i)$$

If we introduce the notation $\tilde{\gamma}_i$ for the costs of the maintenance of the station ω_i, then in this case we can formulate a general optimization problem

$$v^*(p) = arg\ max\ \{\sum^{p} DR\,(\Omega_{p/i})\,v_i\} \tag{3.19}$$

$$v_i = \{\begin{smallmatrix}0\\1\end{smallmatrix}$$

$$\sum_{i=1}^{p} v_i \leqslant N_{max}$$

$$\sum_{i=1}^{p} \tilde{\gamma}_i\,v_i \leqslant \gamma_{max} \tag{3.20}$$

In limitations (3.20) N_{max} is the maximum acceptable number of stations; γ_{max} is the maximum acceptable costs. Now consider the problem of a fixed list of users who are ready to pay for the information received. Let ζ_l be the costs borne by the lth user. Then, denoting $\zeta_0 = \Sigma_l\,\zeta_l$ we write the following optimization problem in the interests of all LN of the information users:

$$v^*(p) = arg\ max\ \{\sum_{i=1}^{LN} \beta_l\,(\sum_{i=1}^{p} DR_{g_l}\,(\Omega_{p/i})\,v_i)\}$$

$$v_i = \{\begin{smallmatrix}0\\1\end{smallmatrix}$$

$$\sum_{i} v_i \leqslant N_{max}$$

$$\sum_{i} \gamma_i\,v_i \leqslant \zeta_0$$

When solving problems of network optimization, it is important that an account be taken of economic factors (cost effectiveness). Below we shall discuss the substantiation of optimization problems connected with the criteria of costs.

3.1.4.3 Minimization of the costs on obtaining information needed

This problem can be solved through minimizing a linear function $\Sigma_i \, \gamma_i \, v_i$ with some constrained parameters: the number of stations, minimum acceptable accuracy, and resolution of the information received. Let's formulate the simplest optimization problem:

$$v^* \, (p) \; = \; arg \; min \; \{ \sum_{i=1}^{p} \tilde{\gamma}_i \, v_i \, \}$$

$$v_i = \{ \begin{smallmatrix} 0 \\ 1 \end{smallmatrix}$$

$$\sum_{j=1}^{p} v_j \leq N_{max}$$

$$\sum_{j=1}^{p} DR \, (\Omega_{p/i}) \, v_j \geq \alpha$$

This formulation does not consider the interests of individual users. In order to take into consideration various needs for information one can formulate the following problem:

$$v^* \, (p) \; = \; arg \; min \; \{ \sum_{i=1}^{p} \tilde{\gamma}_i \, v_i \, \}$$

$$v_i = \{ \begin{smallmatrix} 0 \\ 1 \end{smallmatrix}$$

$$\sum_{j=1}^{p} v_j \leq N_{max}$$

$$\sum_{i=1}^{p} DR_{g_l} \, (\Omega_{p/i}) \, v_j \geq \alpha_l \sum_{i=1}^{p} DR_{gl} \, (\Omega_{p/i})$$

$$(l - 1, \, \ldots, \, LN)$$

An example of solving the optimization problems considered suggests the following conclusions:

1. To formulate the problems of rationalization of the observation network, it is necessary to specify the aim function determined by the chosen optimization criterion (accuracy, resolution, cost, etc.), or by a combination of such criteria.
2. To solve such problems, it is necessary to have complete input information. Parameters and coefficients in the expression for the aim function and in the limitations, can be divided into two groups:

   — information characteristics of the observation network (system),
   — economic characteristics of the system and the cost of information for the users.

3. The formulation and solution of alternative problems determined by various optimization criteria opens up the possibility of a multiple control of the resulting solution $v^*(p)$ and raises the reliability of the final results.

3.2 ANALYSIS OF THE INFORMATION CONTENT OF GLOBAL SYSTEMS OF AEROLOGICAL SOUNDING AND REMOTE SOUNDING OF THE ATMOSPHERE

An analysis of previous results shows that with the existing procedure of processing satellite spectral measurements data and obtaining output information in the SIRS and SATEM codes, transmitted via the international meteorological communication channels, the contribution of the remote sounding data to the numerical analysis of the fields of temperature and geopotential remains moderate. The procedure of comparing the information efficiency indices of the systems of both conventional and remote sensing measurements made earlier cannot be considered correct because of differences in statistical properties of the errors in the respective assessments of meteorological parameters (Pokrovski and Beliavski, 1983 a,b; Pokrovski, 1984). The formulation of a 3-D retrieval problem in the case of remote sounding of the atmosphere (Pokrovski, 1982; Pokrovski and Denisov, 1985; Pokrovski et al., 1985) makes it possible to perform a more correct quantitative comparison of the information efficiency indices of the systems of conventional and satellite observations. Advantages of spectral techniques of numerical analysis of the meteorological fields, connected with considerable saving in computer resources (computation time, volume of operational memory), have determined an interest to apply spectral techniques in the field of 4-D analysis. It has been shown (Pokrovski and Denisov, 1980; Pokrovski, 1984) that the method of spectral analysis can be efficiently used to interpret the data of the temperature of remote sounding of the atmosphere (TRSA). Owing to an efficient approximation of the hemispherical fields with a few EOFs (Pokrovski and Beliavski, 1983 a,b; Pokrovski and Denisov, 1985), it was possible, based on the techniques of spectral analysis, to solve the problem of assessing the information content of hemispherical observation systems. Here we consider the aerological network of the northern hemisphere, its basic regional components, as well as a system of accomplished with the help of meteorological satellites in polar orbits.

3.2.1 Quantitative assessment of the information content of observing systems

This problem consists in estimating the 3-D field X from direct and indirect observations for an arbitrary set of points with horizontal coordinates $\omega_l = (\varphi_l, \lambda_l)$ ($l = 1, \ldots, r$, φ is latitude, λ is longitude). The input field is presented as an expansion:

$$X(h_k, \omega) = \sum_{i=1}^{s} \sum_{j=1}^{y} c_{ij}\, g_i(h_k)\, f_j(\omega) \qquad (3.21)$$

from all vertical $\{g_i\}$ and horizontal $\{f_j\}$ modes. It is assumed that both $\{g_i\}$ and $\{f_j\}$ are families of orthonormal functions. Here h_k ($k = 1, \ldots, s$) is a standard vertical level.

The equation of observation for an arbitrary knot of the horizontal grid can be written as

$$y_l = A_l \cdot x_l + \varepsilon_l \tag{3.22}$$

Here x_l is the vector of values of the field X (h_k, ω_l) at standard levels in the vertical air column for the point $\omega_l; y_l$ is the vector of observations made in the point $\omega_l; \varepsilon_l$ is the error in these observations. In the case of a system of conventional *in situ* observations, the matrix A_l is square, and $A_l = I$ at each point (Pokrovski and Denisov, 1980). In case of indirect observations (remote sounding) the matrix turns out to be rectangular (Pokrovski and Beliavski, 1983 a,b).

Introducing auxiliary functions

$$Z_i(\omega) = \sum_{j=1}^{N} c_{ij} f_j(\omega) \tag{3.23}$$

it is possible to divide the problem of the X field analysis into two stages. The first stage is connected with estimating $Z_i(\omega)$ in points of observations ω_l for each vertical mode g_i. At the second stage the problem is to find a set of unknown coefficients $\{c_{ij}\}$ from approximate values of $Z_i(\omega_l)$. Let us discuss both stages of the solution of this problem.

Let g_i be the vector formed by the values of $g_i(h_k)$ at standard heights h_k. In this case, using (3.21) and (3.23), we find that

$$Z_i(\omega_l) = g_i^{\mathrm{T}} \cdot x_l \tag{3.24}$$

Now it is necessary to estimate $Z_i(\omega_l)$ from the data of y_l observations. The relationship between these parameters is described with Eqs. (3.22) and (3.24). Suppose that the covariance matrices of the vectors x and ε are known *a priori*. Let them be Σ_x and Σ_ε respectively. Here and below the index l is omitted. The variance of the best linear estimate of $\hat{Z}_i$ for $Z_i(\omega_l)$ in (3.24) is the following (Pokrovski and Denisov, 1980):

$$\delta_{\hat{z}}^2 = g_i^{\mathrm{T}} \cdot [\, \Sigma_x - \Sigma_x \cdot A^{\mathrm{T}} \cdot (A \cdot \Sigma_x \cdot A^{\mathrm{T}} + \Sigma_\varepsilon)^{-1} \cdot A \cdot \Sigma_x \,] \cdot g_i \tag{3.25}$$

If the normalized eigenvectors of the matrix Σ_x are used as $\{g_i\}$, formula (3.25) becomes much simpler. Let γ_i $(i = 1, \ldots, s)$ be the respective eigennumbers, the matrix $C = A^{\mathrm{T}} \cdot (A \cdot \Sigma_x \cdot A^{\mathrm{T}} + \Sigma_\varepsilon)^{-1} \cdot A$. Then (3.25) becomes

$$\delta_{\hat{z}}^2{}_i = \gamma_i^2 - \gamma_i^2 \cdot g_i^{\mathrm{T}} \cdot C \cdot g_i$$

Discussion of the first stage of the problem is now completed.

Below is given the solution to the problem of retrieval of the set of coefficients $\{C_{ij}\}_{j=1}^2$ at a fixed index of the number of vertical mode. Since the solution for all values of i is of the same type, the index will be omitted. Let the components of the vector $\hat{Z}$ be an array of the values of the best linear estimate (3.24) in points of observations $\{\omega_l\}$, and the elements of the matrix F with dimension $r \times N$ be determined from the equation $F = \{f_{kl}\} = \{f_k(\omega_l)\}$. Then the vector c of the coefficients to be found C_{ik} (i is fixed) is included in the system of equations

$$\hat{Z} = F \cdot c + \Delta \tag{3.26}$$

The components of the vector Δ are formed from the differences $\delta_l = Z_l - \hat{Z}_l$. In contrast to the classical case, the components of the vectors c and Δ from (3.26) are statistically dependent. Therefore after some matrix transformations, we obtain an expression for the covariance matrix of the best linear estimates for the vector c with

$$S_{\hat{c}}^{-1} = S_c^{-1} + F^{\mathrm{T}} \cdot S_\Delta^{-1} \cdot F + R\,(c, \Delta) \tag{3.27}$$

The matrix $R(c,\Delta)$ from (3.27) contains only the terms including a cross-covariance matrix $S_{c\Delta}$ as a multiplier.

A set of EOFs can be used as a horizontal basis $\{f_j\}$. Then the dimensions of the problem will substantially decrease, since the actually needed number of EOFs, $\bar{N}$, is considerably less than that of the knots N. This makes it easier to solve the problem of inversion of the right-hand-side matrix in (3.27) to find $S_{\hat{c}}$. Note that in the case considered, S_c is a diagonal matrix formed from eigenvalues of horizontal EOFs. Then there is the problem of inversion of S_Δ, whose dimension is $N \times N$, Since S_Δ is a non-diagonal matrix (in contrast to the classic case), and its numerical inversion is impossible, covariations are computed only for the knot inside the squares 6×6 knots, covering the grid of horizontal EOFs. In this case S_Δ is a block-diagonal matrix, for which it is easy to determine S_Δ^{-1}.

3.2.2 Information content of aerological observations in the northern hemisphere

Practically, in some cases for an operational analysis and forecast we should confine ourselves to regional observation data. But even under such circumstances, the role of hemispherical TRSA data is significant. In this section we shall consider their information contribution with respect to several regional networks of aerological soundings in the northern hemisphere. A non-uniform coverage with aerological data determines an abnormal spatial and, hence, spectral distribution of the errors of analysis. Apart from the aerological network in the northern hemisphere (A0), the following regional networks of aerological soundings have been modelled: the territory of the former USSR; North America (A2); Europe (A3); Asia (A4); Pacific Islands (A5); Africa (A6); and ship-borne stations in the Atlantic Ocean basin (A7). Along with the sub-systems of aerological sounding mentioned above, two combinations of regional sub-systems have been modelled:

(i) A2 + A3 + A4,
(ii) A2 + A3 + A5 + A7.

Apart from the total number of aerological stations (680) functioning during the first global GARP experiment (FGGE), a shortened list of stations, regularly providing information, has been considered separately. Table 3.1 gives the quantitative composition of these sub-systems and the list of respective indices of efficiency from the viewpoint of the results of analysis.

3.2.2.1 Variance characteristics

The trace of the residual covariance matrix $R\,(\Sigma_{\hat{x}}) = tr\,(\Sigma_{\hat{x}})$ and the multiple correlation coefficient (MCC) k^2 are calculated based on variances of the vector components $\hat{x}$. Indices A, C, A + C with the parameter R will indicate that calculations were made for the systems of aerological and satellite sounding and

Table 3.1. Indices of efficiency of the NH aerological network and its sub-systems for analysis purposes

Aerological part	Number of stations	R_A	$\sqrt{\sigma^{-2}_x}$	κ	k^2	$\sigma^2_x(0,0)$	$\sigma^2_x(0,2)$	$\sigma^2_x(1,3)$	$\sigma^2_x(2,6)$	$\sigma^2_x(4,8)$	$Z(A0/Ai)$	$ro(Ai/Ar)$
1	2	3	4	5	6	7	8	9	10	11	12	13
A0	$\frac{680}{265}$	$\frac{61}{137}$	$\frac{7.8}{11.7}$	$\frac{0.078}{0.05}$	$\frac{0.99}{0.978}$	$\frac{0.005}{0.01}$	$\frac{1.4}{2.9}$	$\frac{1.6;1.5}{3.8;2.9}$	$\frac{1.5;1.5}{2.8;3.1}$	$\frac{1.3;1.2}{3.1;2.7}$	—	$\frac{13}{0.556}$
A1	$\frac{201}{52}$	$\frac{1527}{2372}$	$\frac{39.1}{48.7}$	$\frac{0.0026}{0.0089}$	$\frac{0.76}{0.63}$	$\frac{0.18}{0.24}$	$\frac{43.6}{69}$	$\frac{59;48}{90;76}$	$\frac{60;52}{83;68}$	$\frac{40;35}{64;58}$	$\frac{0.96}{0.94}$	0.356
A2	$\frac{154}{84}$	$\frac{1216}{1557}$	$\frac{34.9}{39.5}$	$\frac{0.0070}{0.0077}$	$\frac{0.81}{0.69}$	$\frac{0.19}{0.26}$	$\frac{82}{117}$	$\frac{78;20}{95;42}$	$\frac{31;58}{52;74}$	$\frac{20;12}{41;32}$	$\frac{0.95}{0.94}$	—
A3	$\frac{90}{58}$	$\frac{3176}{3432}$	$\frac{56.4}{58.6}$	$\frac{0.0016}{0.0023}$	$\frac{0.50}{0.38}$	$\frac{0.27}{0.33}$	$\frac{120}{149}$	$\frac{49;140}{58;146}$	$\frac{165;103}{122;91}$	$\frac{84;93}{74;92}$	$\frac{0.98}{0.96}$	—
A4	$\frac{177}{52}$	$\frac{2988}{4133}$	$\frac{54.7}{64.3}$	$\frac{0.0082}{0.20}$	$\frac{0.53}{0.35}$	$\frac{0.19}{0.31}$	$\frac{67}{126}$	$\frac{131;112}{180;157}$	$\frac{118;118}{167;150}$	$\frac{70;73}{167;150}$	$\frac{70;73}{107;104}$	$\frac{0.979}{0.967}$
A5	16	5527	74.3	0.076	0.13	0.53	206	189;207	226;198	128;139	0.989	
A6	30	4647	69.6	0.0155	0.24	0.43	178	146;193	233;172	126;149	0.987	
A7	12	3446	58.7	0.0184	0.46	0.32	119	92;138	154;112	74;64	0.982	
A2+A3+A4	$\frac{421}{194}$	$\frac{215}{444}$	$\frac{14.7}{21.1}$	$\frac{0.0184}{0.013}$	$\frac{0.97}{0.93}$	$\frac{0.01}{0.04}$	$\frac{6.8}{18.6}$	$\frac{10;6.0}{18;12}$	$\frac{9.0;7.8}{16;16}$	$\frac{4.0;4.6}{9.1;11}$	$\frac{0.717}{0.691}$	0.515

Note: Numerator—in the period of FGGE; denominator—at usual time.

their combination, respectively. Natural fluctuations of the H500 field are characterized by the interval of values from $R\,(\Sigma_x)$ = 6400 m (complete network) to 5527 m (Pacific Islands, A5). In accordance with this (Table 3.1) MCC varies from 0.99 (A0) to 0.13 (A5). A reduced network A0 has a double value of $R\,(\Sigma_{\hat{x}})$. Considering individual sub-systems, one should mention that a reduction of the network (compared to the FGGE period) markedly increases the variance at A1 and A4, and little affects the standard error characteristics of A2 and A3. This circumstance points to the best spatial distribution of the reduced number of stations A2, A3 compared to A1 and A4.

3.2.2.2 The mean square deviation (MSD) in analysis
The value of the absolute error in analysis (AEA), $\sqrt{\bar{\sigma}_{\hat{x}}^2}$, ($\sigma_{\hat{x}}^2$ is the MSD for analysis errors over the grid) also varies within wide limits. Depending on the sub-system, its value varies from 8 m (A0, FGGE period) to 74 m (A5). A reduction of the network A0 increases the average error of analysis by a factor of 1.5. In the case of sub-systems A1 and A4 the error increases by 10 m. With reducing more efficient sub-systems A2 and A3, the MSD increases only by 2–4 m. The modelled combination of sub-systems (A2 + A3 + A4) ensures a relatively high level of average accuracy of analysis—15 m (full amount), 21 m (reduced amount). These levels of analysis error are lower by a factor of 2.5 than for individual sub-systems, e.g., A1.

3.2.2.3 The spectral structure of the analysis error
Since the functions of the EOF basis used are constructed as linear combinations of spherical harmonics, it is possible to assess the spectral structure of the analysis errors from the data of various observational systems. Table 3.1 shows the MSDs for several spectral components of the error. It is seen that the error $\sigma_{\hat{x}}$ (0,0) in estimating the hemispherical mean value of the H500 field varies from 0.1 m (A0) to 0.74 m (A5). The second zonal component (0.2) is estimated to an accuracy of 1 m (A0) and 14 m (A5). The accuracy of estimating the complex coefficients of expansion for non-zonal components is at a maximum for the components (1,3) and then increasing with a number of the components, rapidly approaching the level of "natural variations" of the respective components.

3.2.2.4 The ill-conditionality index
This index κ, presenting the ratio of minimum to maximum of eigenvalues of the matrix $\Sigma_{\hat{x}}$ in contrast to those considered above, depends not so much on the number of stations as on their location (Pokrovski and Beliavski, 1983b). Therefore the value of κ for regional sub-systems is 8–10 times lower than that of the complete aerological network (A0). A non-rational arrangement of stations in regional sub-systems causes an increase in the ill-conditionality index (ICI) in the transition from the full to the reduced number of stations. The ICI of sub-systems A5–A7 containing a few stations is close to the value $\kappa\,(\Sigma_x)$ of for the *a priori* covariance matrix Σ_x. The point is that for these sub-systems the $\Sigma_{\hat{x}}$ differs little from Σ_x. With an increasing number of stations the values can evolve in the two directions. First, the transition from a decrease to a subsequent increase of κ with a uniform location of stations;

secondly, a monotonic decrease of κ when the stations are concentrated in one region. An example is the European network A3.

3.2.2.5 Deficit of information from the sub-systems

The MCC is a suitable measure to assess the information content of observational systems (Pokrovski and Beliavski, 1983 a,b). When assessing the information contribution of the TRSA data we used its modification (Pokrovski and Beliavski, 1983b), under the assumption that this system is a broadened ground-based aerological network. Considering the A0 network to be the broadening of regional sub-systems A1–A7, we may consider the parameter

$$Z (A0/A_i) = 1 - tr [\Sigma_{\hat{x}} (A0) / tr [\Sigma_{\hat{x}} (A_i)],$$

which characterizes an increase of information due to such a broadening from A_i to A0. For this purpose this characteristic can better be called the information deficit of the sub-system A_i (IDS). The value of the information deficit for sub-systems varies from 0.95 to 1 (Table 3.1). Maximum values of IDS correspond to the smallest systems A5–A7. Combinations of sub-systems enable one to obtain IDS values of 0.7–0.8 and less. The sub-system A2 + A3 + A4, which normally has 194 stations, has an IDS value of 0.69. A similar approach makes it possible to assess the role of individual sub-systems in their combinations. The IDS values for North American sub-system A2 in combinations A2 + A3 + A4 and A2 + A3 + A5 + A7 are 0.713 and 0.823, respectively.

3.2.2.6 The efficiency index for reduced sub-systems

We may introduce the quantitative index of relationship between the information content of full (FGGE period) and reduced sub-systems:

$$ro^2 (A_i / A_i') = tr [\Sigma_{\hat{x}} (A_i)] / tr [\Sigma_{\hat{x}} (A_i')]$$

Here the primes denote the reduced sub-systems. Let us call the parameter ro^2 (A_i/ A_i') the efficiency index for reduced sub-systems (EIRS). The EIRS values vary widely. The least successful reduction of the network is illustrated by sub-system A4. Here, ro (A4/A'4) = 0.28. The reduced sub-systems A2, A3 are most efficient. Here, the EIRS values exceed 0.6. High values of EIRS correspond to combined networks including the sub-system A2. The sub-system of the Russian stations A1 has an intermediate value of 0.36. The data in Table 3.1 show that with the use of data from a different set of aerological stations an approximately equal accuracy of analysis can be obtained. Therefore, considering the cost of stations and maintenance costs, the problem of the rational distribution of aerological stations is rather urgent.

3.2.3 Information contribution of remote sounding data with the use of aerological network data

For assessment, various TRSA systems have been modelled. The presence of one satellite implies an accomplishment of measurements in 18 half-orbits with a 20 longitudinal step. With the use of two satellites, measurements could be made in 35 half-orbits. Two-level measurement errors were modelled, which, taking into account the approximation of the EOF basis, constitute 60 and 80 m, respectively. The horizontal correlation of the measurement errors was taken into account either over the whole hemisphere without considering the boundaries of latitudinal zones (I), or only within three basic latitudinal zones (III). The latter situation is closer to the reality (Pokrovski and Beliavski, 1983a).

We shall now discuss some special features of the efficiency indices of the TRSA systems (without taking into account aerology) from the point of view of the results of analysis (Table 3.2). Along with higher values of R, AEA and κ (compared to the characteristics of aerological networks), which point to a great stability in a short-term forecast, we note some equivalent features of TRSA systems. An increase in the accuracy of remote sounding for H500 by 20 m at each sub-satellite point gives approximately the same result as a doubling of measurements due to the simultaneous functioning of two satellites. Eliminating the horizontal correlation of the input data uncertainties between the main latitudinal zones due to an operational correction of the atmospheric optical model at reference points (Pokrovski and Beliavski, 1983a) ensures only a halved effect in increased average accuracy of analysis. Rather substantial are changes in the spectral structure of the spatial distribution of the analysis errors compared to the data in Table 3.1. Values of the MSD in the estimates of the component (0.0) decrease, at least, by an order of magnitude compared to the data obtained for regional aerological sub-systems. On the other hand, for the whole hemispherical network AO the accuracy of estimation of this component is higher by a factor of 1.5–2 than from the TRSA data. The accuracy of retrieving other spectral components from the data of the whole network AO is also 2–3 times higher than with the use of only the satellite information. However, if the user has only regional aerological information, the relationship between MSDs of estimates of the spectral components from the data of conventional and satellite observations changes is the opposite (compare Tables 3.1 and 3.2). The data in Table 3.2 show that the type of horizontal correlation of the errors in the radiometric satellite information is the basic factor affecting the irregular (in wave and zonal numbers) redistribution of MSD of the estimates of spectral components. Without a correlation between the main latitudinal zones, the MSD of the component (0.0) almost does not change: $\sigma_{\hat{x}}^2$ (0.2) decreases by 20%, $\sigma_{\hat{x}}^2$ (1.3), $\sigma_{\hat{x}}^2$ (2.6)—by a factor of 1.5. In contrast to this, an increase in the number of orbits (twice) leads to a uniform (in wave and zonal numbers) decrease in the MSD in the estimates of spectral components.

Since the combined observational systems are particularly important from the practical point of view, we shall dwell upon the efficiency indices for the aerological network, taking into account the TRSA results (Table 3.3), and making a parallel comparison with the data in Table 3.1.

3.2.3.1 Variance characteristics
The values of R_{A+C} for individual sub-systems A1–A7 are by an order of magnitude less than those of R_A. Fluctuations in R_A values in Table 3.1 reached two orders of magnitude, depending on the sub-system. Here the values of R_{A+C} vary within an order of magnitude. Thus, with the use of the TRSA data the difference between the

Table 3.2. The efficiency indices of the TRSA systems (excluding aerology) for analysis purposes

Number orbits	Level of error	Character of horizontal correlation of error	R_c	$\sqrt{\sigma^{-2}_{\dot x}}$	κ	k^2	$\sigma^2_{\dot x}(0,0)$	$\sigma^2_{\dot x}(0,2)$	$\sigma^2_{\dot x}(1,3)$	$\sigma^2_{\dot x}(2,6)$	$\sigma^2_{\dot x}(4,8)$
18	60	I	317	17.7	0.165	0.950	0.02	7.9	10.5;105	8.6;9.0	8.3;7.7
18	60	III	249	15.8	0.349	0.961	0.02	6.3	8.3;7.4	6.2;6.5	6.2;5.7
18	80	I	531	23.0	0.175	0.917	0.04	15.5	18;18	15;15	14;13
18	80	III	423	20.6	0.354	0.934	0.03	10.8	14;13	11;11	11;10
36	60	I	165	12.9	0.156	0.974	0.01	4.1	5.4;5.4	4.4;4.6	4.3;4.0
36	60	III	128	11.3	0.343	0.980	0.01	3.2	4.3;3.8	3.2;3.3	3.2;2.9
36	60	I	284	16.9	0.163	0.956	0.02	7.1	9.3;9.4	7.7;8.0	7.4;6.9
36	60	III	223	14.9	0.347	0.965	0.01	5.6	7.5;6.7	5.6;5.8	5.6;5.1

information content of individual sub-systems disappears. Nevertheless, there remains some difference between the information content of full (FGGE period) and reduced regional aerological networks. The point is that the sub-systems A1–A7 affect, first of all, the accuracy of the regional analysis. The TRSA system makes an information contribution of a hemispherical scale. Its role for the regional analysis in the aerologically covered regions is not so great.

3.2.3.2 The MSD of analysis
This characteristic has a 3–4 times lesser range of variations than in the case of information available only from aerological networks. If in the case of a hemispherical network A0 inclusion of TRSA information ensures a decrease in the AEA level ($\sqrt{\bar{\sigma}_x^2}$) by 1m, for the sub-systems A5–A7, containing a few stations, a decrease in AEA reaches 40–50m. Note, that in this case a decrease in the maximum errors of analysis can reach 80–90m. For example, it is true for the sub-systems A1, A2, A3. In the case of developed regional sub-systems the contribution of the TRSA data is also rather substantial. For the Russian sub-system the AEA value decreases by a factor of 3, for the North American, 2.5, for the European, 3.6, and for sub-system combinations, 1.5–2.

3.2.3.3 The spectral structure of the analysis error
Standard deviations of the spectral components of the spatial distribution of the analysis error from the data of the combined observation system (Table 3.3) differ markedly from the respective characteristics obtained for aerological networks (Table 3.1). Consideration of the TRSA data for small sub-systems A5–A7 makes it possible to reach a level of accuracy for the estimates of the component (0.0) (i.e. average H500), characteristic of the hemispherical network AO, either combinations A2 + A3 + A4 or A2 + A3 + A5 + A7. In the case of the Russian and North American sub-systems the TRSA contribution ensures an order of magnitude decrease of σ_x^2 (0.0) (see Tables 3.1 and 3.3). An important zonal component (0.2) is characterized by a decrease in MSD values (due to the TRSA data): in the case of the Russian sub-system by a factor of 7, to the North American sub-system, 10, and of the European sub-system, 13. Note, that the respective changes are at a minimum for the full hemispherical network A0. With the zonal and meridional numbers increasing, the selective (for different sub-systems) character of error distribution for spectral components due to the use of satellite information manifests itself more clearly. For less numerous sub-systems (A5–A7) this specification is more substantial than for large sub-systems (A1, A2) or their combinations.

3.2.3.4 The ill-conditionality index (ICI)
A substantial MSD in κ values for aerological sub-systems (Table 3.1) markedly decreases with the use of the TRSA data (Table 3.3). The general use of satellite information raises the ICI of the observation system. In the case of the hemispherical network AO the value of increases by a factor of 1.5–2. For small sub-systems (A5–A7) the index increases by an order of magnitude.

Table 3.3. Indices of efficiency of the NH aerological network and its sub-systems with an account of the TRSA data (18/60/I) for analysis purposes

Aerological network	Number of stations	R_{A+C}	$\sqrt{\sigma^{-2}_{\hat{x}}}$	κ	Z	$\sigma^2_{\hat{x}}(0,0)$	$\sigma^2_{\hat{x}}(0,2)$	$\sigma^2_{\hat{x}}(1,3)$	$\sigma^2_{\hat{x}}(2,6)$	$\sigma^2_{\hat{x}}(4,8)$
1	2	3	4	5	6	7	8	9	10	11
A0	680/265	47.5/99.1	6.9/10	0.109/0.088	0.23/0.28	0/0.01	1.2/2.3	1.4;1.3 / 2.8;2.5	1.2;1.2 / 2.1;2.1	1.0;1.0 / 1.9;1.9
A1	201/52	182/358	13.5/18.9	0.048/0.094	0.85/0.88	0.02/0.03	7.0/9.3	9.7;7.0 / 12.1;9.5	3.9;3.8 / 4.8;4.6	4.1;4.0 / 4.7;4.6
A2	154/84	168/282	13.0/16.8	0.084/0.069	0.80/0.81	0.02/0.02	8.2/8.8	11;5.7 / 11.5;6.8	6.9;7.2 / 7.8;8.9	5.8;5.0 / 6.1;5.2
A3	90/58	235/390	15.3/19.8	0.037/0.036	0.89/0.90	0.01/0.03	5.5/9.6	6.4;8.9 / 11;15	6.5;6.3 / 11;9.8	6.8;5.9 / 11.1;9.4
A4	177/52	250/394	15.8/19.9	0.124/0.086	0.90/0.91	0.03/0.03	9.3/9.3	15;13 / 15;13	14;13 / 13;12	9;10 / 10;11
A5	16	313	17.7	0.167	0.96	0.04	12.5	17;18	13;14	12;11
A6	30	295	17.2	0.174	0.95	0.03	12.0	16;17	13;13	12;12
A7	12	265	16.3	0.183	0.96	0.02	6.8	8.3;9.1	7.3;7.2	6.5;6.0
A2+A3+A4	421/194	93.5/169	9.7/13.0	0.071/0.059	0.57/0.60	0.01/0.01	3.4/4.9	4.5;3.6 / 5.5;4.9	3.0;3.0 / 4.6;4.2	2.2;2.1 / 3.1;3.2

Note: Numerator—in the period of FGGE; denominator—at usual time

3.2.3.5 The relative contribution of TRSA systems

The parameter Z characterizes the relative information contribution of the satellite data. The Z value depends substantially on the composition of the aerological network. For the full network AO the information content of the TRSA data varies from 0.2 to 0.3 (Table 3.3). Extension of the system during FGGE has reduced the contribution of satellite information by 0.05 in the case of AO. For regional sub-systems such a reduction of Z constituted 0.01–0.03. The Z values themselves increase sharply with the transition from the hemispherical network to regional aerological sub-systems. The relative contribution of the TRSA data exceeds the 0.8 level for all the sub-systems A1–A7 considered. The independent aerological information is estimated at 15% for A1, 20% for A2, and 10% for A3. In the case of small sub-systems the relative contribution of aerological information decreases to 2–3%. With the use of data for the combination of large sub-systems, A2 + A3 + A4, the dependent information contained in aerology constitutes about 40%. For the other combination of sub-systems, A2 + A3 + A5 + A7, the share of independent information is estimated at 30%. Thus, in the case of analysis of regional aerological networks data the role of satellite information increases strongly and becomes dominating. This conclusion changes in principle the attitude to satellite information as only desirable and auxiliary in the northern hemisphere. The results show that in several practically important situations the TRSA data become the main source of information, and their role is decisive for the successful accomplishment of the numerical analysis.

The following conclusions can be drawn:

1. With the correct assimilation of satellite data in the scheme of hemispherical analysis, the relative information contribution of the TRSA system constitutes 10–15% in the northern hemisphere and 60–90% with respect to regional sub-systems of the aerological network (the Russian, North American, European, etc.). Therefore, in certain situations the TRSA systems can play a substituting role.
2. Substantially variable characteristics of information content of aerological sub-systems depending on the location of stations bring forth the problem of rational geographical distribution of stations on the basis of solving the optimization problem.

3.2.4 Application of the Shannon measure to obtain a quantitative estimate of the information content of observation systems

For an objective assessment of the information content of the existing systems and sub-systems of observations, it is necessary to use a certain quantitative measure of information. Denisov and Pokrovski (1980) considered the model of an observation system and gave formulas to calculate the Fischer information matrices (FIM). Convex functionals determined on a compact set of FIM can serve as a suitable measure of information.

An observation system providing an extremum for the FIM functional determined by numerical techniques is a problem for the optimal design of an observation system. The optimization criterion determined the choice of an FIM functional. Among these functions is the MSD of the estimates of meteorological parameters for the regular grid knots. In this case we deal with the A-criterion (Pokrovski, 1984). The determinant of FIM, which characterizes the D-criterion, has been used most often in the optimal design of the experiment because the most substantial theoretical results, which serve as the basis for a number of numerical optimization techniques, have been obtained for this information measure. A logarithm of the FIM determinant is included in the expressions for the Shannon information. Bearing in mind the monotonic character of the logarithm function, one can state that the D-optimization corresponds to the optimization as regards the Shannon information measure. This circumstance explains the choice of a given quantitative measure of information in the problems of planning the observation systems.

3.2.4.1 The Shannon measure of information

In the problems of numerical analysis and optimal design of observation systems one faces the necessity to obtain a quantitative estimate of information about a random vector x contained in another random vector y. In the case of the numerical analysis problems considered, the y-vector represents an array of observation data from the network, x is the vector of retrieved values of a meteorological parameter in regular grid knots. A similar interpretation is also possible in the case of studying the information content of the data from various observation systems (satellites, aircraft, balloons, buoys, etc.). In the case of several systems of observations, the vectors x and y can be a set of data obtained with two systems of observations.

A comparison of the characteristics of information content for several pairs of random vectors x and y is the basis to state and solve the problems of planning the systems of observations.

The schemes of objective analysis are usually based on the supposition that the meteorological field under study is random, with the first- and second-order statistical moments known. Moreover, to make the calculations easier, the covariance functions or matrices were used, already centred with average values of the respective elements. It means that in the schemes of analysis the random fields under study are identified with the Gauss fields having the same first and second moments. The Shannon measure of information for the random vector x contained in a random vector y is determined from the following equation:

$$J(x,y) = \frac{1}{2} \log \frac{|\Sigma_x||\Sigma_y|}{|\Sigma_z|} \tag{3.28}$$

where $z = (x/y)$ is a combined random vector; $\Sigma_x, \Sigma_y, \Sigma_z$ are the covariance matrices of the respective random vectors. To make the interpretation of the Shannon measure easier, the multiple correlation coefficient of a pair of random vectors x and y is determined from the equation:

$$k^2\ (x,\ y)\ =\ 1 - \frac{|\ \Sigma_z\ |}{|\ \Sigma_x\ |\ |\ \Sigma_y\ |} \tag{3.29}$$

The connection between (3.28) and (3.29) is apparent. Using the Frobenius formula applied to calculate the determinant of the block matrix,

$$\Sigma_z\ =\ \begin{pmatrix} \Sigma_x & \Sigma_{xy} \\ \Sigma^T_{xy} & \Sigma_y \end{pmatrix}$$

where Σ_{xy}, Σ^T_{xy} are cross-covariance matrices of x and y, Eq. (3.28) and Eq. (3.29) are simplified as follows:

$$J(x,y)\ =\ \frac{1}{2}\ log\ \frac{|\ \Sigma_x\ |}{|\ \Sigma_x - \Sigma_{xy} \cdot \Sigma_y^{-1} \cdot \Sigma^T_{xy}\ |} \tag{3.30}$$

$$k^2(x,y)\ =\ \frac{|\ \Sigma_x\ | - |\ \Sigma_x - \Sigma_{xy} \cdot \Sigma_y^{-1} \cdot \Sigma^T_{xy}\ |}{|\ \Sigma_x\ |} \tag{3.31}$$

These formulas show that calculations of the characteristics of information content are rather simple. The necessity to calculate Σ_y^{-1} points to the fact that only one of the covariance matrices, either Σ_x or Σ_y, should be non-singular. However, even in case of non-singularity the distributions of y in (3.30) and (3.31) are valid when Σ_y^{-1} is replaced by a generalized inverse matrix Σ^+_y.

3.2.4.2 The canonic form of Shannon's measure of information
Consider the Hotteling linear transformation which provides the calculation of canonic correlations for the pair of random vectors x and y. Let $x = (x_1, \ldots, x_r)^T$ (T denotes transpose); Σ_x, Σ_y, Σ_{xy} are the respective matrices of covariances. In this case we can obtain the matrices L and M for transformations: $\tilde{x} = L^T \cdot x$, $\tilde{y} = M^T \cdot y$ which are such that the covariance matrix $\Sigma_{\tilde{z}}$ of the combined vector $\tilde{z} = (\tilde{x}|\tilde{y})$ assumes the following canonic form:

$$\Sigma_{\tilde{z}}\ =\ \begin{pmatrix} I_{r'} & R \\ R^T & I_{p'} \end{pmatrix} \tag{3.32}$$

where $I_{r'}$, $I_{p'}$ are square matrices with r' and p' units on the main diagonal, respectively; R is the matrix $r \times p$, for which the first k diagonal elements are equal to $\rho_1, \ldots, \rho_k$ $(0 \leqslant \rho_i \leqslant 1, i = 1, \ldots, k)$ and the remaining elements of these matrices are equal to zero.

The values $r' \leqslant r, p' \leqslant p$. The equality sign takes place in case of non-singularities of the respective distributions. Here, r', p' are the ranks of the matrices, $k = min\ (r', p')$. Let the matrices of transformations of L and M have a full rank. Then they have the following properties:

$$L^T \cdot \Sigma_x \cdot L\ =\ I_{r'};\ M^T \cdot \Sigma_y \cdot M\ =\ I_{p'};\ L^T \cdot \Sigma_{xy} \cdot M\ =\ R$$

The canonic transformation of the covariance matrices Σ_x, Σ_y, Σ_z from Eq. (3.28) for

Shannon's measure of information makes it possible to obtain the canonic form for J (x, y).

Eq. (3.32) points to the fact that all the components of the vectors $\tilde{x}$ and $\tilde{y}$ are statistically independent, except for the first k components $\tilde{x}_1, \ldots, \tilde{x}_k$ and $\tilde{y}_1, \ldots, \tilde{y}_k$, which in pairs are correlated with the coefficients $\rho_1, \ldots, \rho_k$. For a pair of correlated scalar parameters ξ and η, the expression for Shannon's information is the following:

$$J(\xi, \eta) = -\tfrac{1}{2} \log [1 - r^2 (\xi, \eta)] \tag{3.33}$$

where r (ξ, η) is the coefficient of correlation between ξ and η. Applying Eq. (3.33) to k pairs $(\tilde{x}_1, \tilde{y}_1), \ldots, (\tilde{x}_k, \tilde{y}_k)$, we obtain

$$J(x, y) = -\tfrac{1}{2} \sum_{i=1}^{k} \log [1 - r^2(\tilde{x}_i, \tilde{y}_i)] = -\tfrac{1}{2} \log \prod_{i=1}^{k} [1 - r^2(\tilde{x}_i, \tilde{y}_i)] \tag{3.34}$$

Thus, Eq. (3.34) presents the canonic form of the Shannon information representation. To solve the problem, is necessary to have the values of the coefficients of correlation between the canonic random values. As is known, a set of the sought-after values of correlation coefficients can be obtained in the form of the roots of the characteristic equation:

$$| \Sigma_x - \rho \, \Sigma_{xy} \cdot \Sigma_y \cdot \Sigma^{\mathrm{T}}_{xy} | = 0 \tag{3.35}$$

3.2.4.3 The spectral form
An important feature of the analysis of meteorological fields is that the dimension of the vector x is equal to the number of grid knots n, or the number of observation stations is much larger than the volume N of the statistical sample, which serves as the basis for calculations of the information content of the data of alternative observational systems. As a rule, it is of the order of 10^3–10^4. The number of independent realizations of the annual observations is only about a hundred. In view of the correlation between the time series of the main meteorological parameters (temperature, pressure, wind, etc.), in order to calculate the statistical moments of the meteorological fields mentioned above it is expedient to use the results of observations with a time step of 3–4 days. Thus, in the problem of analysis the relationship $n > N$ is typical.

Now let us discuss the specific features of calculations of statistical moments of the meteorological fields resulting from the circumstance mentioned. Let X be the matrix of the elements of sampling of a volume N of analysis results X_i $(i = 1, \ldots, N)$. We shall consider that X has the following structure: $X = (X_1, \ldots, X_N)$ that is, it is a rectangular matrix $n \times N$. The sampled covariance matrix to represent the meteorological field X over the grid or in observation points

$$S_x = \frac{1}{N-1} X \cdot X^{\mathrm{T}} \tag{3.36}$$

turns out to be singular, since $n > N$. Matrix (3.36) has dimension $n \times n$. Its rank is equal to N, provided the vectors X_i $(i = 1, \ldots, N)$ are linearly independent. The latter circumstance is usually ensured by the procedure of "thinning out" the observational time series and, hence, the succession of analyses of the meteorological fields. Then we shall consider that the rank of S_x is at a maximum and equal to N. In this case, Σ_x, being a symmetrical and non-negatively determined matrix, has N non-negative eigennumbers, $\lambda_1 \geqslant \lambda_2 \geqslant \ldots \lambda_N > 0$ and $n - N$ eigennumbers $\lambda_{N+1}, \ldots, \lambda_n$ equal to zero.

It is apparent that the singular character of the estimate obtained of the covariance matrix Σ_x for the grid presentation of the meteorological field is determined exclusively by the length of the available observation series. There are no grounds to believe that the covariance matrix to be estimated is singular. Therefore, instead of consideration over the whole Euclidean space R^n corresponding to the grid presentation of the field, we shall consider the statistical distribution of the element x in space R with dimension N, for which the respective sampled estimates can be obtained. Of interest is a study of the invariant sub-space $Q^N \subset R^N$ corresponding to a set of eigenvalues Σ_x: $\lambda^1_x, \ldots, \lambda_x{}^N$. The orthonormal basis $Q_x{}^N$ and a set of non-zero eigennumbers $\lambda^1_x, \ldots, \lambda^N_x$ can be found through solving the problem:

$$\tilde{S}_x \cdot \tilde{\varphi}_x{}^i = \lambda^i_x \, \varphi^i_x \qquad (3.37)$$

for the non-singular matrix $\tilde{S}_x = \frac{1}{N-1} X^T \cdot X$. The non-zero eigennumbers S_x and $\tilde{S}_x$ are known to coincide. Let $\Phi_x = (\tilde{\varphi}_x{}^N)$. Then the matrix $\Phi_x = X \cdot \Phi_x \cdot \Lambda / \sqrt{N-1}$ transforms S_x to the canonic form $\Phi^T_x \cdot S_x \cdot \Phi_x = \Lambda_x$, hence the matrix Φ_x is formed with the column vectors $\varphi_x{}^I$, which are the eigenvectors S_x, that is, the main components of the distribution of the vector x. Similarly, one can calculate the non-zero eigennumbers and the respective eigen-vectors of the matrix S_y.

3.2.4.4 The invariance of the Shannon measure

Let us illustrate that the invariance of the Shannon measure with respect to singular linear transformations of the vectors x and y makes it possible to obtain a simple technique to calculate $J(x, y)$ through calculations of the determinants of the Gramm matrix. For any set of independent vectors $a_1, \ldots, a_k$ it is possible to determine the Gramm matrix $G(a_1, \ldots, a_k) = \{(a_i, a_j)\}^k_{i,j}$. The matrix G is symmetrical, positively determined, its determinant being equal to the volume of the k-dimensional parallelepiped, constructed on the vectors $a_1, \ldots, a_k$. Note that

$$S_x = \frac{1}{N-1} G(x_1, \ldots, x_N), \ S_y = \frac{1}{N-1} G(y_1, \ldots, y_N).$$

By introducing stationary directions $\varphi_x{}^i, \varphi_y{}^i$ and angles α_i between hyperplanes $Q_x{}^N$ and $Q_y{}^N$ into R^n it was shown that

$$\prod_{i=1}^{k} (1 - \cos^2 \alpha_i) = \frac{|\,G(\varphi_x{}^1, \ldots, \varphi_x{}^N; \varphi_y{}^1, \ldots, \varphi_y{}^N)\,|}{|\,G(\varphi_x{}^1, \ldots, \varphi_x{}^N)\,|\cdot|\,G(\varphi_y{}^1, \ldots, \varphi_y{}^N)\,|} \qquad (3.38)$$

Here, $\varphi_x{}^i$ and $\varphi_y{}^i$ are, respectively, the eigenvectors S_x and S_y. Considering (3.38) and that

$$\cos^2 \alpha_i = r^2 (\tilde{x}_i, \tilde{y}_i)$$

we have

$$J(x, y) = -\frac{1}{2} \log \frac{| G(\varphi_x^{1}, \ldots, \varphi_x^{N}; \varphi_y^{1}, \ldots, \varphi_y^{N}) |}{| G(\varphi_x^{1}, \ldots, \varphi_x^{N}) | \cdot | G(\varphi_y^{1}, \ldots, \varphi_y^{N}) |} \tag{3.39}$$

Note the following property of the Gramm determinants. Let $\xi = A \cdot x, \eta = B \cdot y$ be linear non-singular transformations of the vectors x and y . Then the following qualities are valid:

$$G (\xi_1, \ldots, \xi_N) = |A| \, G (x_1, \ldots, x_N),$$
$$G (\eta_1, \ldots, \eta_N) = |B| \, G (y_1, \ldots, y_N)$$
$$G (\xi_1, \ldots, \xi_N, \eta_1, \ldots, \eta_N) = |A| \, |B| \, G(x_1, \ldots, x_N, y_1, \ldots, y_N)$$

It follows that $J(x, y) = J(\xi, \eta) = J(\xi, y) = J(x, \eta)$. In this case (3.39) can be rewritten:

$$J(x, y) = -\frac{1}{2} \log \frac{| G(x_1, \ldots, x_N; y_1, \ldots, y_N) |}{| G(x_1, \ldots, x_N) | \cdot | G(y_1, \ldots, y_N) |} \tag{3.40}$$

Eq. (3.40) is useful to calculate $J(x, y)$ in the case of small samples for the vectors x and y. Summarizing, we note that two methods were proposed here to calculate the Shannon information, based on the use of canonic correlations in (3.34) and the Gramm determinants in (3.40).

3.2.4.5 Application to the simplest model of observations

Consider the relationship between the Shannon measure and the MSD of analysis for the model of the observation system $\tilde{x} = x + \varepsilon$, where x is the random vector of true values of meteorological parameters in some set of observation points with a covariance matrix Σ_x characterizing the natural variations of a given parameter. Suppose that the random vector of observation uncertainties ε has a zero average and a covariance matrix $\sigma_\varepsilon^2 I$. This means that the measurements are equally precise and the errors are statistically independent. In this case

$$J(\tilde{x}, x) = -\frac{1}{2} \log (I - \frac{1}{\sigma_\varepsilon^2} \Sigma_x) \tag{3.41}$$

considering that $|A| = \exp\{ \operatorname{tr}(\log A)\}$ ("tr" is the matrix trace), Eq. (3.41) is rewritten as

$$J (\tilde{x}, x) = -\frac{1}{2} \operatorname{tr} [\log (I - \frac{1}{\sigma_\varepsilon^2} \Sigma_x)] \tag{3.42}$$

Using the linear part of the Taylor expansion of the logarithmic function, we obtain an approximate equation for (3.42):

$$J(\tilde{x}, x) \approx \frac{1}{2\sigma_\varepsilon^2} \sum_{i=1}^{n} \sigma_x^{ii} \tag{3.43}$$

where σ_x^{ii} is the diagonal element Σ_x. If the average standard deviation of the meteorological parameter x in (3.43) is written as $\hat{\sigma}_x^2 = \Sigma_i \sigma_x^{ii} / n$ then the value of the Shannon information will be in proportion to σ_x^2:

$$J\tilde{x}, x) \approx \left(\frac{n}{2\sigma_\varepsilon^2}\right) \hat{\sigma}_x^2 \tag{3.44}$$

Based on the approximate relationship (3.44), the following conclusions can be drawn about the properties of the Shannon information:

1. With non-zero MSD of observations σ_ε^2 the value of J cannot be equal to ∞.
2. The Shannon information measure is in proportion to the signal/noise ratio:

$$\delta\hat{\sigma}_x^2 / \sigma_\varepsilon^2$$

3.2.4.6 The technique to calculate the Shannon measure of observational systems and sub-systems

The availability of several systems of observations determines the urgency of solving the problem of assessing the information contribution of the data from each system to the results of an objective analysis of the meteorological fields. For simplicity purposes, consider the case of two observation systems. However, all the results mentioned can be generalized for the case of an arbitrary number of such systems.

Let x be an observational data base formed through combining the data on x_1 and x_2 obtained from the two systems of observation mentioned above. Then $x = (x_1|x_2)$. Similarly, let us determine the structure of an operator $A = (A_1|A_2)$, realizing the objective analysis with the formula $y = Ax$. Then $y = A_1x_1 + A_2x_2$. For covariance matrices the following relationship is valid:

$$S_{yy} = A_1 \cdot S_{x_1x_1} \cdot A_1^T + A_1 S_{x_1x_2} \cdot A_2^T + A_2 \cdot S_{x_2x_1} \cdot A_1^T + A_2 \cdot S_{x_2x_2} \cdot A_2^T \tag{3.45}$$

Consider the amount of information from an observational system about the results of objective analysis. According to (3.28), we have

$$J(x_1, y) = -\frac{1}{2} \log \frac{\begin{vmatrix} S_{x_1x_1} & S_{x_1y} \\ S_{x_1y} & S_{yy} \end{vmatrix}}{|S_{x_1x_1}| \cdot |S_{yy}|} \tag{3.46}$$

where $S_{x_1y} = S_{x_1x_1} \cdot A^T_1$. It can be shown (Pokrovski, 1972) that (3.46) is transformed into:

$$J(x_1, y) = -\frac{1}{2} \log \frac{|S_{y/x_1}|}{|S_{yy}|}$$

$$S_{y/x_1} = A_1 \cdot S_{x_1x_2} \cdot A_2^T + A_2 \cdot S_{x_2x_1} \cdot A_1^T + A_2 \cdot S_{x_2x_2} \cdot A_2^T \tag{3.47}$$

3.2.4.7 Examples of calculations of the Shannon characteristics of the information content of the observational systems

All the examples given below have been modelled and are illustrated. Calculations have been based on the technique of calculations of the information content discussed in Sections 3.2.4.1. to 3.2.4.6. The input data for the calculations are realistic.The EOFs used for the NH H500 field have been obtained from the processed representative statistics of the results of numerical analyses for the winter seasons 1976–1979. Thus, the data given below characterize the information volume of a statistical ensemble for the fields of geopotential H500 obtained with the use of various observations of systems.The real spatial distribution of the aerological stations, characteristics of the spatial and temporal resolution, and the level of uncertainties of the existing satellite systems of observations serve the basis for realistic assessments of the information content.

Example 1. Assessment of the information content of the NH aerological network and its regional sub-systems.
Initial data: The NH aerological network (A0) of 680 stations during the FGGE; the Russian network (A1)—201 stations; the North American network (A2)—154 stations; the European network (A3)—90 stations; the Asian network (A4)—177 stations; AF—a set of 50 of the most informative stations (Pokrovski, 1987). The MSD of the aerological measurements for H500, $\sigma_\varepsilon = 15$ m. Results of calculations of J and K^2 for the stations given above are listed in Table 3.4.

Table 3.4

Parameter	A0	A1	A2	A4	A2 + A3 + A4
AF					
J	3.04	0.65	0.74	0.35	1.51
1.08					
K^2	0.99	0.76	0.81	0.53	0.97
0.89					

Example 2. Assessment of relative information content of the system of satellite remote sounding of the atmosphere with account of the NH aerological network and its components.
Initial data: The aerological network and its components (see Example 1). A system of satellite sounding (C) with a measurement step: 2.5 (latitude), 10 (longitude), as well as with account of the horizontal correlation of measurement errors (Pokrovski and Denisov, 1980). The level of errors $\sigma_\varepsilon = 60$ m. Results of calculations are given in Table 3.5.

Table 3.5

Parameter	A0	A1	A2	A4	A2 + A3 + A4
AF					
J	0.11	0.92	0.87	1.08	0.36
1.62					
K^2	0.23	0.85	0.80	0.90	0.52
0.75					

Example 3. Assessment of relative information content of the oceanic stations functioning in middle and tropical latitudes of the northern hemisphere during the special observational period of FGGE.
Initial data: A set of land aerological stations A0 (668 stations) and four combinations of the oceanic stations (Pokrovski and Denisov, 1985). Results of calculations are given in Table 3.6.

Table 3.6

	Number of stations			
Atlantic Ocean	4	3	1	9
Pacific Ocean	—	3	—	3
K^2	0.037	0.104	0.014	0.136

These examples do not exhaust the possibilities to use this technique. The technique was used (Pokrovski, 1984) to optimize the satellite system of the temperature sounding of the atmosphere from the viewpoint of accuracy of the objective analysis of the NH geopotential field. A similar approach has been used (Pokrovski and Malygina, 1986; Kondratyev et al., 1992) for the optimal combination of the data of the ground ozonometric network with the results of satellite IR and UV measurements.

3.2.5 Comparison of the techniques of optimization of the observational systems

The problem of an optimal design of the observational meteorological networks has attracted attention of the experts for several decades (Pokrovski, 1984). The techniques proposed and the results obtained referred to the solution of two types of problems. The first type is the determination of the dependence of MSD of an optimal interpolation to the regular grid knots on the network density; the second type is the quantitative estimation of the information content of the alternative observation networks (sub-networks), as well as new observation systems. However, neither problem can be considered to be that of optimization, strictly speaking. The solution of such problems makes it possible to give general recommendations to design the network. However, only the solution of an optimization problem gives a concrete scenario of the rational design of the observation network.The present apparatus of the theory of planning an experiment can be applied to the regressive statistical model of the system of observations (Section 3.1.3). A version has been proposed (Pokrovski, 1984) to construct a regression model of a system to observe a given meteorological field with the use of the EOF to observe a given meteorological field with the use of the EOF basis for that field.

The solution of the problem of selection of the most (least) informative stations of the network was based on the method of optimal interpolation, which is widely used in meteorological practice. Here we shall compare both approaches and assess their efficiency to solve the problem of observational network optimization.

3.2.5.1 Optimization of the network based on optimal interpolation

The designer of a network most often faces the problems of either broadening it or reducing it. To solve such problems, it is necessary to have a numerical algorithm, which could rank the existing stations by their information contribution or determine the most favourable location for new stations.

To transfer the observational data from the network to the regular grid, the method of optimal interpolation is usually used. This method can also be applied to retrieve the values of the meteorological parameter directly in observation points from the data of other stations. A station of the network for which the retrieval by the method of optimal interpolation is most successful (minimal retrieval error) can be considered the least informative. This station should be reduced first. When the network is extended, a point should be preferred where the error of the field retrieval (from the data of available stations) is at a maximum. Now, we shall formalize the formulation of the problem.

Let X be a random field of the investigated meteorological parameter. The value of the meteorological parameter $x(\omega)$ in the point with coordinates ω is considered to be a random value with the known average $\overline{x}(\omega) = E[x(\omega)]$ (E denotes mathematical expectation). We assume that for any combination of observation points $\omega_l, \ldots, \omega_k$ the covariance matrix Σ_x is known with elements $\{\sigma_x^2\}_{ij} = E[(x(\omega_i) - x(\omega_j))(x(\omega_i) - \overline{x}(\omega_j))]$ ($i, j = 1, \ldots, $ k). Take a random point ω_i and calculate the MSD of an optimal interpolation of the meteorological parameter x in it: $\tilde{x}(\omega_i / \Omega_{p/i})$ from the data of other stations. Here $= \Omega_{p/i} = (\omega_l, \ldots, \omega_{i-1}, \omega_{i+1}, \ldots, \omega_k)$. According to classic results we have (Belousov et al., 1968; Mathematical theory ... , 1983)

$$\hat{x}(\omega_i, \Omega_{p/i}) = \overline{x}(\omega_i) + \Sigma_x(\omega_i, \Omega_{p/i}) \cdot \Sigma_x^{-1}(\Omega_{p/i}) \cdot (x(\Omega_{p/i}) - \overline{x}(\Omega_{p/i})) \tag{3.48}$$

In (3.48) the following notations are used: $x(\Omega_{p/i}) = (x(\omega_1), \ldots, x(\omega_{i-1}), x(\omega_{i+1}),$ $\ldots x(\omega_k))^{\mathrm{T}}$ (T denotes transpose); $\Sigma_x(\Omega_{p/i})$ is the covariance matrix of the vector $x(\Omega_{p/i})$, $\Sigma_x(\omega_i, \Omega_{p/i})$ is the vector-row comprising the covariations of a random value $x(\omega_i)$ and the components of the vector $x(\Omega_{p/i})$. The MSD of the estimate of $\hat{x}(\Omega_{p/i})$ is as follows:

$$\{\sigma_x^2\}_{ii} = \{\sigma_x^2\}_{ii} - \Sigma_x(\omega_i, \Omega_{p/i}) \cdot \Sigma_x^{-1}(\Omega_{p/i}) \cdot \Sigma_x^{\mathrm{T}}(\omega_i, \Omega_{p/i}) \tag{3.49}$$

By re-enumeration of the observation stations we shall obtain that the observation point considered was the last in the set, that is, was called ω_k. Then, using the known

Frobenius formula for the inversion of the symmetrical matrix, we can find the relationship:

$$\{\sigma_x^{-2}\}_{kk} = 1 \: / \: \{\sigma_x^2\}_{kk} \tag{3.50}$$

which provides a simple method of ranking the observation stations by their information contribution ($\{\sigma_x^{-2}\}_{ij}$ are the elements of the matrix Σ_x^{-1}). According to the considerations mentioned above, such ranking should be made by decreasing values of MSD of the optimal interpolation $\{\sigma_{\tilde{x}}^2\}_{ii}$. Eq. (3.50) enables us to rank the stations by increasing values of diagonal elements $\{\sigma_x^{-2}\}_{ii}$ of the inverse matrix upon its calculation. Besides, this approach enables one to construct an algorithm of successive exclusion of the least informative stations of the network. The number i of a station to be excluded from the set k of stations is determined as follows:

$$i = arg(max \: \{\sigma_x^{-2}\}_{ii}).$$

Now consider the problem of extending the network. Suppose, stations $\omega_1, \ldots, \omega_{k-1}$ have been selected. It is necessary to determine the station ω_k. With an account of the foregoing statement, the location of a new station ω_k should be found from the maximization condition $\{\sigma_x^{-2}\}_{kk}$. It follows from (3.50) that the problem of selection is reduced to finding ω_k for which $\{\sigma_x^{-2}\}_{kk}$ is at a minimum. Thus, the solution of both problems was reduced to analysis of diagonal elements of the inverse matrix Σ_x^{-1}. Consider the structure of Σ_x in more detail. The observation value $\tilde{x}(\omega)$ is the sum of the true values of the meteorological parameter and measurement error $\tilde{x}(\omega) = x(\omega) + \varepsilon(\omega)$. Both $x(\omega)$ and $\varepsilon(\omega)$ can be considered statistically independent. Combine $x(\omega_i)$ in the vector $x(\Omega_0) = (x(\omega), \ldots, x(\omega_k))$. Then

$$\Sigma_{\tilde{x}}(\Omega_0) = \Sigma_x(\Omega_0) + \Sigma_\varepsilon(\Omega_0) \tag{3.51}$$

Since observations at the network are made with the instruments of similar type, it is usually considered that $\Sigma_\varepsilon(\Omega_0) = \delta_\varepsilon^2 I$. The latter means that the measurements are equally precise and the measurement errors are statistically independent. Below we shall take the model $\Sigma_\varepsilon(\Omega_0)$ as the basis. Nevertheless, all that is discussed below can be applied to the matrix $\Sigma_\varepsilon(\Omega_0)$ of an arbitrary structure. Using the method of principal components, the covariance matrix $\Sigma_x(\Omega_0)$ can be presented as

$$\Sigma_x = F \cdot \Lambda \cdot F^T \tag{3.52}$$

Here, Λ is the diagonal $k \times k$ matrix formed with eigennumbers $\lambda_1, \ldots, \lambda_k$ of the matrix Σ_x and the matrix F is formed with $f_1, \ldots, f_k$, which are the respective eigenvectors of the same matrix. In this case, using (3.51) and (3.52), we have

$$\Sigma_{\tilde{x}}^{-1} = (\Sigma_\varepsilon + F \cdot \Lambda \cdot F^T)^{-1} = \Sigma_\varepsilon^{-1} - \Sigma_\varepsilon^{-1} \cdot F \cdot (\Lambda^{-1} + F^T \cdot \Sigma_\varepsilon^{-1} \cdot F)^{-1} \cdot F^T \cdot \Sigma_\varepsilon^{-1} \tag{3.53}$$

As has been mentioned above, $F = (f_1, \ldots, f_k)$. The column vector is expressed as $f_i = (f_i(\omega_1), \ldots, f_i(\omega_k))^T$. Let $f(\omega_i)$ be the ith row of the matrix F. In this case $f(\omega_i) = (f_1(\omega_i), \ldots, f_k(\omega_i))$ and $F = (f(\omega_1) \ldots f(\omega_k))^T$. Taking into account the notations introduced we may write an expression for the ith diagonal element of the matrix. Using (3.53), we have

$$\{\sigma_{\hat{x}}^{-2}\}_{ii} = \{\sigma_x^{-2}\}_{ii} (\{\sigma_x^2\}_{ii} - f(\omega_i) [\Lambda^{-1} + F^{T} \cdot \Sigma_\varepsilon^{-1} \cdot F]^{-1} \cdot f^{T}(\omega_i)) \tag{3.54}$$

It follows from (3.54) that the procedure of selection of the least informative point ω_i is reduced to a minimization:

$$S(\omega_i) = f(\omega_i) [\Lambda^{-1} + F^{T} \cdot \Sigma_\varepsilon^{-1} \cdot F]^{-1} \cdot f^{T}(\omega_i) \tag{3.55}$$

When solving the problem of extending the network, it is necessary to find ω, with $S(\omega)$ at a maximum. Thus, the problem of analysis of the diagonal elements of the inverse matrix Σ_x^{-1} can be replaced by the problem of finding the extrema of functional (3.55). It will be shown below that (3.55) is characteristic of the presentation of the "response function" in the theory of planning the experiment for regression models (Pokrovski, 1984).

3.2.5.2 Optimization of network by developing a regression model of the observation system

An optimal interpolation is a method of objective analysis of the meteorological fields over the grid. In recent years of great concern has been the method of spectral analysis, when the fields are expanded in a certain orthonormal system of functions. Let us discuss the essence of the method. As before, we shall consider that the results of observations at k stations $\omega_1, \ldots \omega_k$ form the vector $x(\Omega_0) = (x(\omega_1), \ldots, x(\omega_k))^{T}$. Suppose that a set of orthonormal functions $\{g_i(\omega)\}_{i=1}^{N}$ is used as a basis. Introduce the rectangular matrix

$$G = \{g_{ji}\} = \{g_i(\omega_j)\}_{i=1}^{N}{}_{j=1}^{k}$$

of dimension $k \times N$. In this case the problem of spectral analysis consists in finding the vector of spectral coefficients $c = (c_1, \ldots, c_N)^{T}$ for the presentation of the vector of observations

$x(\Omega_0) = (x(\omega_1), \ldots, x(\omega_k))^{T}$ from the system of equations

$$x(\Omega_0) = G \cdot c + \varepsilon(\Omega_0) \tag{3.56}$$

Eq. (3.56) includes a random vector $\varepsilon(\Omega_0) = (\varepsilon(\omega_1), \ldots \varepsilon(\omega_k))^{T}$ of the observation error. Let $E[\varepsilon(\Omega_0)] = 0$ and $\Sigma_\varepsilon(\Omega_0)$ be the covariance matrix $\varepsilon(\Omega_0)$. Eq. (3.56) is a regression model of the observation network.

Methods of the theory of planning an experiment should be applied to the functionals of the FIM. In the case of model (3.56) the FIM is written as

$$M = G^{T} \cdot \Sigma_\varepsilon^{-1} \cdot G$$

The matrix $M = M(\Omega_0)$ is directly related to the covariance matrix $\Sigma_{\hat{c}}$ to assess the vector of coefficients $\hat{c}$. The estimate of $\hat{c}$ is obtained from (3.56) using the least squares technique. If c is a set of unknown parameters, then $\Sigma_{\hat{c}}^{-1} = M$. However, of interest is the case when c is a random vector with a known vector of averages $\bar{c}$ and a known covariance matrix Σ_c. The point is that with information available about $\bar{x}$ (Ω_0) and $\Sigma_x(\Omega_0)$ we can move on to the respective characteristics for the spectral coefficients. In this case $\Sigma_{\hat{c}} = (\Sigma_c^{-1} + M)^{-1}$. The matrix $\Sigma_{\hat{c}} = \Sigma_{\hat{c}}(\Omega_0)$, since $M = M(\Omega_0)$. Then the problem of optimal design of the observation network consists in finding $\Omega_0 = \Omega_0^*$ that realizes a minimum of the functional $\Phi = \Phi(\Sigma_{\hat{c}})$.

Consider the D-criterion of optimization, one of the most widely used. In this case, Φ equals $\det(\Sigma_{\hat{c}})$. To draw the algorithms of optimization, we take into consideration the "response function" $\varphi(\omega)$ in an arbitrary point with coordinates ω with a fixed set of the network stations Ω_0. In the case of D-criterion the response function is

$$\varphi(\omega) = g^{\mathrm{T}}(\omega) \cdot (\Sigma_c^{-1} + G^{\mathrm{T}} \cdot \Sigma_\varepsilon^{-1} \cdot G)^{-1} \cdot g(\omega) \qquad (3.57)$$

where $g(\omega) = (g_1(\omega), \ldots, g_N(\omega))^{\mathrm{T}}$. By analogy with the section above, consider two problems: selection of the least informative stations and determination of the location for new stations. In the first case the numerical procedure consists in finding the element $\omega_i \in \Omega_0$, realizing a minimum of $\varphi(\omega)$. The solution of the second problem is based on the determination of ω, realizing a maximum of $\varphi(\omega)$.

3.2.5.3 A comparative analysis of optimization techniques

The numerical procedures of optimization are similar in structure for both approaches to the problem of designing the observational network. They contain formalism for direct and inverse step-by-step optimization. In the case of optimal interpolation the extrema of the functional $S(\omega)$ are found (see (3.56)), and when the regression model is used $\varphi(\omega)$ (see (3.57)). The optimized functionals are then compared. The structure of both functionals is similar. The difference is in the use of vector-functions f and g in (3.55) and (3.57). Another difference consists in the use of the matrices F and G, Λ and Σ_c. So far, the choice of basic functions $\{g_i(\omega)\}$ has not been specified. To compare the two approaches mentioned above, an assumption should be made that in both cases we have similar 'input data. Since in the method of optimal interpolation the covariance matrix was used, it is expedient to use EOFs when applying a regression model. For a finite set of observations of points $\omega_1, \ldots \omega_k$ the EOFs coincide with eigenvectors of the covariance matrix Therefore we may consider $g_l(\omega_i) = f_j(\omega_i)$. Then $G = F$. Besides, $\Sigma_i = \Lambda$, where Λ has been determined in (3.52). Now both (3.55) and (3.57) are completely identical. This means that both approaches are completely equivalent. However, we should dwell on the differences connected with the numerical realization of the two methods. With the use of the method of optimal interpolation to rank the network stations by their information contribution, it is necessary to calculate the diagonal elements of the matrix. The conversion of the covariance matrix is usually a non-stable procedure, which leads to highly erroneous values. For a stable conversion of the covariance matrix some regularizing procedures can be used. However, their application is connected, as a rule, with a distortion of the structure of correlations described with the matrix. With the use of the second approach, it is most difficult is to calculate the EOFs, that is, eigenvectors of the covariance matrix $\Sigma_x^{-1}(\Omega_0)$. This procedure is also generally unstable, especially for eigenvectors with eigenvalues close to zero. Nevertheless, the possibility to divide the EOF into stable and unstable parts (from the viewpoint of calculations) enables one to regularize the regression model and, hence, the procedures of numerical optimization, which ensures that stable results of the optimization problem solution are obtained.

3.3 METHOD OF THE THEORY OF CONJUGATED EQUATIONS FOR OPTIMAL PLANNING OF CONVENTIONAL AND SATELLITE OBSERVING SYSTEMS

In the process of improving the systems of observations to obtain various parameters of the atmosphere, ocean and land, the solution of the problems of an optimal design of observational systems becomes more and more urgent. Among them is the problem of an optimal combination of the existing means of measurements is the most important. The latter include conventional networks of ground and oceanic stations performing discrete observations as well as new systems of continuous observations (satellites, buoys, balloons, aircraft). The dimensions of the respective mathematical problems of optimization can be rather substantial. The number of stations accomplishing routine measurements in the northern hemisphere reaches about one thousand, while the number of points of satellite soundings is tens or hundreds of thousands (Denisov and Pokrovski, 1980). Under such a situation, an approach based on the solution of the conjugated problem has proved to be useful. Pokrovski (1981, 1982) generalized this approach for the case of continuous observations, and a technique was suggested to calculate the functions of information value in the problem of the 4-D analysis of meteorological fields.

   We consider here both the theory and the methods of calculations of the functions of information value which would ensure optimal synthesis of conventional synoptic and new continuous observational systems.

3.3.1 A method to solve the problem

3.3.1.1 The model
Consider the model of the atmosphere or the atmosphere–ocean system as a non-linear system of conventional differential equations, for which the Cauchy problem has been formulated:

$$\dot{x}(t) = f[x(t), t], \quad x(t_0) = x_0 \tag{3.58}$$

A system, such as (3.58), can be obtained by writing the solution $X = X(t,\lambda,\varphi,h)$ of the system of initial equations in partial derivatives in spectral form, that is, in the form of expansion

$$X(t,\lambda,\varphi,h) = \sum_{i=1}^{N} x_i(t) F_i(\lambda,\varphi,h) + \varepsilon_N \tag{3.59}$$

in the system of functions $F(\lambda,\varphi,h)$ orthonormalized on the sphere or hemisphere. The vector-function $x(t) = (x_1(t), \ldots, x_N(t))^{\mathrm{T}}$, where t is the forecast time. The vector ε_N is an approximation error. In particular, when $\{F_i\}$ is an EOF the basis of ε_N is a random function, which in many geophysical applications can be considered Gaussian with the first two moments known.

   The specific feature of system (3.58) is that it is inhomogeneous. The inhomogeneity of (3.58) is determined by the effect on the model of external forcings. In the case of the hydrothermodynamic model it is a question of diabatic heating, condensation, convection, turbulent friction, etc. Using a certain parameter process and denoting through $\alpha = (a_1, \ldots, \alpha_k)$ a set of the parameters used, we rewrite (3.58) in the form

$$\dot{x}(t) = f[x(t), \alpha, t], \quad x(t_0) = x_0 \tag{3.60}$$

An increment of the vector-function f can be written with the use of the matrices of partial derivatives $f_x' = \delta f[\bar{x}]/\delta x$ and $f_\alpha' = \delta f[\bar{\alpha}]/\delta \alpha$ and the vectors of increments $\Delta x = \bar{x}(t) - x(t)$ and $\Delta \alpha = \alpha - \bar{\alpha}$

$$\Delta f = f_x' \cdot \Delta x + f_\alpha' \cdot \Delta \alpha \tag{3.61}$$

Here, $\bar{x}$ is a set of coefficients corresponding to the mean-climatological values of the meteorological parameters. Let $\bar{\alpha}$ be a set of parameters obtained with a preliminary adjustment of the model. The most widely used technique of adjustment is to obtain statistical estimates of α from Eq. (3.60) used as diagnostic relationships for given values of meteorological parameters $x(t_i)$ $(i = 1, \ldots, s)$.

Here we use the requirement of non-biased estimate of $\bar{f} = f[x, \bar{\alpha}, t]$ for the values of x in the empirical statistical ensemble $\{x(t_i)\}$. Clearly, in a real situation this depends on the time coordinate. For simplicity, let $\Delta \alpha$ be a Gauss random vector with the matrix of second moments known: Σ_α. In this case $\Delta_g = f_\alpha' \cdot \Delta \alpha$ will also be a Gauss random vector with the covariance matrix $\Sigma_g = f_\alpha' \cdot \Sigma_\alpha \cdot [f_\alpha']$. This supposition means that for each t the values of α are an individual realization of a random vector with the given characteristics. Thus, we obtain, at last,

$$\Delta f = f_x' \cdot \Delta x + \Delta g \tag{3.62}$$

Accomplishing a linearization of (3.62) into (3.60) and omitting Δ, we obtain a system of linear equations

$$\dot{x}(t) = A(t) \cdot x(t) + g(t), \quad x(t_0) = x_0 \tag{3.63}$$

where $A = \delta f/\delta x$. Eq. (3.63) describes the temporal evolution of fluctuations of the model (3.63) solution with respect to an undisturbed state $(\bar{x}, \bar{\alpha})$.

3.3.1.2 Observation systems

Consider two types of observation systems: discrete and continuous in time. Let discrete observations be made at $t = t_0$, continuous observations in a time interval $[t_0, T]$. Discrete measurements are made at a set of points $\Omega_0 = \{\omega_j^0\} = \{\lambda_j, \varphi_j\}$ determined by the geographical location of the network stations. Using (3.59), we write an expression for the observation results:

$$X_0 = F(\Omega_0) \cdot x_0 + \tilde{\varepsilon}_0 \tag{3.64}$$

Here the columns of the matrix $F(\Omega_0)$ are formed by the vector $F_i(\Omega_0)$, $x_0 = (x_1(t_0), \ldots, x_N(t_0))^T$, $X_0 = X(t_0, \Omega_0)$. Thus, Eq. (3.64) is an equation relating the results of discrete observations with the vector of the model variables x for $t = t_0$. Let (3.64) be called an equation of the discrete observation system.

In the case of continuous observation systems, the set of observation points is a function of time: $\Omega = \Omega(t)$, $t_0 \leqslant t \leqslant T$. Therefore, the respective equation for observations has the form of (3.64), where X, F, x and ε are functions of time, t.

The principal difference between satellite systems of continuous observations consists in indirect measurements (retrievals) of the parameters sought (Pokrovski, 1981, 1984). For simplicity purposes, consider the case of a set of linear functionals $\{l_i(t)\}$ forming a matrix operator $L(t) = \{l_1(t) \mid, \ldots, \mid l_p(t)\}$. If the functionals l_i are non-linear, then performing a linearization in the vicinity of $\bar{X}$, we obtain an expression $\Delta l_i = [l_i]_x' \cdot \Delta X$. Since everywhere, beginning from Eq. (3.63), X stands for ΔX, the functionals l_i can always be considered linear. Thus, instead of $F(\Omega(t)) \cdot x$ the results of continuous observations will be $L(t) \cdot F(\Omega(t)) \cdot x(t)$, where $L(t)$ is some rectangular matrix depending on time, t. The final equation for continuous observations will be:

$$X(t) = B(t) \cdot x(t) + \tilde{\varepsilon}(t) \tag{3.65}$$

where $B(t) = L(t) \cdot F(\Omega(t))$.

3.3.1.3 The estimation problem

Eqs. (3.63)–(3.65) form the basis for solving the problem of optimization of the observation systems. Their common feature is that they are stochastic, since they have stochastic components $g(t)$, $\tilde{\varepsilon}_0$, $\tilde{\varepsilon}(t)$ in their right-hand parts. Suppose, these items are statistically independent of each other. The physical interpretation of this fact is apparent. Considering the linear character of transformations of model (3.63) and Eqs. (3.64) and (3.65) of the observation systems, any linear functional $a^T \cdot x(t)$ of the solution $x(t)$ at the moment of forecast $t = T$ can be represented with linear operations applied to the data of discrete and continuous observations:

$$a^T \cdot x(T) = -\int_{t_0}^{T} p^T(t) X(t) \, dt + p_0^T \cdot X_0 \tag{3.66}$$

The vector p_0^T characterizes the sensitivity of the forecast results to the accuracy of the data of the system of discrete observations X_0. Let p_0^T be the vector of information value of discrete observations. The vector function $p^T(t)$ describes the sensitivity of the predicted parameter $a^T \cdot \hat{x}(t)$ to the errors in the prescribed continuous observation data. Let $p^T(t)$ be a value of function of continuous information. The choice of p_0, $p(t)$ in our approach is determined by the need to minimize the MSD of the estimate (3.66). The solution of three optimization problems will be considered:

(i)   discrete system, p_0;
(ii) continuous system, $p(t)$;
(iii) optimized combination of continuous observations, $p(t)$, with an account of prescribed properties of the discrete system, p_0.

3.3.1.4 Discrete system of observations

Consider the simplest situation of the determination of p_0 under the condition that $p(t) \equiv 0$ in (3.66). The data of continuous observations $X(t)$ are absent in (3.65).

Along with (3.63), consider a conjugate homogeneous system

$$-\dot{x}^*(t) = A^{\mathrm{T}}(t) \cdot x^*(t), \quad x^*(T) = a \tag{3.67}$$

Using (3.63) and (3.67), we obtain

$${}^d\!/\!dt \, [x^{\mathrm{T}}(t) \cdot x^*(t)] = g^{\mathrm{T}} \cdot x^* \tag{3.68}$$

Integration of (3.68) in the interval $[t_0, T]$ and considering (3.67), we obtain an equation

$$a^{\mathrm{T}} \cdot x(T) = x^{\mathrm{T}}(t_0) \cdot x^*(t_0) + \int_{t_0}^{T} g^{\mathrm{T}}(t) \cdot x^*(t) \, dt \tag{3.69}$$

Substracting (3.69) from (3.66), we obtain

$$a^{\mathrm{T}}(\hat{x}\,(T) - x(T)) = (p_0^{\mathrm{T}} \cdot F_0 - x^{*\mathrm{T}}(t_0)) x(t_0) + p_0^{\mathrm{T}} \varepsilon_0 - \int_{t_0}^{T} g^{\mathrm{T}}(t) \cdot x^*(t) \, dt \tag{3.70}$$

considering that $p(t) = 0$. It may be seen from (3.70) that for the estimation of (3.66) to be unbiased, the following condition should be fulfilled:

$$F_0^{\mathrm{T}} \cdot p_0 = x^*\,(t_0) \tag{3.71}$$

from which the vector p_0 can be found.

Supposing that p_0 fulfils condition (3.71), we find an expression for MSD in (3.70):

$$\sigma^2_{a^{\mathrm{T}} \cdot \hat{x}\,(T)} = p_0^{\mathrm{T}} \cdot \Sigma_{\varepsilon 0} \cdot p_0 + \int_{t_0}^{T} (x^*)^{\mathrm{T}} \cdot \Sigma_g \cdot x^* \, dt \tag{3.72}$$

The MSD of the forecast is determined by two components: the uncertainty of the observations system ε_0 at the moment $t = t_0$ in (3.64) and an integral contribution of the stochastic uncertainty of model g in the interval $[t_0, T]$ in (3.63).

The formulated problem can be solved on the basis of applying the techniques of pseudo-inversion of matrix to the problem of the least squares: $\hat{p}_0 = (F_0^{\mathrm{T}})^+ \cdot x^*(t_0)$.

3.3.1.5 Continuous system of observations

With a system of continuous observations defined by (3.65), one can overcome the limitations of the problem in the case of discrete systems of observations. In this case $B(t) \neq 0$, $p(t) \neq 0$. Consider an auxiliary conjugate system of inhomogeneous equations

$$-\dot{x}^*(t) = A^{\mathrm{T}}(t) \cdot x^*(t) + g^*(t), \quad x^*(T) = a \tag{3.73}$$

Suppose that the initial field $\overline{X}_0$ at the moment $t = t_0$ has been prescribed. To this field corresponds a spectral representation $\overline{x}_0 = F_0^{\mathrm{T}} \cdot X_0$ whose uncertainty is characterized by a covariance matrix Σ_{x_0}. Eq. (3.68) in this case is transformed into

$$a^{\mathrm{T}} \cdot \hat{x} = -\int_{t_0}^{T} p^{\mathrm{T}}(t) \cdot X(t) \, dt + p_0^{\mathrm{T}} \cdot X_0 \tag{3.74}$$

Pokrovski (1982) showed that for the estimate of (3.74) to be non-biased, the following equalities should be fulfilled:

$$F_0^T \cdot p_0 = x^*(t_0), \quad g^*(t) = B^T(t) \cdot p(t) \tag{3.75}$$

Thus, the condition of non-biased estimates enables one not only to estimate the vector of sensitivity of p_0 to initial data of the problem X_0 but also to reveal the structure of the still undetermined function $g^*(t)$.

To minimize the MSD of (3.74) taking into account the limitations (3.63) it is necessary to use a technique of Euler–Lagrange canonical equations. Upon some transformations (see Pokrovski, 1982), we come to the solution of two equations. First, the Ricatti matrix equation is integrated in forward time:

$$\dot{S} = S \cdot A^T + A \cdot S - S \cdot B^T \cdot \Sigma_\varepsilon^{-1} \cdot B \cdot S + \Sigma_g, \quad S(t_0) = \Sigma_{x_0} \tag{3.76}$$

then a conjugate system in inverse time:

$$\dot{x}^* = -(A^T + B^T \cdot \Sigma_\varepsilon^{-1} \cdot B \cdot S) \cdot x^*, \quad x^*(T) = a \tag{3.77}$$

After this the function $p(t)$ is determined from the equation

$$p(t) = \Sigma_\varepsilon^{-1} \cdot B(t) \cdot S \cdot x^*(t) = \Sigma_\varepsilon^{-1} \cdot B(t) \cdot \lambda(t) \tag{3.78}$$

Here, $\lambda(t)$ is a function of sensitivity from canonical equations of the problem.

Thus, the problem of an optimal design of the continuous system of observations under discussion requires the solution of not only the basic and conjugate equations from the classic method, but also of auxiliary equation (3.76).

3.3.1.6 The synthesis of continuous and discrete systems of observations

The optimization discussed above does not guarantee a desirable distribution of the function of sensitivity of the forecast results $a^T.\hat{x}(T)$ with respect to the data of a discrete system of observations. The need to obtain a special vector p_0 is determined by that the meteorological networks are distributed non-uniformly over the globe. Therefore, the problem of designing a new system of continuous measurements should be connected with a minimization of the effect of lacking data of conventional discrete observations. It is reduced to the determination of the function of information value $p(t)$, which ensures the transition of the solution of $x^*(t)$ of the conjugate system to a prescribed state x^*_0 at $t = t_0$. In this case the problem can be reformulated in the following way. It is necessary to find the function $p(t)$ which minimizes the functional

$$\int_{t_0}^{T} (p^T(t) \cdot \Sigma_\varepsilon \cdot p(t) + x^{*T}(t) \cdot \Sigma_g \cdot x^*(t)) \, dt \tag{3.79}$$

under condition that

$$x^*(t_0) = x_0^* \tag{3.80}$$

and considering the limits determined by the conjugate system

$$-\dot{x}^* = A^T(t) \cdot x^*(t) + B^T(t) \cdot p(t), \quad x^*(T) = a \tag{3.81}$$

Conditions (3.80) can be related to (3.79) through the vector of Lagrange multipliers μ.

Considering the linear character of the system of Euler–Lagrange canonical equations, write an expression for its solution:

$$\lambda(t) = S(t) \cdot x^*(t) + R(t) \cdot \mu \tag{3.82}$$

$$x_0^* = U(t) \cdot x^*(t) + Q(t) \cdot \mu \tag{3.83}$$

The matrix functions S, R, Q are determined successively from the following equations:

$$\dot{S} = S \cdot A^T + A \cdot S + \Sigma_g - S \cdot B^T \cdot \Sigma_\varepsilon^{-1} \cdot B \cdot S, \quad S(t_0) = 0 \tag{3.84}$$

$$\dot{R} = (A + S \cdot B^T \cdot \Sigma_\varepsilon^{-1} \cdot B) \cdot R, \quad R(t_0) = I \tag{3.85}$$

$$Q = R^T \cdot B^T \cdot \Sigma_\varepsilon^{-1} \cdot B \cdot R, \quad Q(t_0) = 0 \tag{3.86}$$

The matrix function $U(t) = R^T(t)$.

Now we shall formulate the basic stages of the algorithm to solve this problem. First, matrix equations (3.84)–(3.96) are successively integrated. Then, from (3.86) for $t = T$ we can determine the vector μ. Introducing this vector into (3.82) and using the resulting equation in (3.74), we obtain a homogeneous system of adjoint equations, the solution of which $x^*(t)$ with account of (3.78) makes it possible to calculate the function of information value $p(t)$. We have used a formalism based on solution of Ricatti's matrix equations. This formalism has been widely used in the theory of filtration and stochastic control.

3.3.2 Optimization of temperature remote sounding on the basis of the analysis of the information value function

Use of a prognostic hydrodynamic model to optimize the spatial–temporal scheme of remote sounding of the atmosphere (RSA) ensures a flexible approach to the problem of selection and accumulation of information from meteorological satellites. Of course, the geographical location of the regions of a preferable collection of meteorological information strongly varies in time. The technique based on calculations of the satellite information value function (SIVS) $p(t)$ discussed above enables the scheme of RSA data collection to be planned. Use of the technique of "adjoint equations" to study the "function of sensitivity" of the equations of atmospheric hydrothermodynamics to the input data of the forecast problem has been considered by Marchuk et al. (1986). The methodology mentioned above makes it possible to extend the sphere of application of the adjoint equations technique.

3.3.2.1 The problem of the forecast of the averaged geopotential fields

Two versions have been considered to assessments of the linear functionals of the solution $a^T \cdot x(T)$ for a hydrodynamic model that provides a short-term (2–3 days) forecast of the pressure field in the Northern Hemisphere (Beliavski and Pokrovski, 1983). In the first version, $a = a_s$, with a determination of individual spectral components of the presentation of the hemispherical geopotential field from the EOF basis. Here we shall dwell on the first version of the solution of the problem. When considering the problem of SIVF computation to forecast the averaged fields of geopotential $a^T \cdot x(T)$, two types of models have been studied:

(i)   a deterministic dynamic model (3.63) in which $g = 0$;
(ii) a dynamic–stochastic model (3.63) in which the component g was used, estimated from the FGGE data (Beliavski and Pokrovski, 1983).

In simulation experiments the real location of the aerological network stations was used, as well as satellite orbits along the meridional circles with a 20° longitudinal step.

For simplicity of the SIVF analysis, $p(s, t)$ is presented as a product $p(s, t) = pr(t) \cdot ps(s, t)$ of the temporal change $pr(t)$ and spatial distribution $ps(s, t)$. Note that the simplicity of such a presentation is determined by normalizing the function $ps(s, t)$ in s for each value of t, according to the rule: max $p(s, t) = 1$. The character of decreasing of the temporal change $pr(t)$ from $t = T$ to $t = t_0$ shows the "forgetting" of the RSA information as the time of forecast increases, $pt = T-t$. In the case of a purely dynamic prognostic model the value of satellite information halves with pt growing from zero to 96 h (Fig. 3.1). For a more realistic dynamic–stochastic model, the values of temporal tendency of SIVF $pr(t)$ decrease by a factor of 28 in the same time interval. During the first 12 hours the value of satellite information decreases by a factor of 1.5–2; after one day, to 3; after two days by a factor of 7. Thus, a real inadequacy of the prognostic model determines the necessity to renew the satellite information every 6 h. For this purpose, an RSA system of not less than two satellites is needed.

To determine the preferable zones of satellite data collection consider the spatial distribution of SIVF, $ps(s, t)$. We shall discuss, first, the cases of the deterministic prognostic mode. For $pt = 0$, maximum SIVF values are concentrated in the

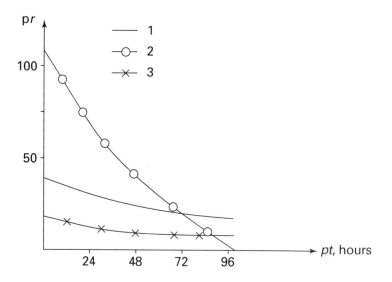

Fig. 3.1. Temporal variations of PSIV $p_r(t)$: 1—a_g functional, determinated forecast model; 2—a_g functional, dynamic–stochastic model; 3—a_s, functional (first EOF component), determinated model.

region of forecast RG. An increase in the range of forecast to two days leads to the appearance of great values of SIVF in the points referring to the satellite orbits over the Atlantic basin. With $pt = 72$ h there is a need for satellite measurements over the Pacific Ocean and Eastern Siberia.

The choice of the region of Eastern Siberia is connected with considerable natural fluctuations of the geopotential field and a more sparse aerological network. At the same time, there is a substantial decrease in SIVF in the region of forecast RG. With the period of forecast pt growing to 12–24 h, the values of SIVF decrease everywhere, except the water basins of both the oceans mentioned above, where some increase in its value is observed. It refers mostly to the Atlantic Ocean and less to the basin of the Pacific (Fig. 3.2). The increase in pt to two days determines a considerable growth of SIVF over the Atlantic Ocean. In the interval of pt from 2 to 3 days the SIVF starts increasing more uniformly in all the regions of the northern hemisphere, which indicates the ceasing of the effect of this method in planning a scheme of RSA data collection.

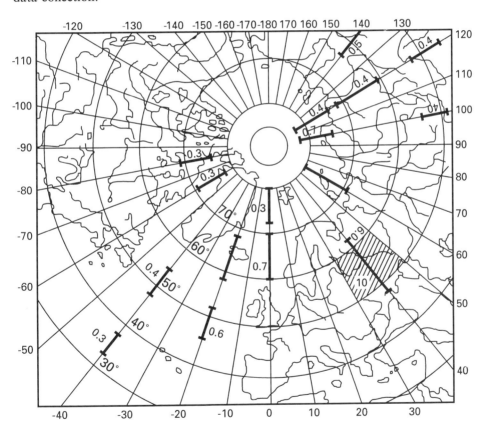

Fig. 3.2. Location of the sections of the orbits corresponding to maximum FSIV "ps"in a 3-day forecast of H_{500} averaged in the shaded area with the use of a dynamic–stochastic model $(pt = 72$ h$)$.

Simultaneously with computation of SIVF, calculations were made of the aerological information value function (AIVF), p_0. At $pt = 72$ h one can point out two regions of abnormally high values of AIVF:

(i)   north-eastern region of North America, in the interval 60–80 N;
(ii) Eastern Siberia and the Far East (Fig. 3.3).

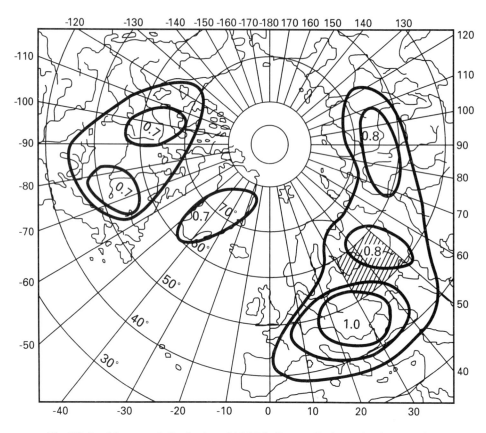

Fig. 3.3. Spatial–temporal distribution of AIVF "ps" anomalies in a 3-day forecast of H_{500} averages in the shaded area with the use of a dynamic–stochastic model ($pt=72$ h).

3.3.2.2 The forecast of large-scale components of the hemispherical field of geopotential

Now we shall analyse the SIVF for the case when the functional $a^{\mathrm{T}}_s \cdot x(T)$ is forecast, which indicates individual spectral components representing the hemispherical field of geopotential in EOF. We shall discuss the case of forecasting the first, third spectral components representing the field X in the EOF basis (Beliavski and Pokrovski, 1983). We shall consider only the case of the determinated prognostic model.

The spectral version of the forecast functional is characterized by a slower decrease in pt of the temporal change in SIVF, pr. For example, when forecasting an EOF, the function pr decreases by 20% over 3 days, and for the third EOF by 25%. Thus, when forecasting the ultralong waves of the pressure field, the process of "forgetting" the satellite information is much slower. With the use of RSA data to forecast the waves on a planetary scale, it is sufficient to renew the information every 2–3 days.

The prognostic problem considered is characterized by a more uniform (compared to that above) distribution of SIVF values over the hemisphere for all pt. Let us first discuss the case of the first EOF forecast (Fig. 3.4). With $pt = 0$ maximum values of SIVF refer to the basins of both oceans, as well as to abnormal zones of maximum fluctuations of the geopotential field in the north-east of North America and in Eastern Siberia. An absolute maximum of SIVF is observed in the Pacific Ocean. With the period of forecast growing to 2–3 days, there appear two types of evolution of the SIVF values. In the continental abnormal zones mentioned

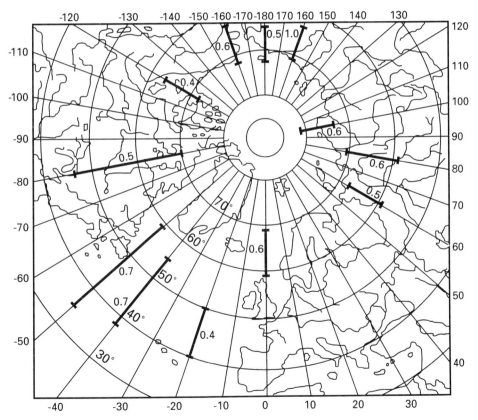

Fig. 3.4. Location of the sections of the orbits corresponding to maximum SIVF "ps" values in a 3-day forecast of the first EOF component of the geopotential field with the use of a determinated model ($pt = 0$ h).

above, values of SIVF remain relatively large. Over the ocean basins there is observed the alternation in time of the neighbouring orbits as the most informative. For the third EOF the time period of such an alternation is markedly less than for the first component.

A further increase in *pt (pt* > 72 h) causes an alternation of the most informative neighbouring orbits over the abnormal continental zones as well as a marked increase in SIVF over the oceans. The region of maximum SIVF values over the Pacific Ocean shifts from middle to high latitudes.

Let us dwell upon special behaviour of SIVF for the case of forecasting the third EOF. With *pt* = 0, maximum values of SIVF refer to the Pacific basin, and with *pt* = 48 h to the western Atlantic. A further increase in *pt* is connected with the SIVF values over the Atlantic basin, over North America and the European sector of the Arctic basin. At the same time, the SIVF decreases over the whole of Europe and Asia.

Thus, when forecasting the ultralong wave components of the hemispheric geopotential field, the method of determination of an optimal scheme of RSA based on account of SIVF leads to non-trivial results, which could not be forecast. It should also be noted that the structure of SIVF can rapidly change. Since the applied hydrodynamic model is far from being ideal, the model results can be considered only as methodical illustrations to the technique proposed. It is most expedient to apply this approach on the basis of the prognostic model used in operational practice.

3.4 ANALYSIS OF THE SATELLITE INFORMATION USERS' REQUIREMENTS OF SATELLITE REMOTE SENSING SYSTEMS AND THE INFORMATION CONTENT OF EXISTING OBSERVATIONAL COMPLEXES

A wide circle of the users of satellite information (SI) is concerned with numerous ecological problems, which need the data of remote sounding from space to be utilized.

3.4.1 Objects of investigations
The general scheme of studies connected with the use of SI in environmental investigations is shown in Fig. 3.5. Two interrelated principal groups of studies— global cycles and geophysical processes—form the basis to solve most of the environmental problems. Among the global cycles of principal importance are the energy and water cycles, as well as several biogeochemical cycles. The latter include, in particular, the cycles of carbon, nitrogen and other elements, which have been studied inadequately. The other direction of global environmental studies is connected with biogeochemical processes in the ocean, on land, and in the atmosphere. The scientific problems mentioned are important for various Earth sciences (geology, oceanology, hydrology, climatology) as well as for different branches of economics agriculture, forestry, etc.

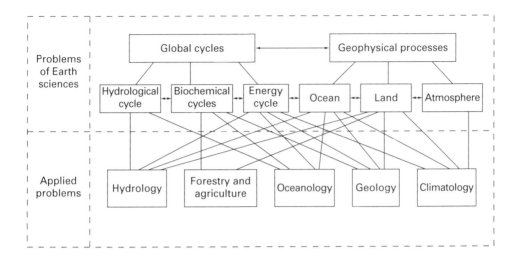

Fig. 3.5. The structure of ecological studies making use of space-borne observation systems.

3.4.2 Users' requirements of satellite information

In most cases the SI users can formulate precisely enough requirements for the principal characteristics of information (spectral channels, geometry of the experiment, spatial and temporal resolution, etc.). In the studies discussed below we used a summary of such requirements incorporating four groups of ecological problems: I—oceanology (102 requirements), II—hydrology (33), III—geology (36), and IV—forestry and agriculture (32).

Table 3.7 illustrates some requirements for several important ecological problems in each group mentioned above. A variety of such requirements brings forth the problem of choosing the optimal conditions for the experiment encorporating all ecological problems.

The difference in the requirements consists, first of all, in the choice of spectral channels for remote sensing. In the upper part of Figs. 3.6 and 3.7 are shown the location and the width of the intervals needed in the optical and near-IR spectral regions.

At the bottom of these figures are given spectral characteristics of some multichannel remote sensing instruments. A comparison of the upper and bottom parts of Figs. 3.6 and 3.7 demonstrates the inadequacy of the instruments and illustrates the necessity for an optimal design of the parameters of the remote sensing instruments. Table 3.8 lists the requirements for the one microwave active/passive system to solve ecological problems of groups I-IV mentioned above. The limits of the spectral sub-intervals are given in Table 3.9.

Table 3.7. Requirements to the optical remote sounding systems

Groups of problems	Ecological problems	Resolution (m)	Viewing angles	Width of covered band (km)	Spectral intervals, μm		
					Visible	Near-IR	IR
1	2	3	4	5	6	7	8
I. Oceanology	1. Mapping the coastal currents and tides	60–90	45–60	200	0.41–0.44;0.45–0.47; 0.51–0.53;0.55–0.57; 0.57–0.64;0.64–0.68; 0.68–0.70	0.77–0.80	10.9–12.6
	2. Water turbidity	50–100	0–30	40–100	0.3–0.5;0.5;0.65	0.90	
	3. Mapping the ocean surface (colour, salinity, oxygen content, polluting bioorganisms, temperature)	30–60	0–20	100	0.37–0.40;0.40–0.53; 0.43–0.45;0.45–0.48; 0.48–0.51;0.51–0.53; 0.53–0.55;0.55–0.57; 0.57–0.61;0.61–0.66; 0.66–0.70	0.70–0.82	10.9–12.6
	4. Sea ice	100–200	0–30	100–200	0.45–0.53;0.53–0.57; 0.50–0.58;0.57–0.64; 0.64–0.69	0.73–0.82 0.8–1.1	10.9–12.6
	5. Propagation and migration of marine organisms. Biologic pollution	1000	0–10	50–100	0.45–0.53;0.53–0.57; 0.57–0.64;0.64–0.69; 0.50–0.58	0.73–0.82	8–14
	6. Coastal water pollution	10–30	0–10	50–100	0.45–0.53;0.53–0.57; 0.57–0.64;0.64–0.69; 0.30–0.40;0.48–0.59; 0.50–0.58	0.73–0.82	10.9–12.6
II. Hydrology	1. River basins	5–10	0–30	200	0.68–0.74	0.78–1.2	—
	2. Spring floods	5–10	0–10	50	0.67–0.75	0.7–1.3	10–14
	3. Marshes	3–5	0–10	50	0.51–0.57;0.62–0.67; 0.53–0.57;0.57–0.64; 0.64–0.69	0.7–1.3	10.9–12.6

4. Snow cover (density, melting)	10–50	0–20	200	0.38–0.51;0.44–0.52; 0.69–0.88;0.50–0.67	0.82–0.84 0.7–1.3 0.49–1.2	—
5. Glaciers and ice cover on rivers and lakes	5–10	0–30	50–100	0.44–0.50;0.50–0.55; 0.46–0.52;0.52–0.58; 0.50–0.58	0.79–0.84 0.7–1.3	8–14
6. Rainfalls and soil moistening	5–30	0–10	50	0.49–1.2	0.78–0.84 0.8–1.3	8–14 10.9–12.6
7. Water basins pollution	5–10	0–10	200	0.3–0.4;0.48–0.59	0.8–0.9	8–14 10–12
III. Geology 1. Topography	10–20	0–30	100–500	0.51–0.63;0.63–0.70	0.70–0.89 0.89–1.0 0.8–1.3	8 – 14
2. Volcanic activity	10–20	0–20	100–200	0.4–0.7	—	10–12 8–14
3. Lithologic mapping	10–20	0–30	100–200	0.51–0.63;0.63–0.70; 0.40–0.48;0.51–0.57; 0.62–0.67	0.70–0.89 0.89–1.0	8–10 10–10.6 10.6–12.6 9.3–12.8
IV. Forestry and agriculture 1. Mapping the soils	5–15	0–45	100–200	0.62–0.67	0.74–0.85 1.5–1.8 2.0–2.6	8–14
2. Soil erosion	5–10	0–45	40–50	0.40–0.48;0.51–0.57; 0.62–0.67	0.73–0.78	—
3. Forest inventory	10–30	0–10	50–100	0.55–0.58;0.70–0.74	1.5–1.8 2.0–2.6	—
4. Forest fires	10–20	0–70	500–1000	0.4–0.7	3.5–5.4	8–14
5. Assessment of the state of crops	5–10	0–10	50–100	0.55–0.58;0.66–0.70; 0.70–0.74;0.51–0.57; 0.59–0.68	0.76–0.83 1.5–1.8	8–14
6. Disease of forest vegetation	10–15	0–10	40–50	0.40–0.44;0.55–0.58; 0.70–0.74;0.51–0.57; 0.58–0.68	0.78–0.84 0.83–0.86	8–14

Table 3.8. Requirements to microwave remote sounding systems

Groups of problems 1	Ecological problems 2	Spectral range 3	System 4	Instruments passive/active 5
I. Oceanology	1. Monitoring the sea ice drifting	Ku, X, C, S, L	Passive	Multichannel radiometer
	2. Control of sea ice return	Ku, X	Passive	Radiometer measuring close to nadir
	3. Ocean topography	Ku	Act./pass.	Altimeter—nadir-viewing radar
	4. Distribution of temperature in the atmosphere near the ocean surface	Ka, K, Ku , X	Passive	Multichannel scanning radiometer
	5. Winds near the ocean surface	Ku, C	Act./pass.	Two-beam radar–scatterometer operating in two azimuthal directions
	6. Mapping the ocean salinity	L	Passive	Radiometer (nadir measurements)
II. Hydrology	1. Mapping the surface waters	C, L	Passive	Radiometer (nadir measurements)
	2. Precipitation	Q, Ka, K	Passive	Radiometer (nadir measurements)
	3. Atmospheric water vapour	Q, Ka	Passive	Radiometer (nadir measurements)
III. Forestry and agriculture	1. Soil moisture	L	Passive	Scanning radiometer
	2. Assessment of the state of vegetation (leaf area index, total biomass, bioproductivity)	C	Act./pass.	Radar with two receivers connected with two antennas for horizontal and vertical polarization
IV. Geology	1. Drawing the structural and morphological maps	Z	Act./pass.	Radar–radiometer (nadir measurements)
	2. Mapping the hidden features of relief	Z	Act./pass.	

Table 3.9. Limits of microwave intervals

Interval	W	Q	Ka	K	Ku
Boundary (cm)	0.13–0.33	0.33–0.63	0.72–1.0	1.0–1.9	1.9–2.5
Interval	X	C	S	L	P
Boundary (cm)	2.5–3.5	3.5–7.1	7.1–15.8	15.8–63	63–100

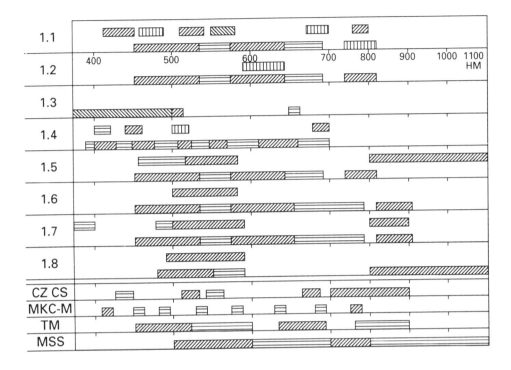

Fig. 3.6. Configuration of spectral intervals needed to solve the problems of group I "Oceanology" (see Table 3.7), as well as corresponding to the known samples of instruments.

3.4.3 Analysis of existing observing systems

The data in Tables 3.7 and 3.8 illustrate the variety of requirements to the instruments. Using the techniques of optimal design of the instrumentation (Pokrovski, 1984), we manage to plan optimal designs for multipurpose systems. We shall dwell here on the analysis of the correspondence of the requirements to instruments for remote sensing (Kondratyev and Pokrovski, 1989).

3.4.3.1 The optical wavelength range

To solve the problems of the oceanology group, the Russian multichannel instrument is most useful. The channels of the MKSM biospectrometer centred at λ = 415, 449, 484, 534, 569,621 and 676 nm ($\Delta\lambda$ = 10 nm) enable one to solve numerous oceanological problems. One of the shortcomings of this instrument is the absence of a measurement channel in the near-UV: 0.37–0.4 and 0.3–0.4 μm, as well as in the near-IR: 0.8–0.9 μm. Note that the MKSM scheme meets the problems of oceanology better, compared to the CZCS spectrometer carried by Nimbus-7.

To solve the problems of hydrology, geology, forestry, and agriculture, the following Russian instruments served as the basis: MKF-6, MSU series, RSS-2, 3,

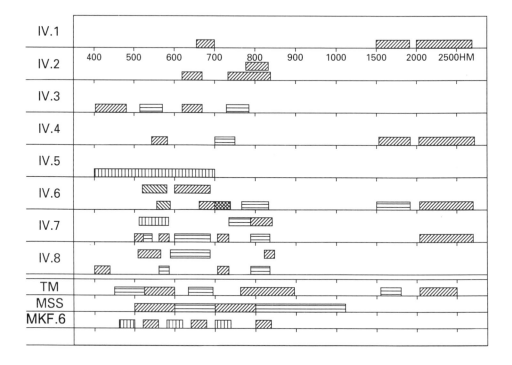

etc. The scheme of measurements for the 6-channel MKF-6 camera is not adequate.

Fig. 3.7. Configuration of spectral intervals needed to solve the problems of group IV "Forestry and agriculture" (see Table 3.7), as well as corresponding to the known samples of instruments.

Measurements in three channels; 660, 720, 820 nm, are affected by ozone and water vapour absorption. The MSU channels chosen by analogy with the American MSS instrument, are also inadequate to solve the concrete problems (see Table 3.7). The Thematic Mapper (TM) complex is much more useful (Table 3.10).

Therefore there are two possibilities. First, to use an instrument of the TM type; secondly, to supplement the MSU or MKF-6 instruments with the RSS-3M spectrometer, which ensures the distribution of radiation in the 0.4–0.7 μm range with a 5-nm resolution.

3.4.3.2 Near-IR region

Here the MSU channels can provide information for the problems of hydrology and geology. For forestry and agriculture the MSU and MKF-6 lack channels 1.5–1.8 and 2.0–2.6 μm, ,as well as the "transparency window" 3.7 μm.

3.4.3.3 The thermal IR region

To solve numerous problems, it is necessary to have not less then two channels in the 8–12 μm "transparency window".

Table 3.10. Comparison of MSU and TM spectral channels

Number	MSU	TM
1	0.5–0.6	0.45–0.52
2	0.6–0.7	0.52–0.60
3	0.7–0.8	0.63–0.69
4	0.8–1.1	0.76–0.90
5	—	1.55–1.75
6	—	10.4–12.5
7	—	2.08–2.35

3.4.3.4 Microwave radiometry

Table 3.8 gives a summary of requirements to an active/passive microwave complex measuring in the 0.1–100 cm wavelength interval. The latest development, the microwave radiometric system IKAR-1, only partly meets the requirements. A unit of nadir-looking radiometers (0.3, 0.8, 1.35, 2.5, 6.0 cm) as well as a unit for similar "Delta" scanning radiometers ensures the solution of two problems:

(i) distribution of temperature and humidity in the atmosphere and near the ocean surface;
(ii) the wind-speed field near the ocean surface.

The R-400 scanning radiometer provides the solution for two other problems:

(i) assessment of the state of vegetation;
(ii) mapping the water surface properties.

The PRV radioaltimeter is meant for the topographic mapping of the ocean. Other problems either cannot be solved or are solved partially.

3.4.4 Optimal planning observing systems

The urgency of the problem for an optimal design of the systems for the remote sensing from space is determined by a number of reasons, including the high cost of space experiments, limited weight of the instruments, energy power supply and in-flight memory volume. Besides, it is necessary to bear in mind a number of scientific aspects of the problem of satellite data interpretation: mathematical incorrectness of inverse problems (from the characteristics of emitted, reflected and absorbed radiation we should retrieve the parameters of the respective medium), uncontrolled fluctuations of the optical characteristics of the atmosphere, etc..

When planning the experiments on remote sensing, two extreme cases should be excluded: an excess or deficit of the obtained information because of inadequate choice of observational conditions. In both cases the solution of inverse problems can be sufficiently distorted in view of its incorrectness.

Two approaches have been developed to solve the problems of multipurpose design of remote sensing systems: informational and economic (Pokrovski, 1988). In both cases it is assumed that the information users dealing with various economic problems can formulate precise requirements for the main characteristics of information (spectral channels, geometry of experiment, spatial and temporal resolution, etc.).

In the studies discussed below a summary of such requirements given in Kondratyev et al. (1975 b) was used.

3.4.4.1 The informational approach

The idea in this approach (Pokrovski, 1981) consists in selecting the most important factors and determining the respective vectors of the factor loadings in the formalized multidimensional space of requirements. The way of constructing the space of requirements and the modification of the scheme used of the factor analysis are given in literature (Kondratyev and Pokrovski, 1977, 1989). The results of the determination of optimal groups of spectral intervals are given in Table 3.11 for the groups of problems I–IV. The results of calculations for various complexes of ecological problems are presented by Kondratyev and Pokrovski (1977). Note that the data in Table 3.11 (first line) have been obtained bearing in mind the requirements of the users of information, which do not take into account the selectivity of its distortion by the atmosphere in different intervals of the electromagnetic spectrum, as well as economic characteristics of the experiments in space. Table 3.11 (second line) shows the limits of spectral channels of sounding, specified with an account of excluded bands of absorption by H_2O, O_3 and NO_3 in the following intervals: 0.38–0.42; 0.57–0.62; 0.755–0.760; 0.785–0.790; 0.810–0.845; 0.910–0.960; 1.10–1.16 μm. An important contribution of molecular scattering by the atmosphere determines a low information content for the 0.30–0.40 μm channel. Therefore this channel is not used in the remote sensing systems (Table 3.12).

Table 3.11. Choice of spectral intervals (μm) **using the factor analysis technique**

Problem groups	Factors						
	1	2	3	4	5	6	7
I. Oceanology	0.45–0.53	0.64–0.69	0.70–0.90	0.57–0.64	0.82–1.30	0.50–0.58	0.40–0.44
	0.45–0.53	0.64–0.69	0.70–0.75	0.62–0.64	0.96–1.10	0.50–0.57	0.42–0.44
II. Hydrology	0.70–1.30	0.51–0.59	0.44–0.52	0.67–0.74	0.57–0.67	0.30–0.40	0.38–0.49
	0.96–1.10	0.51–0.57	0.44–0.52	0.67–0.74	0.62–0.67	0.70–0.75	0.42–0.49
III. Geology	0.51–0.63	0.62–0.70	0.70–0.89	0.40–0.51	0.8–1.30		
	0.51–0.57	0.62–0.70	0.70–0.75	0.42–0.51	0.96–1.10		
IV. Forestry and	0.51–0.57	0.59–0.70	0.75–0.78	0.70–0.74	0.40–0.51	0.55–0.58	0.88–1.30
agriculture	0.51–0.57	0.62–0.70	0.76–0.78	0.70–0.74	0.42–0.51	0.55–0.57	0.96–1.10

Table 3.12. Characteristics of space-borne instruments in the visible and IR spectral ranges

Instrument	Spectral channels, μm	Spatial resolution (nadir)	Viewing band-width, km	Remarks
MSU	0.50–0.60 0.60–0.70 0.70–0.80 0.80–1.10	80 m	185	Multispectral scanner
TM	0.45–0.52 0.52–0.60 0.63–0.69 0.70–0.90	30 m	185	Landsat-4,5 thematic mapper
CZCS	0.43–0.45 0.51–0.53 0.54–0.56 0.66–0.68 0.70–0.80 1.05–1.25	825 m	1636	CZCS
HRV	0.5–0.59 0.61–0.68 0.79–0.89 0.51–0.73	20 m	600	Water basin photography

3.4.4.2 Analysis of capabilities of applied instruments taking account of users' needs

If we arrange the spectral channels of sounding chosen by order of increasing wavelengths, we can establish a relationship between similar channels for different groups of problems (Table 3.13). As can be seen, the shortwave channel 0.42–0.44 μm is needed only to solve the problems of oceanology. It is seen from Table 3.12 that the corresponding 0.43–0.45 μm channels is also used only in the specialized oceanographic instrument CZCS (Table 3.11). The difference in the boundaries of spectral intervals is explained by that the scheme of the oceanographic scanner does not take a proper account of the user's needs (see Table 3.7) and the spectral optical characteristics of the atmosphere. For example, the CZCS scheme lacks the spectral channel 0.62–0.64 μm, which is present in the requirements of each problem of the oceanology group.

The data in Table 3.13 also show that only the problems of the "forestry and agriculture" groups need measurements in two narrow channels: 0.55–0.57 and 0.76–0.78 μm. However, the specialists interested in this group of problems cannot obtain information in these spectral intervals with the help of the instruments considered. Narrow channel No. 6 is needed for the users from the "Oceanology" and "Hydrology" groups. Specialists in "Geology" and "Forestry and Agriculture" are satisfied with information obtained on the broad spectral interval 0.62–0.70 μm, combining channel Nos 5 and 6 for the problems I and II. This spectral range is

Table 3.13. Optimal spectral channels of sounding corresponding to the basic problem groups

Problem group	Spectral channels of sounding								
	1	2	3	4	5	6	7	8	9
I. Oceanology	0.42–0.44	0.45–0.53	0.50–0.57	—	0.62–0.64	0.64–0.69	0.70–0.75	—	0.96–1.10
II. Hydrology	—	0.44–0.52	0.51–0.57	—	0.62–0.67	0.67–0.74	0.70–0.75	—	0.96–1.10
III. Geology	—	0.42–0.51	0.51–0.57	—	0.62–0.70	—	0.70–0.75	—	0.96–1.10
IV. Forestry and agriculture	—	0.42–0.51	0.51–0.57	0.55–0.57	0.62–0.70	—	0.70–0.74	0.76–0.78	0.96–1.10

presented in the instrumentation considered as one spectral interval. It means that the complexes discussed do not meet the requirements of the "Oceanology" and "Hydrology" groups concerning the obtaining of data in channels 5 and 6.

Comparison of data in Tables 3.12 and 3.13 shows that information obtained with the TM agrees best with the requirements of the "Geology" problems and somewhat worse than of the "Hydrology" problems. The multispectral MSS scanner does not provide any information for channel 2 (Table 3.13) at all. In its scheme channels 5 and 6 of an optimal set are merged in one. Information for channels 0.70–0.80 and 0.80–1.10 μm is markedly distorted at the expense of reflected radiation absorbed by atmospheric gases.

These data indicate that the satellite instruments considered are markedly inadequate for the needs of SI users in various branches of ecological investigations.

3.4.4.3 The economic approach

Bearing in mind that in the future the design and accomplishment of space-borne systems of remote sensing should be financed by the economic branches interested in SI, we face the problem of cost-effectiveness of the measuring complexes with their long-term operation on board the space platforms. The multichannel character of SI and its multipurpose applications enable one to analyse the problem of optimal design of the respective observation systems from the viewpoint of maximization of the integral index of economic efficiency of the multipurpose observation system V under condition that individual efficiencies for individual problems v_i ($i = 1, \ldots, N$) are regulated by special limitations of the type of inequalities both from above and from below.

Let us pose the problem. Define: c_{ij} the economic efficiency of the use of the jth measuring channel ($j = 1, \ldots, M$) for the ith partial problem: d_j the full costs of functioning and information processing of the jth channel of the multipurpose measuring system; $l_i{}^+$, $l_i{}^-$, the maximum and minimum economic efficiencies of the observation data for the ith problem. In this case for the cost-effective use of the jth channel k_j we obtain an expression

$$k_j = \sum_i c_{ij} - d_j \quad (j = 1, \ldots, M)$$

Introducing a variable y_j, an indicator for including the jth channel in the observation system $y_j = \{{}^0_1$, we shall formulate the principal problem of optimization in the form of a standard problem of Boolean programming (Kondratyev and Pokrovski, 1989):

$$min \quad \{ - \sum_{j=1}^{M} k_j y_j \} \tag{3.87}$$

$$y_j = \{{}^0_1 \tag{3.88}$$

$$l_i^- \leqslant \sum_{j=1}^{M} c_{ij} y_j \leqslant l_i^+ \quad (i = 1, \ldots, N) \tag{3.89}$$

One of the most efficient numerical algorithms for solving the problems (3.87)–(3.89) is the method suggested by Balash. This method has been applied to substantiate the design of multipurpose systems of environmental remote sensing (Kondratyev and

Pokrovski, 1977). As has been mentioned above, the problems discussed in Kondratyev et al. (1975b) are divided into four large groups: oceanology, hydrology, geology, and forestry and agriculture. Each group, in turn, is divided into subgroups. The number of partial problems in each of the principal groups varies from 9 to 14. As an illustration, consider the results of the choice of an optimal series of spectral channels of sounding for multipurpose survey in the interests of the problems of oceanology (Table 3.14) (Kondratyev et al., 1975b).

Table 3.14. List of partial problems of the "Oceanology" group

Order of priority	Name
1	Sea surface state
2	Water turbidity
3	Sea ice
4	General near-cost sea survey
5	Mapping the coastal currents and tides
6	Global mapping of currents, ocean surface survey
7	Mapping the coastline and shallows
8	Bathymetry and topography of ice
9	Propagation and migration of marine organisms
10	Pollution of coastal waters
11	Effect of pollution on marine medium
12	Study of bars,reefs

The number of spectral channels for 12 problems ($N = 12$) of the "Oceanology" group totals 37 ($M = 37$). The number of spectral intervals m_i to satisfy the requirements for the ith partial problem is within $18 \leqslant m_i \leqslant 33$. This means that the volume of information for each partial problem is rather large. It constitutes not less than half the volume of information for the whole "Oceanology" group. The design of a multichannel instrument complex can proceed from the fact that costs will be in inverse proportion to the width of the spectral interval and in direct proportion to the spectral resolution. Let β be the cost for one channel with a resolution of 1 nm. Then a cost $d_{\Delta\lambda}$ for the channel with resolution $\Delta\lambda$ (nm) will constitute $d_{\Delta\lambda} = \beta/\Delta\lambda$. Let b be the general cost-efficiency of the use of SI in oceanology. Introduce b_i to denote the efficiency of the use of SI in the ith problem of oceanology. Then $b_i = b/N$. Let all b_i be equal. Then $b_i = b/N$ is an average cost-efficiency for some specific problem. Introducing the threshold value $\alpha(0 < \alpha < 1)$ of permissible deviations from average efficiency, we determine the constraints

$$l_i^{+} = (1+\alpha)l_i, \ l_i^{-} = (1-\alpha)l_i \ (i=1,\ldots,M)$$

Let J_i be a multitude of numbers of channels in the requirements to the system of observations for the ith specific problem. Introduce an indicator function of the jth channel according to the equality

$X_j(J) = \{^1_0 \text{ if } j \varepsilon J$ in other cases

Then a series of coefficients c_{ij} used in formulating the optimization problem (3.87)–(3.89) is determined from the equality

$$c_{ij} = \frac{b_i}{m_i} X_j (J_i) \quad (i = 1, \ldots M; \, j = 1, \ldots, N) \quad (3.90)$$

Using concrete numerical values $\beta = 5$, $b = 31$, all the parameters included in (3.87)–(3.89) were calculated. Calculations of the indices of cost-efficiency of the channels k_j $(j = 1, \ldots, N)$ show that some spectral regions are unprofitable (negative values of k_j from the viewpoint of the multipurpose design of the observation system). For oceanology these are channels 0.40–0.45 and 0.69–0.73 μm.

The most economically justified measurements are made in channels 0.53–0.55; 0.66–0.68; 0.59–0.61; 0.61–0.64; 0.55–0.57 μm. Here the values of k_j are at a maximum. Thus, even simple calculations make it possible to choose the spectral channels of remote sensing from the long initial list, which are the most cost-effective.

Channels 1, 7 in the optimal scheme for the "oceanology" problems are less useful economically than others given in Table 3.13. However, this information should be taken into account only when designing a specialized oceanographic instrumentation. Other groups of problems also have their "unprofitable" spectral regions. For example, in cases of problems of forestry and agriculture it is more cost-efficient to obtain]information from the 1.5–1.8 μm channel than from the 0.96–1.10 μm channel. For the problems of the "Hydrology" group all spectral channels are cost-effective.

In summary, we can formulate the basic results:

1. Analysis has been made of the basic objectives of studies when solving environmental problems.
2. The satellite information users' requirements have been systematized for the basic groups of applied problems.
3. A comparison of these requirements with the characteristics of some instrumentation used for meteorological and Earth's resources satellites revealed an inadequacy of these characteristics.
4. An optimization by the criterion of maximum information contribution has made it possible to choose a combination of spectral channels of remote sensing in the interests of four groups of problems: oceanology, hydrology, geology, forestry and agriculture.
5. Use of the models of mathematical programming makes it possible for each group of problems to differentiate the spectral channels of sounding by their cost-efficiency.
6. Concrete results concerning recommendations of an optimal choice of specified channels should be considered as illustrations of a possibility and require further analysis.

There are two principal unsolved problems of environmental remote sensing.

1. The existing satellite remote sensing information is obviously redundant, but, on the other hand, is not complete enough to solve problems of environmental monitoring (an illustration is the recent decision by the US administration to combine civilian and military meteorological satellite observing systems).

2. There is no adequate coordination in the development of conventional (ground- and ship-based, balloons, buoys, aircraft) and satellite observing systems.

These two circumstances put forward the necessity to substantiate an optimized global environmental observing system, including both conventional (*in situ* and remote sensing observations) as well as satellite observations. The chapter contains certain suggestions of how it may be accomplished.

References

1. Aagard K., Carmack E. C. 1989. The role of sea ice and other fresh water in the arctic circulation. J. Geophys. Res., Vol. 94. —p. 14,485–14,498.
2. Abbot M. R. 1984. Biological oceanography. NASA Techn. Memo. 86129. Goddard Space Flight Center. Greenbelt, MD. Vol. 1 (Pt. 2).—p. 11–13.
3. Abrahamson D.E. (Ed.). 1989. The Challenge of Global Warming. Island Press. Washington, D.C.—356 p.
4. Ackley S. F. 1984. Sea ice. NASA Techn. Memo. 86129. Goddard Space Flight Center. Greenbelt, MD.—Vol. 1 (Pt. 2).—p. 41–43.
5. A Document Prepared by the First Meeting of the Special Committee ICSU Secretariat. Paris. 16–19 July, 1987. Global Change Report.—1987.—No. 2.—22 p.
6. Afanasyev V. G. 1981. Society: systematics, knowledge and control. Moscow: Politizdat.—430 p. (in Russian).
7. Aksenov O. Yu., Antonets A.I., Gushchin S.I. 1992. Major results from experiments on detection of forest fires with the help of high-orbit space vehicles. Optical Journal.—No. 8.—p. 21–23 (in Russian).
8. Alajev E.B. 1989. Present-day global-scale problems: methodology of their geographic studies. Izv. AN SSSR, Ser. Geography, No. 2.—p. 23–32 (in Russian).
9. Albert A. 1977. Regression, pseudo-inversion and recurrent estimation. Moscow: Nauka Press.—224 p. (in Russian).
10. Allen S.H., Jr., Boote K.J., Jones J.W., Jones P.H., Valle R.R., Acock B., Rogers H.H., Dahlman R.C. 1987. Response of vegetation to rising carbon dioxide: photosynthesis, biomass, and seed yield of soybean. Glob. Biogeochem. Cycl.—Vol. 1, No. 1.—p. 1–14.
11. Alpatyev A. M. 1983. Development, transformation and protection of the environment. Leningrad: Nauka Press.—240 p. (in Russian).
12. American satellite ERT-1. 1974. Problems of Rocket Engineering.—No.6.—p. 21–43 (in Russian).
13. Anderson D.L. 1989. Composition of the Earth. Science.—Vol. 243, No. 4889.—p. 367–369.

14. Andreae M.O. 1989. The global biogeochemical sulphur cycle: a review. In: Trace Gases and the Biosphere. B. Moore (Ed.). Univ. of Arizona Press.
15. Andronikov V.L. 1979. Aerospace opportunities for soil research. Moscow: Kolos Press.—280 p. (in Russian).
16. Antal E., Farago T., Glantz M.H. 1988. On the concept of extreme meteorological and climatic events. Idojaras.—Vol. 92, No. 5.—p. 269–275.
17. Anuchin V.A. 1982. The geographic factor in the social development. Moscow: Mysl Press.—234 p. (in Russian).
18. Application of radar aerosurvey to geological-geographic investigations. 1981. Ed. by V.M. Glishkov and V.B. Komarov. Leningrad: Nedra Press (in Russian).
19. Application of mathematical models to analysis of ecologo-economic systems. 1988. Ed. by I.A. Bashalkhanov and V.A. Baturin. Novosibirsk: Nauka Press.—216p. (in Russian).
20. A Report from the Second Meeting of the Special Committee. Harvard Univ. Cambridge, MA. 8–11 Febr. 1988. Global Change Report.—1988.—No. 3.—42 p.
21. Armand N.A. 1960. Remote sounding of the Earth's surface and atmosphere in the microwave range. Studies of the Earth from Space.—No. 1.—p. 95–105 (in Russian).
22. Armand N.A., Krapivin V.F., Mkrtchian F.A. 1987. Processing techniques for the data of radiophysical studies of the environment. Moscow: Nauka Press.—271 p. (in Russian).
23. Armand N.A., Bobylev L.P., Bunkin F.V. et al. 1993. Space studies of the Earth as an ecological system and impact of human activities on this system. Programme "ECOS". Preprint 1876.—Institute for Space Studies, RAN.—44 p. (in Russian).
24. Aselmann I. 1985. Zur Beziehung von Nettoprimaproduktion und Biomasse. Berechnungen von Korrelationsgleichungen und ihre Anwendung zur Abschatzung der globalen Biomasse mit Hilfe eines NPP-Modells. Veroff. der Naturforsch. Gesellschaft zu Emden von 1814. Neue Folge.—Emden. Vol. 3, No. 3D2.—197 p.
25. A Strategy for Earth Science from Space in the 1980s and 1990s. Part II: Atmosphere and Interactions with the Solid Earth, Ocean and Biota. Publ. Nat. Res. Council. Nat. Acad. Press. Washington, D.C.—1985.—199 p.
26. Ausbel J.H., Grubber A., Nakicenovic N. 1988. Carbon dioxide emissions in a methane economy. Clim. Change.—Vol. 12, No. 3.—p. 245–263.
27. Avanesov G.A., Glazkov V.D., Ziman Ya.L. et al. 1981a. The multizonal scanning system "Fragment". Studies of the Earth from Space.—No. 5.—p. 45–46 (in Russian).
28. Avanesov G.A., Ziman Ya.L., Sychev A.G., TarnopolskiV.I. 1981b. Metrological support to the Earth surface brightness measurements making use of the multizonal scanning system "Fragment". Studies of the Earth from Space.—No. 5.—p. 65–77 (in Russian).
29. Avanesov G.A., Galeev A.A., Zhukov V.S. et al. 1992. The project ECOS-A:

scientific space studies and development of the models of global ecological and climatological processes and natural disasters. Study of the Earth from Space.—No. 2.—p. 3–14.

30. Avdujevski V. Uspenski G.R. 1985. Economic and scientific complexes. Moscow: Mashinostrojenie Press.—416 p. (in Russian).

31. Bagrov N.A. 1978. Natural constituents of small samples with numerous parameters. Meteorology and Hydrology.—No. 12.—p. 3–9 (in Russian).

32. Ball T.F. 1986. Historical evidence and climatic implications of a shift in the boreal forest tundra transition in Central Canada. Clim. Change.—Vol. 8, No. 2.—p. 121–134.

33. Banin A., Lawless J.G., Whutten R.C. 1984. Global N2O cycles—terrestrial emission, atmospheric accumulation and biospheric effects. Adv. Space Res.—Vol. 4, No. 12.—p. 207–216.

34. Bazilevski K.K., Bezlepko E.V., Pakhomov L.A. et al. 1974. Some problems of measurements and interpretation of polarisation characteristics. Proc. CAO.—Issue 116.—p. 25–37 (in Russian).

35. Becker F., Bolle H.J., Rowntree P.R. 1987. The International Satellite Land Surface Climatology Project. ISLSCP Report.—No. 10.—100 p.

36. Belchanski G.I., Andrejev G.G., Sazonov N.V., Torshin V.I. 1982. On a system of complex processing of aerospace information in the interests of agriculture. Studies of the Earth from Space.—No. 5.—p. 5–11 (in Russian).

37. Beliavski A.I., Pokrovski O.M. 1983. Effect of consideration of the remote sensing data on the numerical analysis of the geopotential field. Meteorology and Hydrology.—No. 1.—p. 14–21 (in Russian).

38. Beliavski A.I., Pokrovski O.M. 1984. An optimization of the system to observe atmospheric pressure in the Northern hemisphere. Studies of the Earth from Space.—No. 3.—p. 8–13 (in Russian).

39. Beliajev V.I., Kisilevski L.I., Pliuta V.E., Smetanin E.A. 1978. The small-sized fast spectrometer MSS-2. J. Appl. Spectroscopy.—Vol. 29, issue 6.—p. 1070–1073 (in Russian).

40. Beliajev V.I., Khudoshina M.Yu. 1989. Principles of logical-informative modelling of complicated geosystems. Kiev: Naukova Dumka Press, 160 p. (in Russian).

41. Beliajev V.I., Zaitseva V.A., Pliuta V.E. et al. 1985. Small-size fast spectro-meter MSS-2P. PTE.—No. 1.—P. 243 (in Russian).

42. Belousov S.L. et al. 1968. Computer processing of operational meteorological information. Leningrad: Gidrometeoizdat.—282 p. (in Russian).

43. Bengtsson L. 1975. Four-dimensional data assimilation of meteorological observations. GARP Publ. Ser. No. 15. Geneva: WMO/ICSU.—76 p.

44. Bengtsson L., Shukla J. 1988. Integration of space and in situ observations to study global climate change. Bull. Amer. Met. Soc.—Vol. 69.—p. 1130–1143.

45. Beregovoi G.T., Buznikov A.A., Kondratyev K.Ya., et al. 1972a. Environmental studies from the manned orbital stations. Leningrad: Gidrometeoizdat.—399 p. (in Russian).

46. Beregovoi G.T., Buznikov A.A., Kondratyev K.Ya., et al. 1972b. Optical

phenomena in the atmosphere as observed from the manned spacecraft. Leningrad: Gidrometeoizdat.—48 p. (in Russian).

47. Berner R.A. 1989. Biogeochemical cycles of carbon and sulfur and their effect on atmospheric oxygen over Phanerozoic time. Global and Planet. Change.—Vol. 1, No. 1–2.—p. 97–122.

48. BEST. Tropical System Energy Budget (Bilan Energetique du Systeme Tropical). CNES. Toulouse.—58 p. , 1988.

49. Bingemer H.G., Crutzen P.J. 1987. The production of methane from solid wastes. J. Geophys. Res.—Vol. D92, No. 2.—p. 2181–2188.

50. Biogeochemical cycle of substances in the biosphere. 1987. Ed. by V.A. Kovda. Moscow: Nauka Press.—143 p. (in Russian).

51. Biosphere: evolution, space, time. 1988. Moscow: Progress Press.—464 p. (in Russian).

52. Bodechtel J. 1981. Satellite remote sensing in Europe. Remote Sens. Soc. Japan. 1st Int. Symp. Earth Resources and Space Age.—p. 95–120.

53. Bogomolov A. F., Popov S. M., Smoliannikov Yu. D., Stepin A.V. 1981. Problems of digital transmission and recording of multizonal video-information and their solution in the experiment "Fragment". Studies of the Earth from Space.—No. 5.—p. 57–64 (in Russian).

54. Bogorodski V. V., Kanareikin D. B., Kozlov A. I. 1981. Polarisation of radiation scattered and emitted by soils.—Leningrad: Gidrometeoizdat.—279 p. (in Russian).

55. Bolin B. 1979. On the role of the atmosphere in biogeochemical cycles—Symons Memorial Lecture. Quart. J. Roy. Met. Soc.—Vol. 105, No. 443.—p. 25–42.

56. Bolin B. 1984. Biogeochemical processes and climate modelling. In: The Global Climate. Ed. by J.T. Houghton. Cambridge Univ. Press.—p. 213–223.

57. Bolle H.-J., Rasool S.I. (Eds.). 1985. Development of the Implementation Plan for the International Satellite Land-Surface Climatology Project (ISLSCP). Phase I. World Climate Pap. WMO/TD-N46.—No. 94.—83 p.

58. Bolshakov V. N. 1983. Ecological forecast.—Moscow: Znanie Press (in Russian).

59. Bolshakov V.N., Lavrova N.P. 1982. Major directions of research in the field of Earth resources using the data of survey from manned spacecraft and manned orbital stations, and their application. Izv. VUZov, Geodesy and Aerophotography.—No. 2.—p. 56–57 (in Russian).

60. Borisenkov E.P. and Kondratyev K.Ya. 1988. Carbon Cycle and Climate. Leningrad: Gidrometeoizdat, 320 pp.

61. Born M., Wolf E. 1970. Principles of Optics.—Moscow: Mir Press.—845 p. (in Russian).

62. Borucki W.J., Pollack J.B., Toon O.B. et al. 1980. The influence of solar UV variations on climate. Proc. Conf. (Boulder, 16–19 Oct. 1979). New York.—p. 513–522.

63. Box E.O. 1988. Estimating the seasonal carbon source-sink geography of natural, steady-state terrestrial biosphere. J. Appl. Meteorol.—Vol. 27, No. 10.—p. 1109–1124.

64. Broecker W. S. 1987. How to build a habitable planet. Eldigio Press, Palisades, NY.—294 p.

65. Broecker W. S., Peng T.-H. 1987. The oceanic salt pump: does it contribute to the glacial-interglacial difference in atmospheric CO2 content?. Glob. Biogeochem. Cycl.—Vol. 1, No. 3.—p. 251–259.

66. Broecker W.S., Denton G.H. 1989. The role of ocean–atmospheric reorganisations in glacial cycles. Geochim Cosmochim. Acta.—Vol. 53.—p. 2465–2501.

67. Brown B.J., Hanson M.E., Liverman D.M., Merideth R.W. 1987. Global sustainability: towards definition. Environm. Manag.—Vol. 11.—p. 713–719.

68. Browning K.A. 1987. Prospects for determining global precipitation from space observations in the years 1995–2000. World Clim. Pap. —No. 137. Appendix I.—8 p.

69. Bruntland G. H. 1989. Global change and our common future. Environment.—Vol. 31, No. 5.—p. 16–20; 40–44.

70. Bryson A., Huo You Sh. 1972. Applied theory of optimal control.—Moscow: Mir Press.—543 p. (in Russian).

71. Buat-Menard P. (Ed.). 1986. The role of air-sea exchange in geochemical cycling.—D. Reidel Publ. Co.—549 p.

72. Buznikov A.A. 1980a. Spectral studies of the atmosphere and natural formations on the Earth surface from the manned spacecraft. In: The XI All-Union Symp. on Actinometry. Pt. II. Instruments and observations techniques.—Tallinn: Est. Acad. Sci.—p. 135–138 (in Russian).

73. Buznikov A. A. 1980b. Spectral studies of the environment in the visible from the manned spacecraft. In: Aerospace and cartographic methods of the environmental studies. Materials of the VI All-Union Geographic Symposium, Frunze.—Leningrad: Geogr. Soc. Press.—p. 11–12 (in Russian).

74. Buznikov A.A. 1981. An occultation experiment on atmospheric sounding in the H2O 2.7-μm band from the orbital station "Salut-4". Izv. LETI.—Issue 290.—p. 3–8 (in Russian).

75. Buznikov A.A. 1982. Experiments on spectral studies of the environment from the manned spacecraft. Izv. VUZov. Geodesy and Aerophotography.—No. 2.—p. 73–74 (in Russian).

76. Buznikov A.A. 1983a. Space-borne spectrophotometry of the geosystems from the manned spacecraft and manned orbital stations. In: Present problems of the remote sounding of the geosystems.—Moscow: Inst. of Geography, USSR Acad. Sci.—p. 131–143 (in Russian).

77. Buznikov A.A. 1983b. Spectral instruments to study the atmosphere-surface system from the manned spacecraft. In: Ibid.—p. 69–74 (in Russian).

78. Buznikov A.A. 1983c. Spectrographic measurements of the terrestrial natural formations from space. Izv. LETI.—Issue 327 (in Russian).

79. Buznikov A.A. 1986. Development and the present state of optical systems to study the Earth agricultural resources from space. In: Application of the data of space studies to the development of agriculture. Express-information, No. 2–86.—Leningrad: USSR Acad. Sci. (in Russian).

80. Buznikov A.A. 1987. Instruments to study agricultural resources making use of

space-borne means. In: Use of the results of aerospace studies in the interests of agriculture. Express-information, No. 1–87.—Leningrad: USSR Acad. Sci. (in Russian).

81. Buznikov A.A. 1990. Optico-electronic systems for remote sounding. Leningrad: LETI Press.—42 p. (in Russian).

82. Buznikov A.A. 1992. Methods and instruments of remote sounding in the global ecological monitoring. Journal of Optical Technology.—No. 8.—p. 4–11 (in Russian).

83. Buznikov A.A. 1994b. Search studies on the substantiation of the conception and development of the principles of designing the system for complex multilevel ecological monitoring of the environment in the north-western region of the European part of Russian Federation. Third St.-Petersburg Int. Conf. "Regional Informatics-94". St.-Petersburg, 10–13 May 1994. Part II. Information technologies in ecology.—p. 4–6 (in Russian).

84. Buznikov A. A. 1975. Special design of spectral instruments for space studies. J. Applied Spectroscopy.—Vol. 21, No. 2.—p. 372–380 (in Russian).

85. Buznikov A.A., Lakhtanov G.A. 1982. A polarisation technique of the remote sounding of oil films on sea surface. Izv. VUZov. Geodesy and Aerophotography.—No. 1.—p. 50–54 (in Russian).

86. Buznikov A.A., Karasev A.B. 1989. International Seminar on satelliete land-surface climatology. Studies of the Earth from Space.—No. 2.—p. 121–123 (in Russian).

87. Buznikov A.A., Orlov V.M. 1989. The satellite hand-operated spectrograph RSS-3 for spectrophotometry of the Earth. In: The XI All-Union Symp. on Actinometry. Pt. II. Instruments and observation techniques. Tallinn: Est. Acad. Sci.—p. 131–134 (in Russian).

88. Buznikov A.A., Lakhtanov G.A. 1991. Polarimeters for aerospace studies of the environment. Studies of the Earth from Space.—No. 1.—p. 103–115 (in Russian).

89. Buznikov A.A., Kondratyev K.Ya., Lazarev A.I., Miroshnikov M.M., Nikolajev A.G., Sevastyanov V.I., Smoktiy O.I., Khrunov E.V. 1972. Visual observations of the daytime, twilight, and nocturnal horizons of the Earth from the manned spacecraft. Space Exploration.—Vol. 10, issue 1.—p. 100–112 (in Russian).

90. Buznikov A.A., Kondratyev K.Ya., Smokty O.I. 1975a. On the formation of the Earth's reflection spectra near the homogeneous media interface. Doklady AN SSSR.—Vol. 222, No. 4.—p. 821–824 (in Russian).

91. Buznikov A.A., Kondratyev K.Ya., Lakhtanov G.A., Orlov V.M. 1975b. Remote sounding of sea surface pollution using the polarization techniques. Water Resources.—No. 3.—p. 128–132 (in Russian).

92. Buznikov A.A., Ivanian G.A., Kondratyev K.Ya., Pozdniakov D.V. 1975c. Application of the effect of polarisation to the remote sounding of the sea surface oil slicks. Doklady AN SSSR.—Vol. 221, No. 5.—p. 1082–1085 (in Russian).

93. Buznikov A.A., Klimuk P.I., Kondratyev K.Ya., Lebedev V.V., Orlov V.M.

1975d. Spectrophotometry of the Earth from the manned spacecraft "Soyuz-13". Doklady AN SSSR.—Vol. 221, No. 6.—p. 1310–1313 (in Russian).

94. Buznikov A.A., Kondratyev K.Ya., Smokty O.I. 1975e. Reflectivity of the Earth's surface near the interface of two uniform areas. Remote Sensing of Earth Res.—Vol. 4.—USA, Tennessee.

95. Buznikov A.A., Lakhtanov G.A., Orlov V.M., Pozdniakov D.V. 1975f. Application of spectral, spectrozonal and polarisation techniques to the remote sounding of oil slicks on the sea surface. In: Geography of the Oceans. Proc. VI Symp. Geogr. Soc. of the USSR.—Leningrad: Geogr. Soc., USSR (in Russian).

96. Buznikov A. A., Kondratyev K. Ya., Orlov V. M. 1976a. Spectra of the twilight horizon from observations from the manned spacecraft "Soyuz-5". Doklady AN SSSR.—Vol. 226, No. 6 (in Russian).

97. Buznikov A.A., Kondratyev K.Ya., Orlov V.M. 1976b. Colorimetric characteristics of the brightness field of the twilight and daytime horizons of the Earth from the "Soyuz-5" data. In: Problems of Atmospheric Physics, issue 14. Leningrad: LGU Press (in Russian).

98. Buznikov A.A., Lakhtanov G.A., Churov V.E. 1977a. On the use of the polarization technique in the remote sounding of soil moisture. Water Resources.—No. 5.—p. 173–179 (in Russian).

99. Buznikov A.A., Kondratyev K.Ya., Pokrovski A.G. 1977b. Application of occultation technique for determining water vapour mixing ratio in the upper stratosphere and mesosphere. Proc. VI Annual Rem. Sens. Earth Resources Conf., March 29–31.

100. Buznikov A.A., Kondratyev K.Ya., Orlov V.M. 1977c. Vertical brightness profiles of the twilight aureole as indicator of the aerosol vertical inhomogeneity. Proc. VI Annual Remote Sens. of Earth Resources Conf., March 29–31.

101. Buznikov A.A., Lakhtanov G.A., Piotrovskaya A.P. 1978. Special features of the polarization of radiation reflected from sand and soils. In: Problems of Atmospheric Physics. Leningrad: LGU.—Issue 15.—p. 44–49 (in Russian).

102. Buznikov A. A., Lakhtanov G. A., Kuznetsov A. N. 1980. the on-board polarimeter for the remote sounding of oil slicks on the sea surface. In: Optical methods to study the oceans and inland water basins. Tallinn: Est. Acad. Sci.—p. 268–272 (in Russian).

103. Buznikov A.A., Grechko G.M., Kondratyev K.Ya. 1983. An experiment on occultation sounding of the atmosphere in the H2O 2.7-μm band from the orbital station "Salut-4". In: Proc. VI Sci. Memorial Lecture on Space Exploration in memory of the soviet scientists—pioneers in mastering the outer space. Moscow: USSR Acad. Sci. (in Russian).

104. Buznikov A.A., Grechko G.M., Kondratyev K.Ya. 1984. The role of researching cosmonauts in accomplishing the spectral geospace experiments from the manned orbital stations. In: Gagarin Memorial Lecture on space exploration and aviation. Moscow: Nauka Press (in Russian).

105. Buznikov A.A., Kondratyev K.Ya., Mishev D.N., Milenova L. 1986. An

experiecne in spectral studies of the environment from the manned orbital stations. In: Int. Workshop of the Socialist Countries' Working Group "Technique and Technology of Remote Sounding".—Tallinn: Est. Acad. Sci. (in Russian).

106. Buznikov A.A., Lakhtanov G.A., Prokhorov V.M., Churov V.E. 1989a. On the measurements of spectro-polarization characteristics of emission from water surfaces at different heights in the atmosphere. Studies of the Earth from Space.—No. 6.—p. 64–69 (in Russian).

107. Buznikov A.A., Borisov A.V., Kovalev A.E. 1989b. A spectrometer to study the spectral transparency of the Earth's atmosphere. Izv. LETI, issue 406 (in Russian).

108. Buznikov A.A., Chekhin L.P., Demidova E.S., Khilov L.P. 1990. Preparation of satellite information to assess the ecological state of the lake Ladoga. Water Resources.—No. 5 (in Russian).

109. Buznikov A.A., Pokrovski O.M., Pchelova T.F. 1991. On the retrieval of the water vapour profile in the upper stratosphere and lower mesosphere using the occulation sounding in the 2.7-μm absorption band. Studies of the Earth from Space.—No. 1.—p. 3–10 (in Russian).

110. Buznikov A.A., Kondratyev K.Ya., Pokrovski O.M., Yanushanets Yu.B. 1992. On the methods of satellite information assimilation to analyse and forecast the atmospheric ozone field. Study of the Earth from Space.—No. 3 (in Russian).

111. Buznikov A. A., Payanskaya-Gvozdeva I.I., Yurkovskaya T.K., Andrejeva E.N. 1993a. The use of remote and ground methods for the control over the ecological situation and transboundary transfer of the Kola Peninsula. Int. Symp. on the Ecological Effects of Arctic Airborne Contaminants. October 4–8, Reykjavik, Iceland.

112. Buznikov A.A., Minkkinen P., Laine P. et al. 1993b. Complex sub-satellite experiments on the study of Lakes Ladoga and Saimaa and adjoining territories. Ist Int. Lake Ladoga Symp. "Ecological problems of Lake Ladoga". November 22–26, 1993. St.-Petersburg.

113. Buznikov A.A., Lakhtanov G.A., Mokijevski K.A., Rumiantsev V.B. 1993c. Combined use of spectral brightness and polarization characteristics of upward radiation in remote sensing of inland water bodies. Ibid.

114. Buznikov A.A., Gorokhov V.L., Tron' A.A. 1994a. Robust-cognitive technology to process the data of ecological monitoring. Third St.-Petersburg Int. Conf. "Regional Informatics-94", St.-Petersburg, 10–13 May 1994. Part II. Information technologies in ecology.—p. 20 (in Russian).

115. Buznikov A.A., Payanskaya-Gvozdeva I.I., Yurkovskaya T.K., Andrejeva E. N. 1994b. Use of remote and ground methods to assess the impacts of smelter emissions in the Kola Peninsula. Proc. of the Int. Symp. on the Ecological Effects of Arctic Airborne Contaminants. October 4–8, 1993. Reykjavik, Iceland.

116. Buznikov A.A., Gorokhov V.L., Lakhtanov G.A. et al. 1994c. Study of the transboundary transfer of pollutants on the Karelian Isthmus through the

control of the state of vegetation and snow covers. Materials of the Scientific-Practical Conf. "Criteria of Ecological Safety". St.-Petersburg.—p. 154–155 (in Russian).

117. Campbell I.M. 1986. Energy and the Atmosphere: A Physical-Chemical Cycling. John Wiley. New York.—337 p.

118. Castri F., di. 1984. Twenty years of international programmes on ecosystems and the biosphere: an overview of achievements, shortcomings and possible new perspectives. Global Change. Proc. Symp. ICSU (Ottawa, Sept. 25, 1984).—ICSU Press.—p. 135–152.

119. Chahine M.T. 1992. Global Energy and Water Cycle Experiment (GEWEX) Third Symp. on Global Change Studies. AMS, Boston.—p. 7–9.

120. Chamberlain J.W. 1986. Theory of Planetary Atmospheres. An Introduction to Their Physics and Chemistry. Int. Geophys. Ser.—Vol. 22.—Acad. Press, New York.—330 p.

121. Charlson R.J., Lovelock J.E., Andreae M.O., Warren S.G. 1987. Oceanic phytoplankton, atmospheric sulphur, cloud albedo, and climate. Nature.—Vol. 326.—p. 655–661.

122. Charlson R. G. 1988. Have concentrations of tropospheric aerosol changed?. In: The Changing Atmosphere. F. S. Rowland and I.S.A. Isaksen (Eds.). Dahlem Workshop Reports.—John Wiley & Sons. Chichester.

123. Chase R., McGoldrick L. 1984. Oceanic transport. NASA Techn. Memo. 86129. GSFC. Greenbelt, MD.—p. 34–36.

124. Chedin A. 1987. WINDMATIC: a wind measuring along-track image-correlator. World Clim. Pap. —No. 137, Appendix F.—7 p.

125. Chelomei V. N., Efremov G. A., Etkin V. S. et al. 1990. The high-resolution radar sounding of sea surface from the satellite "Kosmos-1870". Study of the Earth from Space.—No. 2.—p. 80–90 (in Russian).

126. Chemical Cycles and the Evolution of the Earth. Ed. by C. B. Gregor, R.M. Garrels, F.T. Mackenzie, J.B. Maynard. John Wiley & Sons. New York.—P. XII.—276 p. , 1988.

127. Chemistry and Physics of Terrestrial Planets. Ed. S.K. Saxena. Springer Verlag. Berlin—405 p. , 1986.

128. Chen H.S. 1979. A polarisation scanner for atmospheric radiation monitoring from geosynchronous meteorological satellites. IEEE Reg. V. Annu. Conf., El Paso. RTex., N. Y.—p. 27–29.

129. Chen H.S., Rao N.C.R. 1968. Polarization of light in reflection by some natural surfaces. Brit. J. Appl. Phys. (J. Phys. D). Ser. 2.—Vol. 1, No. 9.—p. 1191–1200.

130. Chenard S. 1989. Apocalypse when?. Space Markets.—Vol. 4, No. 2.—p. 70–81.

131. Cicerone R., Oremland R. 1988. Biogeochemical aspects of atmospheric methane. Global Biogeochem. Cycl.—Vol. 2.—p. 299–327.

132. Cicerone R.J. 1988. How has the atmospheric concentration of CO changed?. In: The Changing Atmosphere. F.S. Rowland and I.S.A. Isaksen (Eds.).—Wiley-Interscience.—p. 49–61.

133. Clark W. C. 1985. Scales of climate impacts. Clim. Change.—Vol. 7, No. 1.—p. 5–27.

134. Clark W.C., Holling C.S. 1984. Sustainable development of the biosphere: human activities and global change. Global Change. Proc. Symp. ICSU (Ottawa, Sept. 25, 1984).—ICSU Press.—p. 283–300.

135. Climate and History: Studies of Past Climates and Their Impact on Man. Eds. T.M. Wigley, M.J. Ingram, G. Farmer.—Cambridge Univ. Press.—530 p. , 1981.

136. Climatic and biological consequences of a nuclear war. 1987. Ed. by E.P. Velekhov. Moscow: Nauka Press.—288 p. (in Russian).

137. Colinvaux P. 1986. Ecology.—725 p.

138. Complete Radiation Experiment. 1976. Ed. by K.Ya. Kondratyev and N.E. Ter-Markariants. Leningrad: Gidrometeoizdat.—240 p. (in Russian).

139. Concepts of Ecosystem Ecology. Eds. L.R. Pomeroy and J.J. Alberts.—Ecological Studies Series. Springer Verlag.—Vol. 67.—384 p. , 1988.

140. Coulson K.L. 1966. Effects of reflection properties of natural surface in aerial reconnaissance. Appl. Opt.—Vol. 5, No. 6.—p. 905–917.

141. Coulson K.L. 1975. Solar and terrestrial radiation (methods and measurements). New York: Acad. Press.—322 p.

142. Coulson K.L., Walraven R.L., Weight G.J., SoohooL. B. 1974. Photocounting polarising radiometer. Appl. Opt.—Vol. 13, No. 3.—p. 497–498.

143. Crutzen P.J. 1986. The role of the tropics in atmospheric chemistry. In: Geophysiology of Amazonia. Ed. by R. Dickinson.—John Wiley & Sons. New York.

144. Crutzen P.J., Graedel T. 1985. The role of atmospheric chemistry in environment-development interactions. In: Sustainable Development of the Biosphere. Eds. W.C. Clark and R.F. Munn. Cambridge Univ. Press.

145. Curran P.J. 1982. Polarized visible light as an aid to vegetation classification. Rem. Sens. Environm.—Vol. 12, No. 6.—p. 491–499.

146. Curran P.J. 1985. Principles of Remote Sensing. Longman Group Ltd. London and New York.—280 p.

147. Curran P.J. 1989. NASA's plans to observe the earth's atmosphere with lidar. IEEE Trans. on Geosci. Remote Sens.—Vol. 27, No. 2.—p. 154–163.

148. Daniulis E.P., Zhirin V.M., Sukhikh V.I., Elman R.I. 1989. Remote sensing in the interests of forestry.—Moscow: Agropromizdat.—223 p. (in Russian).

149. Degens E. T. 1989. Perspectives of Biogeochemistry. Springer Verlag, New York—496 p.

150. Deidvid G. 1979. Ordinal statistics.—Moscow: Nauka Press (in Russian).

151. Delwiche C.C. 1984. Biogeochemical considerations. NASA Techn. Memo. 86129. GSFC, Greenbelt, MD.—Vol. 1 (Pt. 2).—p. 8–10.

152. Denisov S.G., Pokrovski O.M. 1980. Analysis of the information content of the systems of the remote sounding of the geopotential field. Izv. AN SSSR, FAO.—Vol. 16, No. 6.—p. 582–590 (in Russian).

153. Detwiler R.P., Hall C.A.S. 1988. Tropical forests and the global carbon cycle. Science.—Vol. 239.—p. 43–47.

154. Dickinson R. E. 1987. Modelling land-surface processes and hydrology for global climate simulations: a modeller's view of the GEWEX concept. World Clim. Pap. —No. 137, Appendix K.—9 p.

155. Diner D.J., Bruegge C.J., Martonchik J.V. et al. 1989. MISR: a multiangle imaging spectroradiometer for geophysical and climatological research for EOS. IEEE Trans. on Geosci. and Remote Sens.—Vol. 27, No. 2.—p. 200–214.

156. Dutton J.A. 1989. The EOS data and information system: concepts for design. IEEE Trans. on Geosci. and Remote Sens.—Vol. 27, No. 2.—p. 109–116.

157. Dobrovski V.V. 1988. Biogeochemical cycles of heavy metals. Geochemistry.—No. 2.—p. 307–320 (in Russian).

158. Earth observations from space. Science.—Vol. 244, No. 4907.—p. 901–902. 1989.

159. Earth System Science; A Closer View. Report of Earth System Sci. Committee. NASA Advisory Council. NASA, Washington, D.C.—208 p. 1988.

160. Ecologists flirt with chaos. A simple model of chaos. Science.—Vol. 243, No. 4889.—p. 310–312.—1989.

161. Egan W.J. 1968. Aircraft polarimetric and photometric observations. In: Proc. 5th Int. Symp. on Remote Sens. Environm., Michigan.—p. 169–184.

162. Ehrlich P.R., Ehrlich A.H. 1988. Population, plenty, and poverty. National Geogr.—Vol. 174, No. 6.—p. 914–945.

163. Elizarenko A.S., Solomatin V.A., Yakushenkov Yu.G. 1984. Optico-electronic systems in studies of the Earth's resources.—Moscow: Nedra Press (in Russian).

164. Elkington J., Shapley J. 1988. The shrinking planet. U.S. Information Technol. Sustainable Development. World Resources Inst. Pap. —No. 3.—78p.

165. Ellis D. 1989. Environments at Risk. Case Histories of Impact Assessment.–350 p.

166. Enting I.G. 1985. A classification of some inverse problems in geochemical modelling. Tellus.—Vol. D37, No. 4–5.—p. 216–229.

167. Esaias W. E. 1986. Satellite observations of oceanic primary productivity. Climate-Vegetation Interactions. Eds. C. Rosenzweig and R. Dickinson. Rept. OIES-2, UCAR, Boulder, CO.—p. 140–143.

168. Fechner H. 1975. Darstellung der Geopotential winterlichen Nord-halbkugel durch naturliche Orthogonalfunktionen. Ber. Inst. f. Meereskunde.—37 p.

169. Fedorchenko E.I. 1974. On the influence of correlation of meteorological series on the accuracy of sampled moments. Trudy GGO.—Issue 336.—p. 25–47 (in Russian).

170. Final report on studies of the atmosphere-surface system parameters making use of the remote sensing techniques. The 1983–1985 experiment "MKS-M—MKF-6M" at the station "Salut-7". Moscow: Inst. for Space Studies.—242 p. —1987 (in Russian).

171. Fitch B.W. 1981. Effect of reflection by natural surface on the radiation emerging from the top of the Earth's atmosphere. J. Atmos. Sci.—Vol. 38, No. 12.—p. 2717–2729.

172. Flohn H., Fantechi R. (Eds.). 1984. The Climate of Europe: Past, Present and

Future.—D. Reidel Publ., Co., Dordrecht, Holland.—356 p.

173. Fokin A.D. 1986. Soils, biosphere, and life on the Earth.—Moscow: Nauka Press.—177 p. (in Russian).

174. Fortesque D. 1985. The geochemistry of the environment. Moscow: Progress Press.—360 p. (in Russian).

175. Fraser P.J., Rasmussen R.A., Creffield J.W., French J.R., Khalil M.A.K. 1986. Termites and global methane—another assessment. J. Atmos. Chem.—Vol. 4, No. 3.—p. 295–310.

176. Fung I.Y., Tucker C.J., Prentice K.C. 1987. Application of advanced very high resolution radiometer vegetation index to study atmosphere–biosphere exchange of CO2. J. Geophys. Res.—Vol. D92, No. 3.—p. 2999–3015.

177. Gantmacher F.R. 1967. Theory of matrices.—Moscow: Nauka Press.– 408 p. (in Russian).

178. Gates D.M. 1985. Energy and Ecology. Sinsner Assoc., Inc. Sunder land, MA.—377 p.

179. Gates W.L. 1985. The use of general circulation models in the analysis of the ecosystem impacts on climate change. Clim. Change.—Vol. 7, No. 3.—p. 267–284.

180. Geczy B. 1988. The Cretacious/Tertiary boundary and the evolution of the marine invertebrates. Idojaras.—Vol. 92, No. 2–3.—p. 61–68.

181. Geller M.A. 1982. Solar activity-induced stratospheric change and tropospheric climate. Symp. on Solar Constant and Spectral Distribution of Solar Irradiance (Hamburg, 27–28 Aug., 1981). Boulder.—p. 124–132.

182. Geological Implications of Impacts of Large Asteroids and Comets on the Earth. Ed. by L.T. Silver, P.H. Schultz. Special Pap. Geological Soc. Amer. Boulder, CO.—528 p. —1982.

183. Gerasimov I.P. 1985. Ecological problems in the past, present and future geography of the world.—Moscow: Nauka Press.—248 p. (in Russian).

184. Gille J.C. 1984. Middle atmosphere science. NASA Techn. Memo. 86129. GSFC, Greenbelt, MD.—Vol. 1 (Pt. 2).—p. 49–52.

185. Global Environment Change. Recommendations for President-Elect George Bush. Nat. Acad. Sci., Nat. Acad. Engng., Inst. Med. Washington, D. C., Nat. Acad. Press, Washington, D. C.—10 p. —1988.

186. Glushko V.P. 1987. Development of rocket building and space exploration in the USSR.—Moscow: Mashinostrojenie (in Russian).

187. Goetz A.F.H., Herring M. 1989. The high resolution imaging spectrometer (HIRIS) for EOS. IEEE Trans. on Geosci., Remote Sensing.—Vol. 27, No. 2.—p. 136–144.

188. Golitsyn G.S. 1984. The changing atmosphere. Global Change. Proc. Symp. ICSU (Ottawa, Sept. 25, 1984) ICSU Press.—p. 121–134.

189. Gorny V.I., Shilin B.V., Yasinski G.I. 1993. Thermal aerospace survey.—Moscow: Nedra Press.—128 p. (in Russian).

190. Gorshkov V.G., Kondratyev K. Ya. 1988. Conceptual aspects of ecological studies: the role of energy and mass exchange. Bull. USSR Acad. Sci.—No. 10.—p. 62–70 (in Russian).

191. Gorshkov V.G., Kondratyev K.Ya. 1990. The Le-Chatelier principle in the biosphere. Ecology.—No. 1.—p. 7–16 (in Russian).

192. Gorshkov V.G., Kondratyev K.Ya., Losev K.S. 1992. Global ecological perspectives. Bull. Russian Acad. Sci.—No. 5.—p. 70–81 (in Russian).

193. Gorshkov V.G. 1994. Physical and Biological Basis of Life Stability. Man, Biota, Environment. Springer, Heidelberg, 330 p.

194. Goudriaan J., Ketner P. 1984. A simulation study for the global carbon cycle, including man's impact on the biosphere. Clim. Change.—Vol. 6, No. 2.—p. 167–192.

195. Graedel T.E. 1989. Regional and global impacts on the biosphere: a methodology for assessment and prediction. Environment.—Vol. 31, No. 1.—p. 8–13.

196. Graf J.E. 1987. Earth Observing System: the Earth research system of the 1990s. AIAA Pap. —No. 320.—p. 1–13.

197. Grant W.B. (Ed.). 1989. Ozone Measuring Instruments for the Stratosphere. Coll. Works in Optica. Vol. 1. Optical Soc. Amer., Washington, D.C.—X + 438 p.

198. Grigoryev A.A. 1975. Remote sounding of the Earth's landscapes from space.—Leningrad: LGU Press.—156 p. (in Russian).

199. Grigoryev A.A., Kondratyev K.Ya. 1989. The role of space observations in ecological studies: experience and perspectives.—Leningrad: Nauka Press.—36 p. (in Russian).

200. Grishin G.A. 1987. The present state and problems of studies of the ocean from space. Study of the Earth from Space.—No. 6.—p. 94–110 (in Russian).

201. Grove J.M. 1988. The Little Ice Age.—Methuen, London.—498 p.

202. Gubanova S.I., Mashkovich S.A. 1977. On assessment of the infromation content of the system of aerological and satellite measurements. Meteorology and Hydrology.—No. 12.—p. 9–14 (in Russian).

203. Gurney R.J. 1987. Prospects for determining global land surface hydrological parameters from space observations. World Clim. Pap. —No. 137, Appendix L.—9 p.

204. Gvishiani D.M. 1981. Science and global problems of modern life. Problems of Philosophy.—No. 3.—p. 97–108 (in Russian).

205. Halem M., Ghil M., Atras R. 1976. The GISS sounding temperature impact test. NASA Techn. Memo. 78063. GSFC, Greenbelt, MD.—501 p.

206. Hallok H.B., Halajian J. 1983. Polarization imaging and mapping. Appl. Opt.—Vol. 22, No. 7.—p. 964–966.

207. Hamada T. 1987. Prospects of satellite wind sensing systems in the years 1995–2000. Summary. World Clim. Pap. —No. 137. Appendix D.—6 p.

208. Hameed S., Zhang P.-Y., Wang W.-C. 1989. Climate in China after the Tambora eruption in 1815. CIDIAC Commun. Oak Ridge Nat. Lab.—p. 5–8.

209. Hansen A.R., Robinson G.D. 1989. Water vapour and methane in the upper stratosphere: an examination of some of the Nimbus-7 measurements. J. Geophys. Res.—Vol. D94, No. 6.—p. 8474–8484.

210. Hariharan T.A. 1967. A modified skylight polarimeter. J. Sci. Instrum.—Vol. 44, No. 66.—p. 478–479.

211. Hariharan T.A. 1969. An airborne polarimeter for atmospheric radiation studies. J. Sci. Instrum.—(J. Physics E).—Ser. 2.—Vol. 2.—p. 10–12.
212. Hariharan T.A. 1969a. An improved polarimeter for atmospheric radiation studies. Ibid.—p. 1135–1137.
213. Hariharan T.A., Sekera Z. 1966. A photoelectric skylight polarimeter. Appl. Opt.—Vol. 5, No. 9.—p. 1415–1417.
214. Hart M.H. 1978. The evolution of the atmosphere of the Earth. Icarus.—Vol. 33, No. 1.—p. 23–39.
215. Heath D.F., Krueger A.J. 1975. The solar backscatter ultraviolet and total ozone mapping spectrometer (SBUV/TOMS) for Nimbus-G. Optical Engng.— Vol. 14, No. 4.—p. 323–331.
216. Hegg D.A., Radke L.F., Hobbs P.V., Riggan P.J. 1988. Ammonia emissions from biomass burning. Geophys. Res. Lett.—Vol. 15, No. 4.—p. 335–337.
217. Heinecke P., Klosterman H. 1978. Multispectral-Mehrkanal Polarimeter. Dornier-Post.—No. 1.—s. 22–23.
218. Holender M., Wulf D.A. 1983. Non-parametric techniques.—Moscow: Finances and Statistics (in Russian).
219. Hooper N.J., Sherman J.W. III. 1986. Temporal and Spatial analysis of civil marine satellite requirements. NOAA Techn. Rept. NESDIS-16, Washington, D. C.—30 pp.
220. Houghton R.A., Skole SD. L. 1990. Changes in the global carbon cycle between 1700 and 1985. In: The Earth Transformed by Human Action. B.L. Turner (Ed.). Cambridge Univ. Press.
221. Hozin G.S. 1982. Global problems of the present. Critique of bourgeois conceptions.—Moscow: Mysl Press.—280 p. (in Russian).
222. Huneycutt B.L. 1989. Spaceborne imaging radar-C instrument. IEEE Trans. on Geosci. Remote Sens.—Vol. 27, No. 2.—p. 164–169.
223. IAMAP'89. Fifth Scientific Assembly of the International Association of Meteorology and Atmospheric Physics. Brief Review Papers and Abstracts. Univ. of Reading. UK (31 July to 12 Aug. 1989). Vols. 1, 11.
224. Idso S.B. 1989. Carbon Dioxide and Global Change: Earth in Transition. IBR Press. Tempe, Arizona.—292 p.
225. IGBP in Action: Work Plan 1994–1998 (1994a). Global Change Report, No. 28.—151 pp.
226. IGBP Global Modelling and Data Activities 1994–1998 (1994b). Global Change Report, No. 30.—87 pp.
227. IEEE Trans. on Geoscience and Remote Sensing.—1986.—VII. V. GE-24.— No. 4.—p. 443–652.
228. Isachenko A.G. 1987. Geographical aspects of the nature-society interaction and perspectives for integration in geography. Proc. of the All-Union Geogr. Soc.—Vol. 119, No. 1.—p. 3–13 (in Russian).
229. Isidorov V.A. 1985. Organic chemistry of the atmosphere.—Leningrad: Chemistry Press.—265 p. (in Russian).
230. Ismailov T.K. 1980. Development of techniques and means of sub-satellite observations. Study of the Earth from Space.—No. 1.—p. 35–39 (in Russian).

231. Ismailov T.K., Gamidov V.V., Tagijev R.A., Sheikhov R.A. 1982. Problems of the construction of ground-based systems to collect data on the parameters of natural objects. The ground-based mobile information-measurement complex. In: The First All-Union Conference "Biosphere and Climate from the Data of Space Studies". Baku. Elm (in Russian).

232. Ittekkot V., Kempe S., Michaelis W., Spitzy A. (Eds.). 1989. Facets of Modern Biogeochemistry. Festschrift for E. T. Degens.—500 p.

233. Izrael Yu.A. 1984. Ecology and control of the environmental state.—Moscow: Gidrometeoizdat.—560 p. (in Russian).

234. Jackson T.J., Schmugge T.J. 1989. Passive microwave remote sensing system for soil moisture: some supporting research. IEEE Trans. on Geosci. and Remote Sens.—Vol. 27, No. 2.—p. 225–235.

235. Jordan R.L. 1980. The SEASAT—a synthetic aperture radar system. IEEE J. Ocean Engng.—Vol. OE-5.—p. 154–164.

236. Jorgensen S.E. 1988. Fundamentals of ecological modelling. Elsevier, Amsterdam—391 p.

237. Jouzel J., Russell G.L., Suozzo R.J., Koster R.D., White J.W.C., Broecker W.S. 1987. Simulations of the HDO and H218O atmospheric cycles using the NASA GISS general circulation model: the seasonal cycle for present-day conditions. J. Geophys. Res.—Vol. D92, No. 12.—p. 14739–14760.

238. Kadatski B.V. 1986. Climate as a product of the biosphere.—Minsk: Nauka i Tekhnika Press.—112 p. (in Russian).

239. Kadatski B.V. 1988. Biosphere as a system. Bull. Bel. Acad. Sci. p. 32–36 (in Russian).

240. Kagan R.L., Khlebnikova E.I. 1981. On the influence of network density on the variability of interpolated estimates. Meteorology and Hydrology.—No. 5.—p. 39–47 (in Russian).

241. Kalinin G.P., Kurilova Yu.V., Kolosov P.A. 1977. Spaceborne means in the interests of hydrology.—Leningrad: Gidrometeoizdat.—181 p. (in Russian).

242. Kalmykov A.I. et al. (Eds.). 1988. The informative capabilities of the Kosmos-1500 SLR. Special procedures of receiving, processing and interpretation of information.—Moscow: VINITI.—73 p. (in Russian).

243. Kanemasu E.T. 1984. Land biology. NASA Techn. Memo. 86129. GSFC, Greenbelt, MD.—Vol. 1 (Pt. 2).—p. 21–23.

244. Kanevski V.A., Riazantsev V.F., Perekrest O.N. et al. 1985. On possibilities of the laser remote sounding of the state of crops from their luminescence characteristics. Study of the Earth from Space.—No. 6.—p. 37–39 (in Russian).

245. Karl T.R., Tarpley J.D., Quayle R.G., Diaz H.F., Robinson D.A., Bradley R.S. 1989. The recent climate record: what it can and cannot tell us. Revs. Geophys.—Vol. 27.—p. 405–430.

246. Karol I.L., Kudriavtsev A.P. 1990. The seasonal photochemical model of the global troposphere and lower stratosphere. Meteorology and Hydrology.—No. 2.—p. 43–52 (in Russian).

247. Kasting J.F. 1989. Long-term stability of the Earth's climate. Glob. Planet. Change.—Vol. 1, No. 1/2.—p. 83–95.

248. Kazakov A.Ya., Pokrovski O.M. 1980. Assessments of the efficiency of the remote sounding of the geopotential field over the Northern hemisphere. Meteorology and Hydrology.—No. 1.—p. 36–45 (in Russian).249. Kaznachejev V.P., Yanshina F.T. 1986. The theory by V.I. Vernadski on biospheric transformation, and the ecology of man.—Moscow: Znanie Press.—48 p. (in Russian).

250. Khalil M. A.K., Rasmussen R.A. 1988. Carbon monoxide in the Earth's atmosphere: indications of a global increase. Nature.—Vol. 332.—p. 242–245.

251. Khalil M.A.K., Rasmussen R. A. 1988a. Nitrous oxide: trends and global mass balance over the last 3000 years. Annal. Glaciology.—Vol. 10.—p. 73–79.

252. Kiehl J.T., Dickinson R.E. 1987. A study of the radiative effects of enhanced atmospheric CO_2 and CH_4 on early earth surface temperatures. J. Geophys. Res.—Vol. D92, No. 3.—p. 2991–2998.

253. Kienko Yu. P. 1987. The spaceborne system "Resurs-F". Study of the Earth from Space (in Russian).

254. King A.W., DeAngelis D.L., Post W.M. 1987. The seasonal exchange of carbon dioxide between the atmosphere and the terrestrial biosphere: extrapolation from site-specific models to regional models. Oak Ridge Nat. Lab. ORNL/TM-10570. Oak Ridge, Tenn.—281 p.

255. Kirchner J.W. 1989. The GAIA hypothesis: can it be tested?. Revs. Geophys.—Vol. 27, No. 2.—p. 223–235.

256. Kneizys F.X., Shettle E.P., Fenn R.W. 1983. Atmospheric transmittance/radiance: Computer code LOWTRAN-6.—AFGL Rep. ERP No. 846, Ma.—200 p.

257. Knox F., McElroy M.B. 1984. Changes in atmospheric CO_2: influence of the marine biota at high latitude. J. Geophys. Res.—Vol. 89.—p. 4629–4637.

258. Kobak K.I. 1988. Biotic components of the carbon cycle.—Leningrad: Gidrometeoizdat.—248 p. (in Russian).

259. Kohlmaier G.H., Sire E.O., Janecek A., Keeling C.D., Piper S.C., Revelle R. 1989. Modelling the seasonal contribution of a CO_2 fertilisation effect of the terrestrial vegetation to the amplitude increase in atmospheric CO_2 at Mauna Loa Observatory. Tellus.—Vol. 41B.—p. 487–510.

260. Kondratyev K. Ya. 1966. Actinometry.—Leningrad: Gidrometeoizdat.—691 p. (in Russian).

261. Kondratyev K.Ya. 1980a. Perspectives of meteorological observations from the space orbital stations in the USA. Study of the Earth from Space.—No. 3.—p. 111–120 (in Russian).

262. Kondratyev K.Ya. 1980b. Monitoring the climate parameters from satellites. Trudy GGO, issue 488.—p. 75–102 (in Russian).

263. Kondratyev K.Ya. 1980c. The World Climate Programme: Principal aspects and prospects of realisation. Inf. Bull. of the Seminar "Atmosphere–Ocean–Outer Space". Int. Centre NII GKNT, Moscow: issue 1.—p. 26–46 (in Russian).

264. Kondratyev K.Ya. 1982. The World Climate Research Programme: the state, perspectives and the role of observations from space. Progress in Sci. and

Technol., Meteorology and Climatology, Vol. 8. Moscow: VINITI.—274 p. (in Russian).

265. Kondratyev K.Ya. 1985a. The effect of land surface processes on climate change and the International Satellite Land-Surface Climatology Project. Study of the Earth from Space.—No. 6.—p. 106–115 (in Russian).

266. Kondratyev K.Ya. 1985b. Key problems of environmental studies: International Geosphere–Biosphere Programme. Z. Meteorol.—Vol. 35, No. 6.—p. 309–333.

267. Kondratyev K.Ya. 1987a. The International Geosphere–Biosphere Programme: the role of observations from space. Study of the Earth from Space.—No. 4.—p. 104–118 (in Russian).

268. Kondratyev K.Ya. 1987b. Global climate changes and their causes. Gerl. Beitr. z. Geophys.—Vol. 96, No. 1.

269. Kondratyev K.Ya. 1988a. Key aspects of biospheric and ecological studies (on the results of the VII General Assembly SCOPE). Proc. All-Union Geogr. Soc.– Vol. 120, No. 6.—p. 481–489 (in Russian).

270. Kondratyev K.Ya. 1988b. Comparative meteorology of planets. Progress in Sci. and Technol., Astronomy. Vol. 37. Moscow: VINITI.—138 p. (in Russian).

271. Kondratyev K.Ya. 1988c. Energy- and mass-exchange in the biosphere. Bull. USSR Acad. Sci.—No. 11.—p. 27–30.

272. Kondratyev K.Ya. 1988d. Climate shocks: Natural and anthropogenic.– John Wiley & Sons, New York—296 p.

273. Kondratyev K.Ya. 1989a. The International Geosphere–Biosphere Programme (IGBP): the role of observations from space. Ecological Sustainability of Regional Development (Eds. L. Kairukstic, A. Buracas, A. Straszak). IIASA. Polish Acad. Sci., Warszawa.—p. 49–63.

274. Kondratyev K.Ya. 1989b. The International Geosphere–Biosphere Programme: the role and place of sun-atmosphere interrelationships. Geofis. Int.—Vol. 28, No. 2.—p. 453–466.

275. Kondratyev K.Ya. 1990a. Key problems of global ecology and geography. Proc. All-Union Geograph. Soc.—Vol. 122, No. 2.—p. 113–120 (in Russian).

276. Kondratyev K.Ya. 1990b. The International Geosphere–Biosphere Programme (IGBP): the status and perspectives. Proc. All-Union Geogr. Soc.—No. 6.—p. 234–243 (in Russian).

277. Kondratyev K.Ya. 1990c. The International Space Year: priorities and perspectives. Study of the Earth from Space.—No. 1.—p. 3–13 (in Russian).

278. Kondratyev K.Ya. 1990d. Key problems of global ecology. Progress in Sci. and Technol., Ser. "Theoretical and General Problems of Geography". Vol. 9.— Moscow: VINITI.—454 p. (in Russian).

279. Kondratyev K.Ya. 1992. Global Climate.—St.-Petersburg: Nauka Press.—359 p. (in Russian).

280. Kondratyev K.Ya. 1993a. The Second U.N. Conference on Environment and Development: some results and perspectives. Bull. Russian Acad. Sci.—No. 2.—p. 169–173 (in Russian).

281. Kondratyev K.Ya. 1993b. Paradigms of global ecology. I. The Environment. Study of the Earth from Space.—No. 4.—p. 109–122. II. Socio-economic aspects. Ibid.—No. 5.—p. 118–126 (in Russian).

282. Kondratyev K.Ya. 1993c. A system for global climate observations. Study of the Earth from Space.—No. 6.—p. 104–115 (in Russian).

283. Kondratyev K.Ya. 1994. Perspectives of the programme "Mission to Planet Earth" and "Systems of Earth Observations". Study of the Earth from Space.—No. 1.—p. 105–108 (in Russian).

283a. Kondratyev K.Ya. 1995. The present-day stage of research development in the field of global change: the U. S. Programme. Study of the Earth from Space, No. 2.—p. 98–105.

284. Kondratyev K.Ya., Pokrovski O. M. 1977g. Planning the multipurpose experiments on the remote sensing of the environmental parameters. Proc. USSR Acad. Sci., Ser. Geography.—No. 3.—p. 83–89 (in Russian).

285. Kondratyev K.Ya., Buznikov A. A. 1981. Spectrophotometry of the environment from the manned spacecraft and orbital stations: experience and perspectives.—Materials of the Workshop "Space–Ocean–Atmosphere". Ed. by G.I. Marchuk. Moscow: VINITI.—42 p. (in Russian).

286. Kondratyev K.Ya., Fedchenko P.P. 1982. Assessment of crops choking from spectral studies. Study of the Earth from Space.—No. 2.—p. 59–62 (in Russian).

287. Kondratyev K. Ya., Pozdniakov O.M. 1988. Optical properties of natural waters and remote sounding of phytoplankton.—Leningrad: Nauka Press.—181 p. (in Russian).

288. Kondratyev K.Ya., Pokrovski O.M. 1989a. The International Geosphere–Biosphere Programme: key aspects of requirements for observational data. Proc. USSR Acad. Sci., Ser. Geography.—No. q.—p. 20–27 (in Russian).

289. Kondratyev K.Ya., Pokrovski O.M. 1989b. Space Meteorology.—Leningrad: Nauka Press.—47 p. (in Russian).

290. Kondratyev K.Ya., Adamenko V.N., Henderson-Sellers B. et al. 1990. Using large lakes as analogues for oceanographic studies. Modelling Marine Ecosystems. Ed. by A. M. Davies. Vol. 2. CRC Press, Boca Raton, p. 299–344.

291. Kondratyev K.Ya., Moreno-Pena F., Galindo I. 1994. Global Change: Environment and Society. Univ. de Colima Publ., Mexico.—47 pp.

292. Kondratyev K.Ya., Danilov-Danilyan V.I., Donchenko V.K. and Losev K.S. 1993. Ecology and Politics. St. Petersburg, Rus. Acad. Sci. Publ., 286 pp.

293. Kondratyev K.Ya., Grassl H. 1996. Global Climate Dynamics as an Interactive Component of Global Change. Springer, Heidelberg (in press).

294. Kondratyev K.Ya. and Cracknell A.P. 1996. Observing Global Climate Change. Taylor & Francis, London (in press).

295. Kondratyev K.Ya., Grassl H. 1993. Global climate change in the context of global ecology.—St.-Petersburg: PROPO.—195 p. (in Russian).

296. Kondratyev K.Ya., Buznikov A.A., Volkov V.N. et al. 1970. Some results from spectrophotometry of the Earth from Soyuz-7. Doklady AN SSSR.—Vol. 195, No. 5.—p. 1084–1087 (in Russian).

297. Kondratyev K.Ya., Buznikov A.A., Vasilyev O.B. et al. 1971a. Some results from the sub-satellite geophysical experiment. Doklady USSR Acad. Sci.—Vol. 196, No. 6.—p. 1333–1336 (in Russian).

298. Kondratyev K.Ya., Buznikov A.A., Vasilyev O.B. et al. 1971b. Combined studies of natural formations from the spacecraft Soyuz-7 and aircraft laboratories. In: Problems of Atmospheric Physics. Leningrad: LGU Press.—Issue 10.—p. 3–29 (in Russian).

299. Kondratyev K.Ya., Buznikov A.A., Volkov B.H., Gorbatko V.V. 1971c. Spectrophotometry of the Earth from the manned spacecraft. Space Research XI. Akademie-Verlag, Berlin.

300. Kondratyev K.Ya., Buznikov A.A., Nikolajev A.G., Sevastyanov V.I., Smokty O.I. 1971d. Results of visual observations of the nocturnal, twilight and daytime horizons of the Earth as observed from Soyuz-9. Doklady AN SSSR.—Vol. 197, No. 3 (in Russian).

301. Kondratyev K.Ya., Buznikov A.A., Vasilyev O.B. et al. 1972a. Some results from spectrophotometry of natural formations from the manned spacecraft Soyuz-9. Space Exploration.—Vol. 10, No. 2.—p. 245–254 (in Russian).

302. Kondratyev K.Ya., Buznikov A.A., Pozdniakov D.V. 1972b. The optical remote sounding of water basins pollution and phytoplankton. Water Resources.—No. 3.—p. 65–75 (in Russian).

303. Kondratyev K.Ya., Vasilyev O.B., Mironova Z.F. 1972c. On the coding technique for the optical reflection spectra of natural formations. In: Problems of Atmospheric Physics. Leningrad: LGU Press.—Issue 10.—p. 29–63 (in Russian).

304. Kondratyev K.Ya., Buznikov A.A., Vasilyev O.B. et al. 1972d. Experience in the interpretation of the natural formations spectra from manned spacecraft Soyuz-7 and Soyuz-9. Proc. VII Int. Symp. on Remote Sensing of Environment, 17–21 May 1971. Vol. III. Ann Arbor, Michigan.

305. Kondratyev K.Ya., Buznikov A.A., Vasilyev O.B., Grishechkin V.S. 1974a. Vertical profiles of the parameters of the atmospheric transfer operator. In: Problems of Atmospheric Physics.—No. 12.—p. 11–23 (in Russian).

306. Kondratyev K.Ya., Buznikov A.A., Vasilyev O.B., Sevastyanov V.I. 1974b. Results of spectrophotometric measurements of natural formations from the spacecraft Soyuz-9 and investigation of environment from space. Remote Sens. Environm.—No. 3.—p. 15–27.

307. Kondratyev K.Ya., Buznikov A.A., Kozlov V.N., Pokrovski A.G. 1974c. On the information support to measurements of stratospheric and mesospheric humidity. Izv. AN SSSR, FAO.—Vol. 10, No. 10.—p. 1040–1054 (in Russian).

308. Kondratyev K.Ya., Buznikov A.A., Smokty O.I. 1974d. Influence of the atmosphere on spectral radiance and contrasts of natural formations measured from space. Proc. UCLA Int. Conf. on Radiation and Remote Probing of Atmosphere. August 28–30, 1973. University of California, USA.

309. Kondratyev K.Ya., Buznikov A.A., Vasilyev O.B., Smoktiy O.I. 1975a. The effect of the atmosphere on spectral brightnesses and contrasts of natural formations in spectrophotometry of the Earth from space. Proc. USSR Acad. Sci., FAO.—Vol. 11, No. 4.—p. 348–361 (in Russian).

310. Kondratyev K.Ya., Grigoryev A.A., Pokrovski O.M. 1975b. The information content of the data of the remote sensing of the environmental parameters and Earth's resources from space.—Leningrad: LGU Press.—146 p. (in Russian).

311. Kondratyev K.Ya., Buznikov A.A., Grechko G.M., Gubarev A.A., Pokrovski A.G. 1976a. Measurement of the atmospheric water vapour mixing ratio in the stratosphere and the mesosphere using spectral instruments carried by Salut-4. Doklady AN USSR.—Vol. 226, No. 3.—p. 563–565 (in Russian).

312. Kondratyev K.Ya., Buznikov A.A., Orlov V.M. 1976b. Spectra of the Earth's twilight horizon as observed from Soyuz-5. Doklady AN SSSR.—Vol. 226, No. 6.—p. 1315–1318 (in Russian).

313. Kondratyev K.Ya., Buznikov A.A., Vasilyev O.B., Smoktiy O.I. 1977a. Effect of the atmosphere on the albedo during the aerospace survey of the Earth in the visible. Proc. USSR Acad. Sci., FAO.—Vol. 13, No. 5.—p. 471–487 (in Russian).

314. Kondratyev K.Ya., Marchuk G.I., Buznikov A.A. et al. 1977b. The emission field of a spherical atmosphere.—Leningrad: LGU Press.—215 p. (in Russian).

315. Kondratyev K.Ya., Buznikov A.A., Pokrovski A.G. 1977c. Remote sounding of the upper atmosphere layers on slant paths. Proc. X Int. Symp. on Remote Sensing of Environment.

316. Kondratyev K.Ya., Buznikov A.A., Pokrovski A.G. 1977d. Investigations of the vertical distribution of water vapour be the technique of occultation sounding of the atmosphere in the 2.7-μm H2O band. Proc. X Int. Symp. on Remote Sensing of Environment.

317. Kondratyev K.Ya., Buznikov A.A., Pokrovski O.M. 1977e. Determination of the vertical profile of aerosol in the atmosphere from results of spectro-photometry of the Earth's twilight horizon from the spacecraft Soyuz-13. Doklady AN SSSR.—Vol. 235, No. 1.—p. 53 (in Russian).

318. Kondratyev K.Ya., Buznikov A.A., Orlov V.M. 1977f. Spectral study of the brightness field near the Earth's twilight horizon from the manned spacecraft. In: Space methods to study the environment. The USSR Geogr. Soc., Leningrad.—p. 42–57 (in Russian).

319. Kondratyev K.Ya., Buznikov A.A., Pokrovski O.M. 1978. Determination of trace gases in the stratosphere making use of occulation sounding. Izv. AN SSSR, FAO.—Vol. 14, No. 12.—p. 1235–1248 (in Russian).

320. Kondratyev K.Ya., Baibakov S.N., Nikolski G.A. 1985a. Nuclear war, atmosphere, and climate. Science in the USSR.—No. 2 (P. 3–13), No. 3 (P. 3–11, 97–101) (in Russian).

321. Kondratyev K Ya., Smokty O.I., Kozoderov V.V. 1985b. Effect of the atmosphere on studies of the Earth's resources from space. Moscow: Mashinostrojenie.—272 p. (in Russian).

322. Kondratyev K.Ya., Buznikov A.A. et al. 1986a. An experience of the complex remote monitoring of lakes. In: The Int. Workshop of the socialist countries' Working Group on remote sounding of the Earth "Technique and Technology of Remote Sounding". Tallinn: Est. Acad. Sci. (in Russian).

323. Kondratyev K.Ya., Kozoderov V.V., Fedchenko P.P. 1986b. Aerospace

studies of soils and vegetation.—Leningrad: Gidrometeoizdat.—231 p. (in Russian).

324. Kondratyev K.Ya., Melentyev V.V., Nazarkin V.A. 1989. The retrieval of the water surface temperatures from the data of microwave remote sounding. Study of the Earth from Space.—No. 5.—p. 14–19 (in Russian).

325. Kondratyev K.Ya., Efremov G.A., Buznikov A.A. et al. 1990. Experimental processing of high-resolution SAR images. Doklady USSR Acad. Sci.—Vol. 317, No. 1.—p. 70–77 (in Russian).

326. Kondratyev K.Ya., Kozoderov V.V., Smokty O.I. 1992a. Earth's Resources Studies: Atmospheric Correction. Springer, Berlin—478 p.

327. Kondratyev K.Ya., Buznikov A.A., Pokrovski O.M. 1992b. Global ecology: remote sounding. Progress in Sci. and Technol.—Vol. XIV. Moscow: VINITI.—307 p. (in Russian).

328. Kondratyev K.Ya., Danilov-Danilyan V.I., Donchenko V.K., Losev K.S. 1994. Ecology and Policy.—St.-Petersburg, Russian Acad. Sci.—286 p. (in Russian).

329. Korbut A.A., Finkelstein Yu. Yu. 1969. Discrete programming. Moscow: Nauka Press.—368 p. (in Russian).

330. "Kosmos-1870" of the series "Almaz". A space vehicle for all-weather radar sounding of the Earth's surface and the World Ocean.—Moscow: Mashinostrojenie, No. 4/1961950.—P90.—1990.—28 p. (in Russian).

331. Kostitsyn V.A. 1984. The evolution of the atmosphere, biosphere, and climate. Moscow: Nauka Press.—96 p. (in Russian).

332. Kotliakov V.M. 1988. The International Geosphere–Biosphere Programme: "Global Change". Bull. USSR Acad. Sci.—No. 1.—p. 92–102 (in Russian).

333. Kotliakov V.M., Mather J.R., Sdasyuk G.V., White G.F. 1988. Global change: geographical approaches (a review). Proc. Nat. Acad. Sci. USA.—Vol. 85.—p. 5986–5991.

334. Kozlov N.P., Sagdejev R.Z., Sheremetyevski N.N. 1981. A complex experiment on the satellite "Meteor"—an important step in the development of operational studies of the Earth from space. Study of the Earth from Space.— No. 6.—p. 5–7 (in Russian).

335. Krinov E.L. 1947. Spectral reflectivity of natural formations.—Moscow, Leningrad: USSR Acad. Sci.—271 p. (in Russian).

336. Kronberg P. 1988. Remote sensing of the Earth.—Moscow: Mir Press.– 349 p. (in Russian).

337. Ksanfomaliti L. V., Moroz V. I., Dolfus A. 1975. A polarimetric experiment on "Mars-5". Space Exploration.—Vol. 13, No. 1.—p. 92–98 (in Russian).

338. Kulbak S. 1967. Information theory and statistics.—Moscow: Nauka Press.– 408 p. (in Russian).

339. Kump L.R. 1989. Chemical stability of the atmosphere and ocean. Glob. Planet. Change.—Vol. 1, No. 1–2.—p. 123–136.

340. Kurbatkin G.P., Siniajev V.N., Yantsen A.G. 1974. Analysis of the forecasts using a spectral model with mean-climatic limitations. Proc. USSR Acad. Sci., FAO.—Vol. 10, No. 1.—p. 3–31 (in Russian).

341. Lakhtanov G.A., Piotrovskaya A.P. 1983. A study of the polarization of radiation reflected from some types of vegetation cover. In: Remote sounding of the environment making use of the optical and radiophysical techniques.— Leningrad: LGU Press.—p. 84–90 (in Russian).

342. Lakhtanov G.A., Churov V.E. 1988. On polarization of radiation from water surface. Bull. LGU, Ser. &, issue 3.—p. 112–117 (in Russian).

343. Landner L. (Ed.). 1989. Chemicals in the Aquatic Environment. Advanced Hazard Assessment. Springer Series on Environmental Management.—350 p.

344. Lashof D.A. 1989. The dynamic greenhouse: feedback processes that may influence future concentrations of atmospheric trace gases and climatic change. Clim. Change.—Vol. 14, No. 3.—p. 213–242.

345. Lavrov S.B., Sdasiuk G.V. 1985. This world of contrasts: the geographic aspects of some global problems.—Moscow: Mysl' Press.—207 p. (in Russian).

346. Lavrova N.P. 1983. Photography from space.—Moscow: Nedra Press.– 288 p. (in Russian).

347. Lavrova N.P., Stetsenko A.F. 1981. Aerial photography. The instrumentation.—Moscow: Nedra Press.—295 p. (in Russian).

348. Leovy C. B. 1984. Tropospheric Science. NASA Techn. Memo. 86129. GSFC, Greenbelt, MD.—Vol. 1 (Pt. 2).—p. 44–48.

349. Le Vine D.M., Wilheit T.T., Murphy R.E., Swift C.T. 1989. A multi-frequency microwave radiometer of the future. IEEE Trans. on Geosci. and Remote Sens.—Vol. 27, No. 2.—p. 193–199.

350. Lieth H., Whittaker R.H. (Eds.). 1976. Primary productivity of the biosphere. Studies. Springer-Verlag. New York—Vol. 14.—339 p.

351. Lieth H., Fantechi R., Schnitzler H. (Eds.). 1984. Interaction between climate and biosphere. Progress in Biometeorology.—Vol. 3. Swets and Zeitlinger B. V., Lisse.—392 p.

352. Likens G.E. 1989. Long-term studies in ecology: approaches and alternatives. Springer, New York—214 p.

353. Lindzen R.S. 1986. A simple model for 100 K—year oscillations in glaciation. J. Atmos. Sci.—Vol. 43, No. 10.—p. 986–996.

354. Link L.E. 1984. Compatibility of present hydrologic models with remotely sensed data. Proc. 17th Int. Symp. Remote Sens. Environm. Ann Arbor, MI.— Vol. 1.—p. 133–153.

355. Lorenz E.N. 1960. Maximum simplification of dynamic equations. Tellus.– Vol. 12.—p. 243–254.

356. Losev K.S., Gorshkov V.G., Kondratyev K.Ya. et al. 1993. Ecology of Russia.—Moscow: VINITI.—348 p. (in Russian).

357. Lovelock J.E. 1975. Thermodynamics and the recognition of alien biospheres. Proc. Roy. Soc. London.—B.—Vol. 189.—p. 167–181.

358. Lovelock J.E. 1986. Geophysiology: a new look at Earth science. Bull. Amer. Meteorol. Soc.—Vol. 67, No. 4.—p. 392–397.

359. Lovelock J.E. 1989. Geophysiology the science of Gaia. Revs. Geophys.—Vol. 27, No. 2.—p. 215–222.

360. Lukashev K.I. 1984. Man and Nature.—Minsk: Nauka i Tekhnika Press.– 295

p. (in Russian).

361. Malingreau J.-P., Tucker C.J. 1988. Large-scale deforestation in the south-eastern Amazon basin of Brazil. Ambio.—Vol. 17, No. 1.—p. 49–55.
362. Malone T.F. 1986. Mission to planet Earth. Integrating studies of global change. Environment.—Vol. 28, No. 8.—p. 6–11; 39–42.
363. Marchuk G.I. 1964. An equation to assess the value of information from the meteorological satellites and setting the inverse problems. Space Exploration.—Vol. 2, No. 3.—p. 462–477 (in Russian).
364. Marchuk G.I., Mikhailov G.A., Nazaralijev Sh.A., Darvinian R.A. 1968. Solution of direct and some inverse problems of atmospheric optics using the Monte-Carlo technique.—Novosibirsk: Nauka Press.—283 p. (in Russian).
365. Marchuk G.I. 1974. Basic and conjugate equations of the atmosphere and ocean dynamics.—Novosibirsk: USSR Acad. Sci. Computing Center, Siberian Branch.—p. 3–31 (in Russian).
366. Marchuk G.I. 1979. Modelling the climate change and the problem of long-range weather forecast. Meteorology and Hydrology.—No. 7.—p. 25–36 (in Russian).
367. Marchuk G.I., Kondratyev K.Ya., Kozoderov V.V. 1988. Earth Radiation Budget: key aspects.—Moscow: Nauka Press.—224 p. (in Russian).
368. Marchuk G.I. and Kondratyev K.Ya. 1992. Priorities of Global Ecology. Moscow: Nauka Press, 264 pp.
369. Marland C. 1988. The prospect of solving the CO2 problem through global reforestation. U.S. Dept. of Energy, Carbon Dioxide Res. Div. TRO39. Washington, D.C.—66 p.
370. Marshall H.G., Walker J.C.G., Kuhn W.R. 1988. Long-term climate change and the geochemical cycle of carbon. J. Geophys. Res.—Vol. D93, No. 1.—p. 791–802.
371. Mashkovich S.A. 1981. Spectral techniques to solve non-linear prognostic problems. Trudy GMTs.—Issue 224.—p. 3–30 (in Russian).
372. Mass C.F., Portman D.A. 1989. Major volcanic eruptions and climate: a critical evaluation. J. Climate.—Vol. 2.—p. 566–593.
373. Mathematic models of ecosystems. The ecological and demographic consequences of a nuclear war. 1986. Ed. by A. A. Dorodnitsyn. Moscow: Nauka Press.—76 p. (in Russian).
374. Mathematic theory of planning an experiment. 1983. Moscow: Nauka Press.–391 p. (in Russian).
375. Matson P.S., Harriss R.C. 1988. Prospects for aircraft-based gas exchange measurements in ecosystem studies. Ecology.—Vol. 69.—p. 1318–1325.
376. Matthews E., Fung I. 1987. Methane emission from natural wetlands: global distribution, area, and environmental characteristics of sources. Global Biogeochem. Cycles.—Vol. 1.—p. 61-86.
377. McCarthy J.J. 1986. Marine ecosystem aspects of the carbon cycle. Clim. Veg. Interact. Proc. Workshop. Greenbelt, MD, 27–29 Jan. 1986. Boulder, CO.– p. 117–119.
378. McElroy M.B., Wofsy S.C., Yung Y.L. 1977. The nitrogen cycle: perturbations

due to man and their impact on atmospheric N2O and O3. Phil Trans. Roy. Soc. London B. Biological Sciences.—Vol. 277, No. 954.—p. 159–181.

379. McElroy M.B. 1983. Atmospheric composition: influence of biology. Planet. Space Sci.—Vol. 31, No. 9.—p. 1065–1074.

380. McElroy J.H., Schneider S. R. 1985a. Earth observations and the polar platform. NOAA Techn. Rept. NESDIS-18. Washington, D. C.—16 p.

381. McElroy J.H., Schneider S.R. 1985b. The space station polar platform: integrating research and operational missions. NOAA Techn. Rept. NESIDIS-19. Washington, D.C.—19 p.

382. McElroy M.B. 1985. Change in the natural environment of the Earth: the historical record. In: W.C. Clark and R.E. Munn (Eds.). Sustainable Development of the Biosphere. Cambridge Univ. Press.

383. Meehl G.A. 1990. Seasonal cycle forcing of El Nino—Southern Oscillation in a global coupled ocean–atmosphere GCM. J. Clim. Vol. 3.—p. 72–98.

384. Megreditchian G. 1985. Methodes statistique d'analyse et d'interpolation des champs meteorologiques.—WMO, Geneve.—300 p.

385. Melack J.M. 1984. Inland aquatic resources and biogeochemical cycles. NASA Techn. Memo. 86129. GSFC, Greenbelt, MD.—Vol. 1 (Pt. 2).—p. 15–17.

386. Mel'nik Yu. A., Zubkovich S.G., Stepanenko V.D. et al. 1980. Radar techniques to study the Earth (Ed. by Yu. A. Mel'nik). Moscow: Sov. Radio Press.—264 p. (in Russian).

387. Melua A.I. 1988. Nature-protective investigations from space. Leningrad: Nauka Press.—176 p. (in Russian).388.
Meszaros E. 1988. On the possible role of the biosphere in the control of atmospheric aerosols: biospheric effects on the climate and water cycle. Idojaras.—Vol. 92, No. 1.—p. 11–16.

389. Meszaros E. 1983. Atmospheric Chemistry. Fundamental Aspects.—Akademiai Kiado, Budapest.—201 p.

390. Mintz Y., Sellers P.J., Willmot C.J. 1983. On the design of an interactive biosphere for the GLAS general circulation model. NASA Techn. Memo. 84973. GSFC, Greenbelt, MD.—57 p.

391. Mirzojeva L.A., Kameshkov G.B., Lustberg E.A., Makovtsov G.A., Zakharenkov V.F. 1992. Spaceborne optico-electronic instruments to detect the forest fire centers. Optical Journal.—No. 8.—p. 17–23 (in Russian).

392. Mishev D.N. 1980. Spectral reflective characteristics of natural formations and their use in the remote sounding of the Earth. Study of the Earth from Space.-No. 1.—p. 16–21 (in Russian).

393. Mishev D.N. 1985. Remote Sounding of the Earth from Space.—Moscow: Mir Press.—229 p. (in Russian).

394. Mitchell J.F.B. 1989. The greenhouse effect and climate change. Revs. Geophys.—Vol. 27.—p. 115–139.

395. Models and techniques to assess the anthropogenic changes in the geosphere.-Novosibirsk: Nauka Press.—1986.—149 p. (in Russian).

396. Mohnen V. 1984. Tropospheric chemistry. NASA Techn. Memo. 86129. GSFC, Greenbelt, MD.—Vol. 1 (Pt. 2).—p. 24–27.

397. Moisejev N.N., Alexandrov V.V., Tarko A.M. 1985. Man and the biosphere. An experience in a system analysis and experiments with the models.- Moscow: Nauka Press.—272 p. (in Russian).

398. Molnar Gy., Nika J. 1982. Combined physical-statistical estimate of global changes due to solar constant variations based on model results. Symp. Solar Constant and Spectral Distribution of Solar Irradiance (Hamburg, 17–18 Aug. 1981). Boulder, CO.—p. 146–154.

399. Monin A.S., Shishkov Yu.A. 1979. History of climate. Leningrad: Gidrometeoizdat.—407 p. (in Russian).

400. Moore B., III. 1984. Global biogeochemistry: an overview. NASA Techn. Memo. 86129. GSFC, Greenbelt, MD.—Vol. 1 (Pt. 2).—p. 5–7.

401. Moore B. III, 1994. The EOS payload panel. The Earth Observer.—Vol. 6, No. 4.—p. 4–15.

402. Moore B., III, Braswell B.H., Jr. 1994. Planetary metabolism: understanding the carbon cycle. Ambio.—Vol. XXIII, No. 1.—p. 4–12.

403. Morone J.G., Woodhouse E.J. 1986. Averting Catastrophe: Strategies for Regulating Risky Technologies. Univ. of Calif. Press. Berkeley.—215 p.

404. Munn R.E. 1986. Environmental prospects for the 21st century: implications for long-term policy and research strategies. Preprint. Int. Inst. for Appl. Syst. Analysis, Laxenburg.—29 p.

405. Munn R.E. 1987. Environmental prospects for the next century: implications for long-term policy and research strategy. IIASA RR-87-15. Laxenburg, Austria.– 20 p.

406. Munn R.E. 1988. Towards sustainable development: an environmental perspective. Preprint for Int. Conf. on Environment and Development. Milano, Italy. 24–26 March 1988.—22 p. 407.
Nature of the models and the models of nature. (Ed. by D.M. Gvishiani, I.B. Novik, S.A. Platov). Moscow: Mysl Press.—272 p. 1986. (in Russian).

408. Newell R.E. 1974. The Earth's climatic history. Technol. Rev.—Vol. 77, No. 2.—p. 2–17.

409. Newell R.E., Reichle H.G., Seiler W. 1989. Carbon monoxide and the burning Earth. Sci. American.—p. 82–88 (October 1989).

410. Obukhov A.M. 1960. On the statistically orthogonal expansions of empirical functions. Izv. AN SSSR. Ser. Geophysics.—No. 3.—p. 432–439 (in Russian).

411. Oleinikov Yu.V. 1987. Ecological alternatives to the scientific-technical revolution.—Moscow: Nauka Press. –161 p. (in Russian).

412. On ecological safety: strategy of the long-range survival. The XVIII Congress of the Socialist International, Stockholm, 20–22 July 1989.—The Working Class and the Present World. 1989, No. 6; 1990, No. 1.—p. 111–122 (in Russian).

413. Pellicori S.F., Gray P.R. 1967. An automatic polarimeter for space applications. Appl. Opt.—Vol. 6, No. 6.—p. 1121–1127.

414. Peltier W.R., Tushingham A.M. 1989. Global sea level rise and the greenhouse effect: might they be connected?. Science.—Vol. 244.—p. 806–810.

415. Penenko V.V. 1981. Techniques of the numerical modelling of atmospheric

processes.—Leningrad: Gidrometeoizdat.—352 p. (in Russian).

416. Perlov V.V., Krasnikov D.N., Sergejev V.P. 1981. Thermal scanner to study the Earth's resources. Optico-Mechanical Industry.—No. 4.—p. 27–29 (in Russian).

417. Permanently operating manned orbital complex of the module type "Mir". User's Manual. 1990.—Moscow.—43 p. (in Russian).

418. Petropavlovskaya M.S. 1988. Remote sounding of the cryolite zone.- Leningrad: Gidrometeoizdat.—72 p. (in Russian).

419. Petrosian L.A., Zakharov V.V. 1986. Introduction to mathematical ecology.— Leningrad: LGU Press.—222 p. (in Russian).

420. Platt C.M.R. 1987. Global measurement of winds by Doppler lidar. World Clim. Pap. —No. 137, Appendix E.—6 p.

421. Pliuta V.E., Beliajev B.I., Zabirko S.P. et al. 1984. The spaceborne spectro-metric system SKIF-A. In: Optical instruments. Preprint No. 333. Inst. of Physics, Bel. Acad. Sci., Minsk.—p. 3–5 (in Russian).

422. Pollack J.B. 1979. Climatic change on the terrestrial planets. Icarus.- Vol. 37, No. 3.—p. 479–553.

423. Pokrovski O.M. 1972. On the optimal conditions of indirect sounding of the atmosphere. Izv. AN SSSR, FAO.—Vol. 8, No. 10.—p. 1094–1097 (in Russian).

424. Pokrovski O.M. 1981. Problems of optimising the systems of remote sensing of the parameters of the atmosphere, ocean and the environmental objects. Preprint No. 12. Moscow: VINITI.—28 p. (Materials of the Seminar "Atmosphere–Ocean–Space") (in Russian).

425. Pokrovski O.M. 1982. On the information value functions appearing in planning the global observation systems. In: Urgent problems of applied mathematics and mathematic modellling.—Novosibirsk: Nauka Press.—p. 60–69 (in Russian).

426. Pokrovski O.M. 1984. An optimisation of the meteorological sounding of the atmosphere from satellites.—Leningrad: Gidrometeoizdat (in Russian).

427. Pokrovski O.M. 1986. Methods of the theory of conjugate equations to design the systems of conventional and satellite observations. Study of the Earth from Space.—No. 3.—p. 107–116 (in Russian).

428. Pokrovski O.M. 1987. On the rationalisation of the system of selecting the NH climate information about the geopotential field. Trudy GGO.—Issue 507.- p. 161–176 (in Russian).

429. Pokrovski O.M. 1988. Optimal planning of the space-borne remote sounding systems. Trudy GGO.—Issue 518.—p. 28–35 (in Russian).

430. Pokrovski O.M. 1989a. On an application of the Shannon measure to the quantitative estimation of the information content of the hydro-meteorological observation systems. Trudy GGO.—Issue 528.—p. 19–32 (in Russian).

431. Pokrovski O.M. 1989b. Analysis of the efficiency of the techniques of optimisation of the ground-based observation systems. Trudy GGO.—Issue 528.—p. 82–88 (in Russian).

432. Pokrovski O.M., Bykov S.Y. 1975. A choice of optimal spectral intervals to

measure reflected solar radiation in the interval 0.4–0.85 μm to identify the natural formations. Meteorology and Hydrology.—No. 12.—p. 34 (in Russian).

433. Pokrovski O.M., Denisov S.G. 1980. On a possibility of the remote sensing of relative altitudes of basic isobaric surfaces. Meteorology and Hydrology.—No. 5.—p. 15–21 (in Russian).

434. Pokrovski O.M., Beliavski A.I. 1983a. On the technique of operational correction of an optical atmospheric model when solving the problems of thermal sounding. Izv. AN SSSR, FAO.—Vol. 19, No. 6.—p. 613–621 (in Russian).

435. Pokrovski O.M., Beliavski A.I. 1983b. On a 4-D assimilation of asynoptical information based on the non-linear filtering scheme. Meteorology and Hydrology.—No. 8.—p. 44–54 (in Russian).

436. Pokrovski O.M., Denisov S.G. 1985. The information content of the oceanic network for an objective analysis of the NH geopotential field. Meteorology and Hydrology.—No. 10.—p. 37–43 (in Russian).

437. Pokrovski O.M., Malygina A.K. 1986. On a rationalization of the scheme of collection of the NH ozone remote sounding data. Study of the Earth from Space.—No. 1.—p. 10–16 (in Russian).

438. Pokrovski O.M., Beliavski A.I., Denisov S.G. 1985. A comparative analysis of the information content of the systems of the aerological and remote sounding of the atmosphere. Study of the Earth from Space.—No. 5.—p. 106–116 (in Russian).

439. Prather M. 1988. European sources of halocarbons and nitrous oxide: update 1986. J. Atmos. Chem.—Vol. 6, No. 4.—p. 375–406.

440. Price J.C. 1987. Calibration of satellite radiometers and the comparison of vegetation indices. Remote Sens. Environm.—Vol. 21.—p. 15–27.

441. Principal scientific directions and subjects of the "Programme of biospheric and ecological studies of the USSR Academy of Sci. for the period to the year 2015".– Moscow: USSR Acad. Sci., Commission on Ecological Problems.—74 p. , 1989 (in Russian).

442. Programme of biospheric and ecological studies of the USSR Academy of Sciences. Bull. USSR Acad. Sci., 1988, No. 11.—p. 1–160 (in Russian).

443. Prosch T., Hennings D., Raschke E. 1983. Video polarimetry: a new imaging technique in atmospheric science. Appl. Opt.—Vol. 22, No. 9.—p. 1360–1363.

444. Pszenny A.A.P., Castelle A.J., Galloway J.N., Duce R.A. 1989. A study of the sulphur cycle in the Antarctic marine boundary layer. J. Geophys. Res.—Vol. D94, No. 7.—p. 9818–9830.

445. Pyke T.N., Jr. 1989. U.S. perspectives on data management for global change. Preprint. 40th IAF Congress, Beijing.—34 p.

446. Radar sounding of the Earth from space. 1990. Ed. by L.M. Mitnik and S.V. Viktorov. Leningrad: Gidrometeroizdat.—200 p. (in Russian).

447. Rampino M.R., Volk T. 1988. Mass extinctions, atmospheric sulphur and climatic warming at the K/T boundary. Nature.—Vol. 332.—p. 63–65.

448. Rampino M.R., Sanders J.E., Newman W.S., Konigsson L.K. 1987. Climate:

History, Periodicity, and Predictability.—Van Nostrand Reinhold. New York.—588 p.

449. Rango A. 1984. Global Hydrological Cycle. NASA Techn. Memo. 86129. GSFC, Greenbelt, MD.—Vol. 1 (Pt. 2).—p. 1–4.

450. Rao S.P. 1968. Linear statistical tehniques and their application.—Moscow: Nauka Press.—517 p. (in Russian).

451. Paper J. (Ed.). 1989. 3-Dimensional G. I. S.. Taylor & Francis, Ltd.—260 p.

452. Rasool S.I. 1984. On monitoring global change by satellites. Global Change. Proc. Symp. of ICSU (Ottawa, Sept. 25, 1984). ICSU Press.—p. 269–282.

453. Rasool S.I. (Ed.). 1987. Potential of remote sensing for the study of global change. Adv. Space Res.—Vol. 7, No. 1.—p. 97.

454. Raup D.M. 1986. Biological extinction in Earth history. Science.—Vol. 231, No. 4745.—p. 1528–1533.

455. Raven P.H. 1987. The Global Ecosystem in Crisis. A MacArthur Foundation Occasional Paper. Chicago, IL.—24 p.

456. Raven P.H. 1988. State of the world: 2000—what we should do to affect it. Preprint. Wingspread Conf.—April 15, 1988. Missouri Botanical Garden.– 29 p.

457. Report of the ISY Mission to Planet Earth Conf. (Durham, New Hampshire, April 29—May 1, 1988). US-ISY Association.—38 p.

458. Report of Science Steering Group for a Tropical Rainfall Measuring Missions (TRMM). 1988. Ed. by J. Simpson. GSFC, Greenbelt, MD.—94 p.

459. Report from the START Regional Meeting for Southeast Asia. 1992. Global Change Report, Stockholm, No. 22, 114 pp.

459a. Report of the Fifteenth Session of the Joint Scientific Committee. Geneva, Switzerland, 14–18 March 1994. WMO/TD. No. 632.—September 1994.—86 pp. (Appendix B)

459b. Report of the Fourth Session of the Joint Scientific and Technical Committee for GCOS (Hamburg, Germany, Septemeber 19–22, 1994). GCOS-4 (WMO/TD. No. 637), WMO, Geneva, 1994.—26 pp. , Appendices.

459c. Report of the GCOS Atmospheric Observation Panel. First session (Hamburg, Germany, April 25–28, 1994). GCOS-6 (WMO/TD. No. 640), WMO, Geneva.– 16 pp. , Appendices.

459d. Report of the GCOS Space-Based Observation Task Group (Darmstadt, Germany, May 3–6, 1994). GCOS-7 (WMO/TD. No. 641), WMO, Geneva, 1994.—10 pp. , Appendices.

459e. Report of the GCOS/GTOS Terrestrial Observation Panel. First Session (Arlington, VA, USA, June 28–30, 1994). GCOS-8 (WMO/TD. No. 642), WMO, Geneva.—21 pp. , Appendices.

460. Research needs in heterogeneous tropospheric chemistry. Proc. Workshop (Sarasoto, FL, Jan. 9–13, 1984). NASA Conf. Publ. 2320. Washington, D.C.— 73 p.

461. Research Strategies for the US Global Change Research Program. 1990. Natl. Res. Council, Washington, D.C., 291 pp.

462. Research and production association "Planeta". Data products.—Moscow: Gidrometeoizdat.—1993.—36 p. (in Russian).

463. Revelle R. 1984. Soil dynamics and sustainable carrying capacity of the earth. Global Change. Proc. Symp. of ICSU (Ottawa, Sept. 25, 1984). ICSU Press.– p. 341–350.

464. Rhind D., Mounsey H. (Eds.). 1989. Understanding G.I.S. (Geographic Infromation System). Taylor & Francis, Ltd.—240 p.

465. Riadchenko V.A. 1990. A parameterisation of the sources and sinks of biogens in the ocean. Meteorology and Hydrology.—No. 2.—p. 78–87 (in Russian).

466. Rinne J. 1971. Investigation of the forecasting error of a simple barotropic model with the aid of the empirical orthogonal functions. Geophysics. Helsinki.—Vol. 11, No. 2.—p. 11–32.

467. Robin G. de Q. 1984. Polar glaciology. NASA Techn. Memo. 86129. GSFC, Greenbelt, MD.—Vol. 1 (Pt. 2).—p. 37–40.

468. Robinson J.M. 1989. On uncertainty in the computation of global emissions from biomass burning. Clim. Change.—Vol. 14, No. 3.—p. 243–262.

469. Rock B.N., Vogelmann J.E., Williams D.L., Vogelmann A.F., Hoshizaki T. 1986. Remote detection of forest damage. Bioscience.—July/August.– p. 439–445.

470. Roederer J.G. 1984. The proposed international geosphere-biosphere programme: some special requirements for disciplinary coverage and programme design. Global Change: Proc. Symp. of ICSU (Ottawa, Sept. 25, 1984). ICSU Press.—p. 1–20.

471. Rossow W.B., Brest Ch.L., Garder L.C. 1989. Global, seasonal surface variations from satellite radiance measurements. J. Climate.—Vol. 2, No. 2.– p. 214–247.

472. Rovinski F.Ya. 1986. The complex global monitoring of the state of the biosphere. Meteorology and Hydrology.—No. 6.—p. 108–114 (in Russian).

473. Rovinski F.Ya., Egorov V.I. 1986. Ozone, nitrogen and sulphur oxides in the lower atmosphere.—Leningrad: Gidrometeoizdat.—184 p. (in Russian).

474. Rowland F.S., Isaksen I.S.A. (Eds.). 1988. The Changing Atmosphere.—John Wiley & Sons, Ltd. Chichester.—281 p.

475. Rozanov B.G. 1984. Principles of the Environment Science.—Moscow: MGU Press.—376 p. (in Russian).

476. Rozenberg G.V. 1955. The Stocks vector-parameter (matrix techniques to take into account the polarization in the ray optics approximation). Progress in Physical Sciences.—Vol. 56, No. 1.—p. 77–109 (in Russian).

477. Rozenberg G.V., Nikolajeva-Tereshkova V.V. 1965. Stratospheric aerosol as observed from spacecraft. Izv. AN SSSR, FAO.—Vol. 1, No. 4.—p. 373–379 (in Russian).

478. Sagoff M. 1988. The Economy of the Earth: Philosophy, Law, and the Environment. Cambridge Univ. Press, England.—X + 251 p.

479. Salganik P.O., Efremov G. A., Neronski L. B. et al. 1990. Radar sounding of the Earth from the satellite "Kosmos-1970". Study of the Earth from Space.— No. 2.—p. 70–79 (in Russian).

480. Salomonson V.V., Barnes W.L., Maymon P.W., Montgomery H.E., Ostrow H. 1989. MODIS: advenced facility instrument for studies of the earth as a system.

IEEE Trans. on Geosci. and Remote Sens.—Vol. 27, No. 2.—p. 145–153.

481. "Salut" in the orbit.—1973. Moscow: Mashinostrojenie.—160 p. (in Russian).

482. Saulski V.K. 1989. Optimal orbits and structures of the satellite systems for the periodic survey of the Earth. Study of the Earth from Space.—No. 2.—p. 104–115 (in Russian).

483. Savijarvi H. 1988. Global energy and moisture budgets from radiosonde data. Mon. Weather Rev.—Vol. 115.—p. 417–430.

484. Schneider S.H. 1986. A goddess of the Earth? The debate on the Gaia hypothesis—an editorial. Clim. Change.—Vol. 8, No. 1.—p. 1–4.

485. Schneider S.H. 1987. An international programme on "Global Change": can it endure?—An editorial. Clim. Change.—Vol. 10, No. 3.—p. 211–218.

486. Schneider S.H. 1989. Cloud Warming. Sierra Club Books. San Francisco.—317 p.

487. SCOPE-21. The major biogeochemical cycles and their interactions. 1983. B. Bolin and R. Cook (Eds.).—John Wiley. Chichester, UK.—554 p.

488. SCOPE-29. The greenhouse effect, climate change, and ecosystems. 1986. B. Bolin, B.R. Doos, J. Jager, and R.A. Worrick (Eds.). John Wiley. Chichester, UK.—574 p.

489. Sedjo R.A. 1989. Forests: a tool to moderate global warming?. Environment.—Vol. 31, No. 1.—p. 14–20.

490. Sekera Z. 1967. Determination of atmospheric parameters from measurements of polarization of upward radiation by satellite or space probe. Icarus.—Vol. 6, No. 3.—p. 348.

491. Sekera Z., Rao N.C.R., Dibble D. 1963. Photoelectric skylight polarimeter. J. Sci. Instrum.—Vol. 34, No. 7.—p. 764–768.

492. Selivanov A.S., Tuchin Yu.M. 1981 A radio-TV complex of the satellites "Meteor" to study the Earth's resour s. Study of the Earth from Space.—No. 5.—p. 28–34 (in Russian).

493. Selivanov A.S., Gektin Yu.M. 1982. On the use of a circular scanning to observe the water basins in the optical range. Study of the Earth from Space.—No. 4.—p. 122–124 (in Russian).

494. Selivanov A.S., Tuchin Yu.M., Ovodkova O.G., Seregin V.A. 1977. Cinema and TV Technology.—No. 3.—p. 43–45 (in Russian).

495. Selivanov A.S., Tuchin Yu.M., Narajeva M.K., Nosov B.I. 1981. An experimental on-board information complex to observe the Earth. Study of the Earth from Space.—No. 5.—p. 35–39 (in Russian).

496. Selivanov A.S., Narajeva M.K., Nosov B.I. et al. 1985. Multizonal cone-sweep scanner to study the Earth's resources. Study of the Earth from Space.—No. 1.—p. 4–11 (in Russian).

497. Sellers P.J. 1985. Canopy reflectance, photosynthesis, and transpiration. NASA Contr. Rept. CR 177822. NASA/GSFC. Greenbelt, MD.—66 p. , ill.

498. Sellers W.D. 1982. The response of a climate model to variations in the solar constant. Symp. Solar Constant and Spectral Distribution of Solar Irradiance (Hamburg, 17–28 Aug. 1981). Boulder, CO.—p. 134–138.

499. Serdiuk V.K., Toliarenko N.V. 1989. The space orbital stations. Progress in

Sci. and Technol. Rocket Building and Space Technology.—Moscow: VINITI.—No. 10.—p. 192 (in Russian).

500. Serdiukov V.M. 1987. Aerospace techniques of geographical studies.—Kiev: Higher School Press.—223 p. (in Russian).

501. Sergin V.Ya. 1980. Origin and mechanism of large-scale climatic oscillations. Science.—Vol. 209, No. 4464.—p. 1477–1481.

502. Shaffer G. 1989. A model of biogeochemical cycling of phosphorus, nitrogen, oxygen, and sulphur in the ocean: one step toward a global climate model. J. Geophys. Res.—Vol. C94, No. 2.—p. 1979–2004.

503. Shakhnazarov G.H. 1985. Where the mankind goes to?—Moscow: Finances and Statistics.—487 p. (in Russian).

504. Shercliff W. 1965. The polarised light.—Moscow: Mir Press.—264 p. (in Russian).

505. Shestopalov V.P., Dranovski V.I., Flimov V.B., Kalmykov A.I. et al. 1984. Complex studies of the environment using the optical and radar techniques. Doklady AN SSSR.—Vol. 279, No. 3.—p. 621–623 (in Russian).

506. Shestopalov V.P., Kalmykov A.I., Komiak V.A., Kuprin A.S. 1985. Complex studies of the Earth environment using the radiophysical techniques. Doklady AN SSSR.—Vol. 284, No. 1.—p. 98–102 (in Russian).

507. Shilin B.V. 1982. The thermal aerial survey.—Leningrad: Gidrometeoizdat.—162 p. (in Russian).

508. Shirokov P.A. 1934. Tensor calculation.—Leningrad: Gostekhizdat.—464 p. (in Russian).

509. Shugrin S.M., Obot A.M. 1986. Solar activity and the biosphere.—Novosibirsk: Nauka Press.—128 p. (in Russian).

510. Shukla J.B., Hallam T.G., Capasso V. (Eds.). 1987. Mathematical Modelling of Environmental and Ecological Systems. Ser. Developments in Environmental Modelling.—Vol. 11.—254 p.

511. Siachenov V.I., Zimmermann G. 1989. The spectrometer carried by the orbital station "Salut-7". Study of the Earth from Space.—No. 2.—p. 65–70 (in Russian).

512. Sidiakin V.G., Temuryants N.A., Makejev V.B., Vladimirski B.M. 1985. Space Ecology.—Kiev: Naukova Dumka Press.—231 p. (in Russian).

513. Siegenthaler U., Oeschger H. 1987. Biospheric CO2 emissions during the past 200 years reconstructed by deconvolution of ice core data. Tellus.—Vol. 39B.—p. 140–154.

514. Simulation modelling of the natural system "lake-catchment area".—Leningrad: Nauka Press.—232 p. , 1987 (in Russian).

515. Slater P.N. 1987. Reflectance- and radiance-based methods for the in-flight absolute calibration of multispectral sensors. Remote Sens. Environm.—Vol. 22.—p. 11–37.

516. Smoktiy O. I. 1969. Light scattering in an aerosol spherical atmosphere. Izv. AN SSSR, FAO.—Vol. 5, No. 1.—p. 46–61 (in Russian).

517. Snopko V.N. 1983. Analysis of polarised radiation. Preprint. Inst. Physics. Bel. Acad. Sci., No. 307. Minsk.—55 p. (in Russian).

518. Sobolev V.V. 1972. Light scattering in planetary atmospheres.—Moscow: Nauka Press.—335 p. (in Russian).
519. Solomon A. 1989. Envisaged climate changes could kill boreal forests. OPTIONS.—Sept.—p. 8–11.
520. Soyuz-22 explores the Earth. 1980. Moscow: Nauka Press.—231 p. (in Russian).
521. Space-based studies accomplished abroad. 1977.—Annual Great Soviet Encyclopaedia.—p. 498–509.
522. Space-based remote sensing of the Earth (a Report to the Congress). NOAA and NASA. U.S. Government Print. Office. Washington, D.C.—1987.—123 p.
523. Space Opportunities for Tropospheric Chemistry Research. Proc. Workshop held in New York City. N.Y., September 9–13, 1985. NASA Conf. Publ.—1987. NNo. 2450.—86 p.
524. Stable statistical techniques for data assessment. 1984. Ed. by R.L. Lorner, G.N. Wilkinson.—Moscow: Mashinostrojenie (in Russian).
525. Staelin D.H. 1987. Capabilities of the advanced microwave sounding unit (AMSU). World Clim. Pap. —No. 137, Appendix B.—9 p.
526. Status of satellite observing possibilities for studies of climate physical processes. Rept. of the COSPAR WG-6, Boulder, CO.—113 p. —1978.
527. Stepanov V.N. 1989. The planetary-scale role of the energy and matter exchange in the World Ocean. Izv. AN SSSR. Ser. Geogr.—No. 2.—p. 5–16 (in Russian).
528. Stevenson F.J. 1985. Cycles of Soils. Carbon, Nitrogen, Phosphorus, Sulphur, Micronutrients. Wiley, New York.—400 p.
529. Stewart R.W., Bretherton F.P. 1984. Atmosphere–ocean interaction. Global Change. Proc. Symp. of ICSU (Ottawa, Sept. 25. 1984). ICSU Press.– p. 53–74.
530. Stothers R.B. 1989. Structure and dating errors in the geologic time scale and periodicity in mass extinctions. Geophys. Res. Lett.—Vol. 16, No. 2.—p. 119–122.
531. Stowe L.L. 1977. Polarization of reflected sunlight as measured from a high-altitude balloon. Proc. Soc. Photo-Opt. Instrum. Eng.—Vol. 112.—p. 176–183.
532. Straskraba M., Gnauck A.H. 1985. Freshwater ecosystems: modelling and simulation. Ser. Developments in Environm. Modelling.—Vol. 8.—310 p.
533. Studies of the environment from the manned orbital stations. 1972. Ed. by K.Ya. Kondratyev.—399 p. (in Russian).
534. Survey of environment related monitoring programmes of international organisations. Economic Summit. Neuherberg, FRG.—38 p.
535. Sytnik K.M., Bryon A.V., Gordetski A.V. 1987. Biosphere. Ecology. Environmental protection.—Reference Book. Kiev: Naukova Dumka Press.—523 p. (in Russian).
536. Tachi K., Arai K., Sato Y. 1989. Advanced microwave scanning radiometer (AMSR): requirements and preliminary design study. IEEE Trans. on Geosci. and Remote Sens.—Vol. 27, No. 2.—p. 177–183.
537. Taylor F.W. 1987. Infrared remote sensing of the middle atmosphere from satellites: the stratospheric and mesospheric sounder experiment 1978–1983.

Surv. Geophys.—Vol. 9, No. 2.—p. 123–148.

538. Taylor F.W., Eyre J.R. 1989. Future satellite missions. Weather.– Vol. 44, No. 7.—p. 298–302.

539. The Atmospheric Sciences: A Vision for 1989–1994. Report of the NSF-UCAR Long-Range Planning Committee. National Acad. Press. Washington, D.C.— 48 p.

540. The expedition "Bering". 1989. (Ed. by K.Ya. Kondratyev). Leningrad: Gidrometeoizdat.—290 p. (in Russian).

541. The International Global Atmospheric Chemistry (IGAC) Programme. IAMAP.—1989.—55 p.

542. The Noordwijk Declaration on Climate Change. Atmospheric Pollution and Climatic Change Ministerial Conference (Noordwijk, The Netherlands, 6–7 Nov. 1989).– 12 p.

543. The Spirit of Rio: Earth Summit 1992. 1992. Brundtland Bull., issue 16, p. 3–5.

544. The Stratosphere 1981: Theory and measurements.—WMO Global Research and monitoring project. Rep. No. 11, May 1981.—118 p.

545. Thompson A.M., Stewart R.W., Owens M.A., Herwehe J.A. 1989. Sensitivity of tropospheric oxidents to global chemical and climate change. Atmos. Environm.—Vol. 23.—p. 519–532.

546. Tjuki J. 1981. An analysis of observation results.—Moscow: Mir Press (in Russian).

547. Tomlinson R., Mounsey H. (Eds.). 1988. Building data bases for global science. Taylor & Francis, Ltd.—419 p.

548. Treshnikov A.F., Kondratyev K.Ya. 1986. Interaction between biosphere and geosphere as the key aspect of the International Geosphere–Biosphere Programme (IGBP). Environm. Pollution Monitor. Res. Programme No. 45. Techn. Doc. WMO/TD-N151.—p. 63–80.

549. Trifonov Yu.V. 1981. Satellites of the series "Meteor" to study the Earth from space. Study of the Earth from Space.—No. 5.—p. 8–27 (in Russian).

550. TRMM. A satellite mission to measure tropical rainfall. NASA GSFC, Greenbelt, MD.—94 p. —1988.

551. Toon O.B., Keating J.F., Turco R.P., Liu M.S. 1987. The sulphur cycle in the marine atmosphere. J. Geophys. Res.—Vol. D92, No. 1.—p. 943–964.

552. Tucker C.J., Fung I.Y., Keeling C.D., Gammon R.H. 1986. Relationship between atmospheric CO2 variations and a satellite-derived vegetation index. Nature.—Vol. 319, No. 6050.—p. 195–199.

553. Turchin V.F., Kozlov V.P., Malkevich M.S. 1970. The use of the mathematical statistics techniques to solve non-correct problems. Progress in Physical Sciences.—Vol. 102, No. 3.—(in Russian).

554. UARS. Upper Atmosphere Research Satellite. NASA. Washington D.C.—28 p. —1989.

555. UNEP. The state of the world environment. UNEP. Nairobi, Kenya.—76 p. — 1987.556.
United States Environmental Protection Agency: 1988. Report to Congress on the Effects of Global Change.

557. Usher P. 1989. Special Report. World Conf. on the Changing Atmosphere: Implications for Global Security. Environment.—Vol. 31, No. 1.—p. 25–38.

558. Uspenski A.B., Fedorov V.V. 1975. Computation aspects of the least squares technique in analysis and planning of regression experiments.—Moscow: MGU Press.—196 p. (in Russian).

559. Valentine J.W. 1989. Phanerozoic marine faunas and the stability of the earth system. Glob. Planet. Change.—Vol. 1, No. 1–2.—p. 137–155.

560. Vallentyne J.R. 1978. Presidential Address. Today is yesterday's tomorrow. Verh. Intern. Verein. Limnol.—Vol. 20.—p. 1–12.

561. Vallentyne J.R. 1986. The necessity of a behavioral code of practice for living in the biosphere, with special reference to an ecosystem ethics. Ecosystem Theory and Application. John Wiley & Sons, Ltd.—p. 406–414.

562. Vanderbilt V.C. 1980. A model of plant canopy polarization response. In: 6th Ann. Symp. : Machine Processing of Rem. Sens. Systems (West Lafayette, Ind., 1980).—New York.—p. 98–108.

563. Varhelyi G. 1985. Continental and global sulfur budgets. 1. Anthropogenic SO2 emissions. Atmos. Environm.—Vol. 19, No. 7.—p. 1029–1040.

564. Varvarin G.A. 1984. Bacteria and the atmospheric composition.—Moscow: Nauka Press.—199 p. (in Russian).

565. Vasilyev B.I. 1969. Optics of polarization instruments.—Moscow: Mashinostrojenie.—140 p. (in Russian).

566. Vasilyev L.N. 1982. Decoding the soil and vegetation covers with the use of numerical information. Study of the Earth from Space.—No. 1.—p. 68–73 (in Russian).

567. Vasilyev O.B., Vedeshin L.A. 1989. The International Symposium "Remote Sensing. Application to Cartography". Study of the Earth from Space.—No. 2.—p. 119–121 (in Russian).

568. Vasilyev L.N., Mironova Z.F. 1974. A technique for coding the reflection spectra of natural formations from observations in the wavelength interval 0.4–0.7 μm. In: Problems of Atmospheric Physics.—Issue 11.—p. 22–26 (in Russian).

569. Veil I.G., Kordzakhia G.I., Mashkovich S.A., Sonechkin D.M. 1976. On a dynamic-stochastic approach to the continuous assimilation of asynchronous information. Meteorology and Hydrology.—No. 6.—p. 3–10 (in Russian).

570. Vernadski V.I. and Modern Life. 1986. (Ed. by B.S. Sokolov and A.L. Yanshin).—Moscow: Nauka Press.—390 p. (in Russian).

571. Vernadski V.I. 1987. The Chemistry of the Earth's Biosphere and its Environment.—Moscow: Nauka Press.—340 p. (in Russian).

572. Vetlov I.P. 1980. the spaceborne system "Meteor" in the service of hydrometeorology. Study of the Earth from Space.—No. 2.—p. 11–27 (in Russian).

573. Vinogradov M.E. 1990. On the present problems in studies of the ocean ecosystems. Bull. USSR Acad. Sci.—No. 1.—p. 88–97 (in Russian).

574. Vladimirski B.M., Kislovski L.D. 1986. The cosmic impact and the evolution of the biosphere.—New in Life Science and Engineering. Space Exploration

and Astronomy.—Moscow: Znanie Press.—No. 1.—64 p. (in Russian).

575. Vlasov D.V., Mirkamilov D.M., Mukhamedov A.A. et al. 1989. Determination of the spectral indicators for the remote laser sounding of plants. Study of the Earth from Space.—p. 84–88 (in Russian).

576. Voitkevich G. V., Bessonov O. A. 1986. The chemical evolution of the Earth.—Moscow: Nedra Press.—212 p. (in Russian).

577. Volkova E. A. 1974. Polarization measurements.—Moscow: Standards Press.—156 p. (in Russian).

578. Vidal A., Perrier A. 1989. Analysis of a simplified relation for estimating daily evapotranspiration from satellite thermal IR data. Int. J. Remote Sens.—Vol. 10, No. 8.—p. 1327–1337.

579. Vupputuri R. K. 1988. Potential effects of anthropogenic trace gas emissions on atmospheric ozone and temperature structure and surface climate. Atmos. Environm.—Vol. 22, No. 12.—p. 2809–2818.

580. Walter H. 1985. Vegetation of the Earth and Ecological Systems of the Geobiosphere. Third revised and enlarged edition. Springer-Verlag, New York– 318 p. , ill.

581. Walter H., Breckle S.-W. 1985. Ecological systems of the Geobiosphere. Vol. 1: Ecological Principles in Global Perspective. Springer-Verlag. New York– 242 p.

582. WCED. Our Common Future. Oxford Univ. Press. Oxford, U.K.—383 p. — 1987.

583. Wessman C.A., Aber J.D., Peterson D.L. 1989. An evaluation of imaging spectrometry for estimating forest canopy chemistry. Int. J. Remote Sens.—Vol. 10, No. 8.—p. 1293–1316.

584. Wigley T.M.L. 1989. Possible climate change due to SO 2-derived cloud condensation nuclei. Nature.—Vol. 339.—p. 365–367.

585. Woodwell G.M. (Ed.). 1984. The role of terrestrial vegetation in the global carbon cycle. SCOPE-23. John Wiley & Sons. Chichester—247 p.

586. Woodwell G.M., Jansen D.H., Milcox H.A., North W.J., Swartz A., Hoyer H. 1988. CO2 reduction and reforestation. Science.—No. 4885.—p. 1493–1497.

587. Woodwell G.M. 1989. The warming of the industrialised middle latitudes 1985–2050: causes and consequences. Clim. Change.—Vol. 15, No. 1/2.—p. 31–50.

588. Wright J.W. 1968. A new model for sea clutter. IEEE Trans. on Ant. and Propag.—Vol. AP-16, No. 2.—p. 217–223.

589. Yablokov A.B., Ostroumov S.A. 1985. The level of protection of animate nature.—Moscow: Nauka Press.—176 p. (in Russian).

590. Yakovlev S.G., Dobrozrakov A.D., Kondratyev Yu.M., et al. 1983. A helicopter spectrometric complex for sub-satellite experiments in test areas to study the Earth's resources. Scientific Space Instrument Making. Issue 2: Optico-electronic instruments. Moscow: Metallurgy.—p. 23–25 (in Russian).

591. Yasamanov N.A. 1985. The ancient climates of the Earth.—Leningrad: Gidrometeoizdat.—296 p. (in Russian).

592. Yeh T., Fu C. 1984. Climatic change—a global and multidisciplinary theme.

Clim. Change. Proc. Symp. of ICSU (Ottawa, Sept. 25, 1984). ICSU Press.– p. 101–120.

593. Yugas L., Kudela K. 1989. An assessment of the spectral characteristics of soils from the Landsat-5 TM data. Study of the Earth from Space.—No. 6.—p. 49–53 (in Russian).

594. Zagorodnikov A.A. 1978. The radar sounding of sea surface roughness from the flying platforms.—Leningrad: Gidrometeoizdat.—239 p. (in Russian).

595. Zakharov V.M., Kostko O.K., Birich L.N., Kruchenitski G.M., Portosov V.S. 1988. The laser sounding of the atmosphere from space.—Leningrad: Gidrometeoizdat.—215 p. (in Russian).

596. Zaletajev V.S. 1989. An ecologically destabilised medium (The ecosystems of arid zones in a changed hydrological regime).—Moscow: Nauka Press.—150 p. (in Russian).

597. Ziman Ya.L., Sazhko M.Yu., Tsitovich V.S. 1976. The flying laboratories and an experience from their use in working out the techniques and means of remote sounding of the Earth's resources. In: Studies of the Earth's resources from space.—Moscow: Nauka Press (in Russian).

598. Zimmermann P.H., Feichter J., Rath H.K., Crutzen P.J., Weiss H. 1989. A global three-dimensional source-receptor model investigation using 85Kr. Atmos. Environm.—Vol. 23, No. 1.—p. 25–36.

599. Zinke P. 1984. Forest environments. NASA Techn. Memo. 86129. GSFC, Greenbelt, MD.—Aug.—Vol. 1 (Pt. 2).—p. 18–20.

600. Zolotarev V.A., Sdasiuk G.V. 1989. Earth in danger.—Moscow: Znanie Press.—44 p. (in Russian).

601. Zuev V.E. 1981. The use of lasers for an operational control of the state of the atmosphere. Materials of the Seminar "Space–Ocean–Atmosphere". Ed. by G.I. Marchuk. Moscow: VINITI.—21 p. (in Russian).

602. Zumnich K.H. 1989. The multichannel spectrometer MKS-L—laboratory studies, in-flight calibration, and testing its functioning. Study of the Earth from Space.—No. 2.—p. 71–77 (in Russian).

Index